Iconic Arithmetic

Volume III

Any comments, corrections, refinements or
suggestions you may have will be greatly appreciated.

You can reach me via email at
william@iconicmath.com

Thanks.

In this series, available from Amazon Books:

Iconic Arithmetic (2019)
  Volume I   The Design of Mathematics for Human Understanding
  ISBN: 978-1-7324851-3-6

Iconic Arithmetic (2019)
  Volume II   Symbolic and Postsymbolic Formal Foundations
  ISBN: 978-1-7324851-4-3

Iconic Arithmetic (2021)
  Volume III   The Structure of Imaginary and Infinite Forms
  ISBN: 978-1-7324851-5-0

Iconic Arithmetic

simple

sensual

postsymbolic

Volume III
The STRUCTURE of IMAGINARY
and INFINITE FORMS

William Bricken

in memoriam
Richard G. Shoup
George Spencer Brown

Chapters Volume I

Preface   xxiii

1. Context   1

2. Ensembles   33

3. Depth   65

4. Dynamics   87

5. Structure   119

6. Perspective   133

7. Units   161

8. Transformation   183

9. Accumulation   207

10. Reflection   239

11. Numbers   261

12. Extension   287

13. Dialects   305

14. Alternatives   341

15. Next   369

Chapters Volume II

Preface   xxiii

16. Crossing   1

17. Equality   23

18. Composition   53

19. Concurrency   73

20. Boundary   107

21. Foundation   131

22. Architects   145

23. Diversity   173

24. Formalism   197

25. Computation   231

26. Postsymbolism   267

27. Sets   297

28. Logic   321

29. Containment   341

30. Connection   365

Chapters Volume III

Preface xxi

31. Artifacts 1

32. Invention 11

33. History 27

34. Behavior 59

35. Features 87

36. Revision 113

37. Derivative 143

38. Mapping 175

39. Complex 207

40. Trigonometry 239

41. Non-numeric 269

42. Indeterminate 307

43. Exotics 325

44. Concrete 349

45. Return 375

Chapter Map

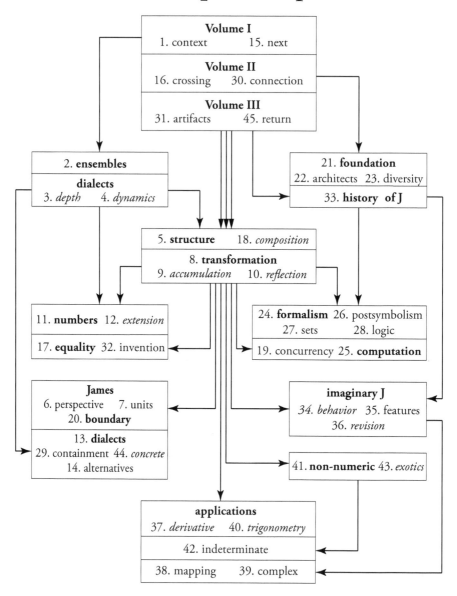

Arrows indicate flow of content.
Bold font indicates the focus of the block of chapters.
Italic font indicates a focus on demonstration of transformations.

Contents Volume III

Chapters   i
Chapter Map   ii
Table of Contents   iii
List of Figures   xiii
Cast of Characters   xv
Preface   xxi

Chapter 31. Artifacts   **1**

31.1 Pre-computational Thought   2
31.2 Adventure   3
      Treasures
      The Edges
      The Structure of Numbers
31.3 Remarks   9
      Endnotes

Chapter 32. Invention   **11**

32.1 Inventing Numbers   12

$$x + 0 \ = 0$$
$$x + 1 \ = 0$$
$$2x - 1 = 0$$
$$x^2 - 1 = 0$$
$$x^2 + 1 = 0$$
$$2^x + 1 = 0$$
$$x + x \ = 0$$

32.2 Remarks   25
      Endnotes

Chapter 33. History   27

33.1 Historical Perspective   27
     Nonexistence
     An Infinity of Logarithms
33.2 The Great Mathematicians   30
     Impossible Numbers
     Logarithms
     Euler's Definition
33.3 Leibniz, Bernoulli and Euler   39
     $J = 0$, Reason 1
     $J = 0$, Reason 2
     $J = 0$, Reason 3
     $J = 0$, Reason 4
33.4 Euler's Solution   48
     Euler Constructs J
33.5 Remarks   54
     Endnotes

Chapter 34. Behavior   59

34.1 Creation   60
     Systems of Units
34.2 Features and Theorems   63
34.3 The Nature of J   64
     A New Unity
     J as a Fundamental Unit
34.4 J is Non-accumulating   69
     Self-inverse
     J-void Process
     Tallying J
34.5 J is Transparent   73
     Permeability
34.6 J-conversion   75
     J-occlusion
     Invariance
34.7 Axiomatic Structure Revisited   81
34.8 Remarks   82
     Endnotes

Chapter 35. Features   87

35.1 Special Structures   88
    J Frames
35.2 J in Action   90
    Negative Base Logarithms
    Roots of Negative Unity
35.3 Unconventional Behavior of J   93
    J Stands Alone
    Sign-blind
    Arrangement Inconsistency
    Tally Failure
35.4 Oscillation   100
    Without Memory
    With Memory
35.5 Counting J Tokens   102
    J-parity
    Self-multiplication of Negatives
35.6 J Unit Fractions   106
    J-Fractions
    Unit Fractions
35.7 Remarks   109
    Endnotes

Chapter 36. Revision   113

36.1 Sign Calculus   114
    Euler's Rationale
    An Algebraic Rationale
    A Distributive Rationale
    An Ensemble Rationale
    A James Rationale
36.2 Martínez' Experiment   122
    Non-commutative Containment
36.3 The Square Root of Unity   126
    Sign-blind Self-multiplication
    Multiple Values
    Bipolar Values from J Replication
36.4 When Exponents Break   132
36.5 When Logarithms Break   136

36.6 Loss of Confluence   138
36.7 Remarks   140
        Endnotes

Chapter 37. Derivative   143

37.1 Form Limits   145
        Form of the Base
37.2 Form Derivatives   146
        Differentiation Frame
        Definition
        Round Derivative
        Square Derivative
        Angle Derivative
        Variable and Constant Derivatives
37.3 Void-based Differentiation   155
        Round Unit Transparency
        Construction of e
37.4 Chain Rule   160
        Differentiation Templates
37.5 Generalization   163
        Product Rule
        Quotient Rule
        Power Rule
        Generic Exponential Template
37.6 Remarks   172
        Endnotes

Chapter 38. Mapping   175

38.1 Inversion   176
38.2 Plane Thinking   178
        Extrinsic and Intrinsic Perspective
        Radians
38.3 Rotation as Reflection   181
        J Reflection
38.4 Drawing the Line   183
        Perspective
        Quadratic Space
        Birth of i

Exponential Space
Birth of J
Logarithmic Space
38.5 Conic Sections   192
38.6 Composite Number Lines   193
      James Number Line
38.7 Equivalence of Systems   198
      Homomorphism
      Pattern Matching
38.8 Remarks   202
      Endnotes

Chapter 39. Complex   **207**

39.1 J-frames   208
      J-frame Reflection
      The J/2 Frame
39.2 i and J   210
      Reentrant Definitions
      Shared Structure
39.3 Cyclic Forms   214
39.4 The Complex Plane   216
      Real and Imaginary Units
      Getting Around
39.5 Euler's Equation   219
      Euler's Identity
39.6 π and J   223
      Imaginary Pi
39.7 Reflection   226
      Fractional Reflection
      Alignment
      The N Roots of −1
      Sign-blind Reflection
      Sign-blind Rotation
39.8 Euler Rotation   231
      Complex Logarithms
39.9 Powers of J   234
39.10 Remarks   235
      Endnotes

Chapter 40. Trigonometry   239

40.1 The Form of Reflection   241
    S_α Notation
40.2 Cosine   243
    Cosine Symmetry
    Cosine Squared
    Cosine Identities
    Sum of Angles
40.3 Sine   249
    Sine as Cosine
    Exponential Sine
    Sine Symmetry
    Sine Squared
40.4 Pythagorean Theorem   254
    Tangent
    Euler Form
    DeMoivre's Theorem
40.5 Derivatives   257
    dCosine
    dSine
40.6 Reflective Trigonometry   259
    Reflective Cosine
    Cyclotomic Alternative
    Fractions of Polarity
    Reflective Sine
    Reflective Identities
40.7 Remarks   266
    Endnotes

Chapter 41. Non-numeric   269

41.1 Infinity   272
    Not Actual, Not Potential
41.2 The Square Unit   277
    Separation
41.3 [ ] as Negative Infinity   278
41.4 <[ ]> as Positive Infinity   280
    Non-numeric Reflection
    Independence of Reflection

Unification

Square Replication

41.5 (<[ ]>) as Divide-by-Zero   285

Incommensurable

Direction of Approach

41.6 Infinite Interpretation   290

Progress

41.7 Complex Infinity   291

[[ ]] as Complex Infinity

Absorption of J

Sign-Blind Absorption

Reflection of Infinity

41.8 Arithmetic of Infinity   299

The Infinite Number Line

41.9 Remarks   301

Endnotes

Chapter 42. Indeterminate   **307**

42.1 Indeterminate Variables   308

Indeterminate Expressions

Assimilating Infinity

42.2 Indeterminate Forms   314

Negotiable Indeterminism

Design Choices

42.3 Indeterminate Series   319

42.4 Form of Indeterminacy   321

Restrictions on Dominion

42.5 Remarks   322

Endnotes

Chapter 43. Exotics   **325**

43.1 Zero or Nothing   329

Sum of Nothing

Self-multiplying Nothing

43.2 Infinitesimals   332

43.3 Infinite Concept   335

Infinite Exponents

The Source of Indeterminacy

43.4 Exotic Bases   337
    Negative Exponential Bases
    Powers of Negative Infinity
43.5 Exotic Logarithms   342
    Base-0 Logarithm
    Base-1 Logarithm
    Base-∞ Logarithm
43.6 Remarks   346
    Endnotes

Chapter 44. Concrete   349

44.1 Revisiting Iconic Dialects   350
    Varieties of J
    Perspective
    About the Dialects
44.2 i, π and e   356
    Iconic i
    Iconic π
    Iconic e
44.3 Euler Transformations   363
44.4 Dnet Differentiation   364
    The Round Derivative
    The Chain Rule
44.5 Dnet Rcosine   368
44.6 Tally Failure in Dnets   369
44.7 Dnet Non-numeric Forms   370
    Triple-square
44.8 Remarks   372
    Endnotes

Chapter 45. Return   375

45.1 Evolution   375
    Return to Postsymbolism
45.2 Crossing the Boundary   377
    Logic Begets Numerics
45.3 Violation of Symbolic Canons   380
    Symbolic Dogma

45.4 Non-conformity   384
    General Computational Technique
    Behavior of J
    Base-free Differentiation
    Rational Reflection
    Infinity
45.5 Grand Strategy   388
45.6 Remarks   390
    Endnotes

Bibliography   393
Index to the Index   397
Index   398
  People   398
  Primary Reference Figures   400
  Typographic Delimiters   400
  Symbolic Concepts   401
    general
    arithmetic and algebra
    geometry and trigonometry
    imaginary and complex
    infinite and indeterminate
    logic and proof
    computer science
    education
    history and philosophy
    typography
  Iconic Concepts   407
    general
    applications
  Structure   412
    brackets
    axioms and theorems
    applied patterns
  Symbols and Icons   414
  Volumes   414
  Cover   415
    cover words
  Bumper Stickers   416
  Websites   418

List of Figures

Figure 31-1: *Summary of definitions, axioms and theorems (Figure 16-1)*   6
Figure 31-2: *The structure of conventional and James numbers*   8

Figure 32-1: *New concepts introduced by simple equations*   13
Figure 32-2: *Simple equations with multiple solutions*   24

Figure 34-1: *Features of* J   62
Figure 34-2: J *theorems*   63
Figure 34-3: *The* J *form of common inverse operations*   76
Figure 34-4: *Exponential form of common inverse operations*   77
Figure 34-5: *Angle-bracket theorems converted to* J*-frame theorems*   81
Figure 34-6: *Some concerning features of* J   83

Figure 35-1: *Some special labels*   88
Figure 35-2: *Frame-types incorporating* J   89
Figure 35-3: *Comparison of bivalent laws*   104

Figure 36-1: *The conventional sign calculus*   119
Figure 36-2: *Options for substitution of signed units*   120
Figure 36-3: *A James version of the Martínez sign calculus*   125

Figure 37-1: *Limit rules for boundaries*   145
Figure 37-2: *Derivatives of boundaries*   147
Figure 37-3: *Derivatives of boundary forms in* base-# *and* base-e   155

Figure 38-1: *Reflection through line and circle*   176
Figure 38-2: *Self-multiplication projected onto the* x-axis   185
Figure 38-3: *Imaginary self-multiplication projected onto the* x-axis   187
Figure 38-4: *The exponential function projected onto the* x-axis   189
Figure 38-5: *The imaginary exponential function projected onto the* x-axis   190
Figure 38-6: *The positive composite number line*   194
Figure 38-7: *The entire composite number line*   195
Figure 38-8: *Numeric domains on the composite number line*   196
Figure 38-9: *James forms on the composite number line*   197
Figure 38-10: *Structure preserving maps*   199

Figure 39-1: *Structural comparison of* i *and* J   213

Figure 39-2: *Cyclic forms of* i   214

Figure 39-3: *Structural comparison of* π, i *and* J   225

Figure 39-4: *Models of the relationship between* i *and* J   227

Figure 39-5: *Turning around*   235

Figure 40-1: *Angles, reflections and their exponential form*   242

Figure 40-2: *James cosines for multiples of* π/2   246

Figure 40-3: *James sines for multiples of* π/2   252

Figure 41-1: <[ ]> *theorems*   282

Figure 41-2: *Axioms and theorems of* [ ] *and* <[ ]>   291

Figure 41-3: *Operations on non-numeric expressions*   299

Figure 41-4: *Types of infinity on the composite number line*   300

Figure 42-1: *The James form of indeterminate expressions*   315

Figure 42-2: *Design decisions to suppress ambiguity*   318

Figure 43-1: *Some of the exotics*   326

Figure 43-2: *Concepts that ground James algebra*   327

Figure 43-3: *Problematic operations on zero*   328

Figure 43-4: *The diversity of an infinite exponent*   334

Figure 43-5: *Powers of negative infinity*   341

Figure 43-6: *Values of exotic logarithms*   343

Figure 43-7: *Exotic results*   346

Figure 44-1: *Roadmap for generating iconic dialects (Figure 13-1)*   351

Figure 44-2: *Iconic forms of* J   352

Figure 44-3: *Iconic forms of* divide-by-zero   353

Figure 44-4: *Iconic forms of* √–1   357

Figure 44-5: *Iconic forms of* π   360

Figure 44-6: *Iconic forms of* e   362

Figure 44-7: *Demonstration of Euler's identity*   363

Figure 44-8: *Demonstration of J-self-occlusion*   364

Figure 44-9: *Construction of the round derivative*   365

Figure 44-10: *Dnet chain rules and demonstration of the product rule*   367

Figure 44-11: *The reflective* rcosine   368

Figure 44-12: *Tally failure*   369

Figure 44-13: *Double-square theorem*   370

Figure 44-14: *Triple-square theorem*   371

Cast of Characters

Visionaries

Aristotle
Gregory Bateson
John Horton Conway
Leonhard Euler
David Hilbert
Gottfried Leibniz
Benoit Mandelbrot
Charles Sanders Peirce
George Spencer Brown
Francisco Varela
Stephen Wolfram

Voices

Johann Bernoulli
Augustus DeMorgan
Leonhard Euler
Jeffrey James
Louis Kauffman
Gottfried Leibniz
Alberto Martínez
Charles Sanders Peirce
Richard Shoup
George Spencer Brown
John Stillwell

Research and Perspective

Gregory Chaitin
Louis Kauffman
Morris Kline
Barry Mazur
Joseph Mazur
Tristan Needham
John Stillwell
Gerald Weinberg

Colleagues

George Burnett-Stuart
Arthur Collings
Andrew Crompton
Graham Ellsbury
Jack Engstrom
Thomas Etter
Fred Furtek
Robert Horn
Jeffrey James
Louis Kauffman
David Keenan
Bernie Lewin
Thomas McFarlane
Meredith Bricken Mills
Daniel Shapiro
Richard Shoup
Andrew Singer
William Winn

Special Thanks to

Paul Allen
Colin Bricken
Ian Bricken
Julie Bricken
Andrew Crompton
Graham Ellsbury
Doug Emory
Jeffrey James
Louis Kauffman
Jaron Lanier
Amy Morrison
Ted Nelson
Daniel Shapiro
Richard Shoup
John Walker
Stephen Wolfram

Historical Figures

Historical Figures	*circa*	*chapter*
Anaximander	500 BCE	41
Pythagoras	500	36, 40, 41
Plato	400	40
Aristotle	350	38, *41*
Euclid	300	*43*
Bhaskar	1150 CE	41
Descartes	1640	33, 38, 40
Pascal	1680	*open-41*
Leibniz	1700	32, *33*, 42, 43
Johann Bernoulli	1720	*33*, 34
Newton	1720	33, 41-43
Euler	1760	*32, 33, 34, 35, 36,* 37, *38*, 39-42, 44
Gauss	1840	39, *41*
DeMorgan	1860	*33*, 39
Riemann	1860	41
Cantor	1880	41
Hilbert	1900	31, *41*, 45
Peano	1900	32, 34, 41
Peirce	1900	39, 45
Poincaré	1900	*41*
Wittgenstein	1940	41, *42*

Quotes (in italics) and Concepts

Quotes (in italics) and Concepts	*chapter*
Antonin Artaud	*open-37*
Alain Badiou	45
Deepak Bal	*33*
John Barrow	*open-32*
Claude Bernard	*open-42*
János Bolyai	*open-33*
Jorge Luis Borges	*41*
David Bressoud	*open-43*
Gerolamo Cardano	*33*, 39
Gregory Chaitin	41
Winston Churchill	*open-35*
Alain Connes	*41*
John Horton Conway	*34*, 41, 43

Tobias Dantzig	33, 41
Keith Devlin	39
William Dunham	41
Timothy Gowers	41, 42
Ivor Grattan-Guiness	33
Jacques Hadamard	open-39
Godfrey Hardy	open-34
Daniel Kahneman	45
Louis Kauffman	35, 45
Donald Knuth	42
Leopold Kronecker	35, 41
Pierre-Simon Laplace	33
Penelope Maddy	41
Benoit Mandelbrot	43, open-44
Alberto Martínez	33, 34, 36, 41
Francis Maseres	33
Hōsaku Matsuo	32, 45
Barry Mazur	36
Paul Nahin	33, 39
Tristan Needham	38
John vonNeumann	open-36
Paul Painlevé	39
Benjamin Peirce	39
John Playfair	33
George Pólya	open-40
George Spencer Brown	open-preface, 33, 45
John Stillwell	open-31, 34, 39
Patrick Suppes	41
Calvin Trillin	open-45
Edward Tufte	open-38, 45
Varela, Thompson & Rosch	45
Gary Zukav	36

Mentioned *chapter*

Jean-Robert Argand	39
S. Ball	45
G. Baron	33
Gregory Bateson	45
Benacerraf & Putman	41

Berlekamp, Conway & Guy	34
Ludwig von Bertalanffy	45
Bernard Bolzano	41
Rafael Bombelli	39
D. Boyle	45
W. Bricken	44
W. Bryant	33
Florian Cajori	39
K. Cole	41
Conway & Guy	41
Courant & Robbins	39
Jean D'Alembert	33
Richard Dedekind	31
Abraham DeMoivre	40
N. Eberstadt	45
Fauvel & Grey	33
Harvey Friedman	31
Kurt Gödel	42
Graham, Knuth & Patashnik	42
John Graves	34
Ernst Haeckel	45
William Hamilton	34
Hardie & Gaye	41
Hartshorne & Weiss	45
Felix Hausdorff	43
Householder, Forsythe & Germond	41
Hutton, Shaw & Pearson	33
K. Inada	32, 45
Kasner & Newman	39
V. Katz	33
F. Klein	33
Morris Kline	33, 41, 42
Péter Körtesi	33
A. Krailsheimer	41
James Lovelock	45
J. Muller	45
Roger Penrose	39
Ilya Prigogine	45
A. Robinson	43
G. Schubring	33
A. Shtern	39

S. Sontag	37
F. Smith	36
G. Thomas	39
Wachsmuth, Rollinger & Brauer	44
Caspar Wessel	39
Eugene Wigner	33
J. Williams	45
S. Wolfram	45

Preface

*For the purposes of communication, a choice has to be made,
but such a choice necessarily limits the presentation
and ignores the unlimited delights of the exploration itself.*
— *George Spencer Brown (1996), Introduction to Appendix 4: An algebra for the
natural numbers, Laws of Form revised fifth English edition (2009) p.118.*

Well, the end of a seven year project. I recently met a correspondence friend for the first time. He immediately asked: "Why can't you write a *small* book?" My honest reply was that I had tried to write for an audience, and found that it was a skill not within my reach. So I'm writing to meet my personal goals and standards, and for consistency with a couple of (um, perhaps risky) decisions made early. The goal is to show the simplicity of iconic arithmetic with an abundance of examples in order to convey a single message: the entire content of school mathematics can be described by a few definitions that anchor how iconic constants might behave, supported by three visually simple pattern-recognition axioms that animate the behavior and transformation of James forms. The half-dozen useful theorems are simple combinations of the axioms, usually standing in place of no more than four or five substitution steps. Volume I seeks to describe and to illustrate the visual dynamics of James algebra while emphasizing the conceptual beauty of void-based thinking and thus to motivate a completely different way of thinking about and understanding elementary arithmetic. The meta-goal is also simple: to demonstrate that *symbolic mathematics* is a choice rather than a necessity by providing a viable iconic alternative.

The first volume went smoothly and relatively quickly given the hundreds of accompanying illustrations. The goal of Volume II is to relate iconic thinking to the evolution of metamathematics and to the revered contributions of the founders of modern axiomatic arithmetic. That volume developed significantly slower since it involved substantial and substantive research. The seminal work from over a century ago had not yet clearly formulated fundamental ideas about meaning and structural transformation. The formal concepts being explored were also (obviously) pre-computational and pre-electronic. I struggled with antiquated motivations that were simultaneously prescient and anachronistic. Volume II is a journey into feeling inadequate yet opinionated. The primary challenge was learning how to see through the nearly universal acceptance of the axiomatic structure of sets and logic and whole numbers to find underneath an elegant, postsymbolic alternative.

This volume though has been the most challenging of the three, for mainly human reasons. Many technical details needed to be refined in order to expand James algebra into topics that were not originally intended but do serve as useful application examples. The goal is to present each application domain from an innovative, postsymbolic perspective. While trying to finish the first volume I elected to put aside nearly completed explorations until the "next volume", a decision directly caused by, yes, too many words. While updating the "nearly finished" content from 2015 and on, I was fully expecting an editing and compilation task. What I found was a whole lot of redundancy. Over the years the same ideas were repeated many times in many different contexts. My understanding had evolved, my errors had moved from one dimension to another, complicated dilemmas turned simple while new tangles were exposed, and worst of all, integrating a two-foot stack of new notes into already written words was a nightmare. I had thought that what *was* could be converted into what is, while holding a totally inappropriate belief that time is in short supply. Truth is, time doesn't care. And then 2020 pushed back and yet another year passed without completion.

Volume III is an exploration of the interplay between formal symbolic knowledge and void-based iconic innovation. The sections on history, the imaginary J, applications of James algebra and non-numeric forms are relatively independent. The heart of arithmetic consists of three concepts: zero, one and infinity. The heart of James algebra embraces three grounding concepts: the nonexistent *void*, the accumulator ( ) and the unifier [ ]. This volume begins with a resurrection of Euler's work on the logarithms of negative numbers in the form of the numeric constant [<( )>], abbreviated as J. The first three chapters explore the history, behavior and issues associated with log −1 and its apparent neglect in modern arithmetic. The next three chapters examine the intimate relationship between π, i and J established by Euler. Then follows a collection of applications of postsymbolic formal thinking to selected subfields of elementary mathematics. If iconic arithmetic is more than an isomorphism, then its application should suggest entirely different perspectives on established mathematical systems. These four chapters are unabashedly exploratory, recounting experiments, dead ends and forced structural conclusions. The next three chapters wrestle with the role of [ ], a fundamental "unit" within the James arithmetic that does not accumulate and in that sense is non-numeric. Some call it infinity. The final content chapter in this volume revisits the spatial dialects of Volume I.

This volume opens the door to several partially explored radical re-visions of the concepts of numeric arithmetic, including
— arithmetic without addition and multiplication
— quasi-numeric illusions that create the impression of complexity
— the additive imaginary J as a numeric unit
— a non-distributive constant
— sign-blind and bipolar numbers and operations
— quantized fractions of polarity
— e as defined by the transparency of ( )
— a generic form of the derivative
— i as a compound imaginary
— reflection as a foundation for rotation
— trigonometry without memory
— the non-numeric infidel [ ] and its reflection <[ ]>
— organized indeterminate expressions
— exotic powers and bases, and of course
— the ever absent *void*.

The postsymbolic dialects of Volume I are constrained in Volumes II and III to the convenience of the **parens** dialect, a typographic yet still iconic notation. At the cost of introducing some unintended symbolic artifacts (called *accidents* in the text) such as reading "(" and ")" as different tokens, bracket notations allow a concise visualization of the dynamics of James transformations by enlisting successive lines of the page to display temporal evolution.

The side columns on each page hold handy illustrations and reminders in support of the text. In the case of formal transformation sequences, the rules being applied are listed line-by-line in the sidebar.

All structural necessities for understanding James algebra are included in Figure 31-1 of Chapter 31.

In reading the text, backward reference to Chapters 1 through 15 refer to Volume I, while Chapters 16 through 30 refer to Volume II.

All references to online content have been verified as accessible during mid-2020.

The iconicmath.com website is the nexus for the content in these volumes and for potentially forthcoming volumes focused on computational logic.

•• • ——————————————— • ••

The notation within the three volumes is consistent but does include a few symbolic characters that have unusual roles.

I've used typographic delimiters, ( ), [ ], < > and others rather than Spencer Brown's spatial mark, ⌐ , for easier typography and to make available several different representations for types of spatial containers.

A fixed width Monaco font identifies mathematical forms and functions, while the linguistic narration and discussion, the metalanguage so to speak, is printed in Cochin font.

The finger ☞ indicates a change in formal system, usually transcription between iconic James forms and conventional string expressions.

The numeric unit represented by a round-bracket has two forms, ( ) and o.

The arbitrary James base is represented by #.

The quasi-token *void* is meant not to exist.

A *frame* is the recurrent James structure (A [B]) with A the *frame type* and B the *frame contents*.

•• • ——————————————— • ••

Should you find typographic and/or conceptual errors in these pages, please freely contact me at william@iconicmath.com with corrections, suggestions and general discussion.

Take care.

william bricken
Snohomish Washington
December 1, 2020

Iconic Arithmetic

Volume III

Chapter 31

Artifacts

Who would have thought that almost everything, in the vast world of mathematics, follows from a few basic facts?[1]
— John Stillwell (2016)

We are exploring James algebra and in the process discovering the structure of an iconic formal system. The objective is to experience new methods of formal thinking rather than to discover new mathematical truths. Rearranging symbolic expressions is more efficient than redrawing boundary forms by virtue of hundreds of years of evolution. But do symbolic systems engender particular habits of thinking? Which cognitive processes does symbolic thinking discourage? Does memorizing rules for symbol manipulation constrain visualization of images or intuitive understanding or behavioral flexibility? Boundary numerics bridges two worlds, the ancient and the electronic. Ensemble arithmetic and James form are much closer to the physical interactive mathematics prevalent Before the Common Era. With fewer types of transformation, with atomic steps taken in parallel, and with the power of void-equivalence, boundary math also resembles optimized computer architectures.[2] Coupled with multisensory interaction, iconic methods encourage **embodied cognition** by removing the barrier between representation and meaning.

31.1 Pre-computational Thought

The apparent simplicity of the arithmetic and algebra of numbers is an artifact of a particular type of processing architecture that may be characterized as **pre-computational human symbolic abstraction** from about 1830 to 1980. Prior to that period numbers were more magic than skill-based. After that numbers adopted a binary format suitable for newer, more efficient silicon architectures. During the 150 intervening years culture and technology underwent profound changes, changes that have only presaged the greater transformation that humanity is now experiencing. The last half of last century endured an awkward transitional period during which our cultural expectation was that humans *need* to be able to process (as opposed to understand) symbolic numeric structure. In *this* century however it has become increasingly clear that humans need to understand how to use the exceptional silicon and algorithmic tools we have developed, regardless of whether or not we understand (or can understand) the 10^{18} transistor transitions per second from which a modern silicon computer generates multimedia experiences.

Educators have traversed the growth of technology with great trepidation. The debatable purpose of schooling is to acculturate as well as to educate. Educational bureaucracies are not designed for accelerated exponential change so much as for preservation of historical values. At the turn of the twentieth century, prior to both electric and silicon technologies and concurrent with the invention of universal schooling, the architects of curriculum for elementary education nominated memorization of arithmetic facts as a cultural and cognitive necessity. Group theoretic algebra was entombed as the *rules* of arithmetic and they too were deemed essential for an educated child to have memorized. As tools designed to replace memorization of facts and paper-and-pencil algorithms evolved, educators reluctantly gave up their belief that it is necessary for school children to be able to compute the square root of a number by hand.[3] Within decades after that, belief in the need to do long division by hand was abandoned. Multi-digit multiplication and even addition of large numbers are now hanging tenaciously by a thread.[4] However the dominant feature of classroom mathematics is that its functional content is *not* how modern relational computation is conducted, is not even close to the algorithms used in silicon computation and is not composed of skills needed for success in the 21st century.

Our extended exploration of iconic arithmetic and pattern-directed transformation has been motivated by fundamental cultural questions about mathematics education and about the tyranny of symbolic arithmetic. Is *symbolic numeric processing* a necessary skill for humans to have mastered by the time they reach their teens? Is *functional thinking* a necessary skill within a world that has moved decisively into relational and contextual values? Indeed is the universal embrace of symbolic algorithms appropriate for an age in which the majority of the Earth's population have in their hands or in their pockets a superb tool for parallel processing of patterns, whether they be numeric, pictorial, temporal or behavioral?

31.2 Adventure

Stepping aside from educational, technological and cultural considerations this journey into iconic arithmetic can be seen as an adventure, an *exploration of a foreign territory*. The role of an explorer is to visit new and exotic lands and to bring back stories and artifacts. An explorer of cognitive realms, whether they be philosophical or literate or mathematical or neurological or psychedelic, journeys inward, often in isolation, exploring non-physical territories and seeking to bring back conceptual artifacts that may be of interest to others. These volumes then are the diaries of a particular kind of adventure by a particular adventurer who is insufficiently acculturated to believe that formal knowledge is embedded exclusively within long strings of arbitrary tokens.

The territory is **formal cognitive distinction**. Formality assures stable and replicable artifacts. The formal structure of the explored territory is three algebraic pattern axioms, or beliefs, about how configurations of mutually nested containers can be transformed. The vehicle of exploration is pattern equivalence between forms of containment. The found artifacts brought back are patterns, or theorems, that depend upon both the structural constraints imposed by the axioms and their medium of expression. For a cognitive explorer to avoid traps and chasms within the imaginary realm a *map* is extremely valuable. For this exploration the map is from iconic distinction to the structure and behavior of symbolic arithmetic. Found artifacts are thus anchored by formal constraint, by conventional familiarity and by the shape of their forms.

Prior to the James axioms and in an attempt to characterize the natural numbers, Volume I postulates *unit ensembles* that support both containment and accumulation. The strategy was to begin with the mind of a preschool toddler to build patterns of discrete units. The spatial patterns themselves mimic the operations of arithmetic with forms that can be manipulated by both hand and eye. The postsymbolic containment patterns enabled by the James form provide a simple way to represent and to understand symbolic numeric expressions. But to see the simplicity naturally requires familiarity with iconic formal thinking.

What stands out within iconic form is the absence of many old and familiar numeric artifacts that have been assumed to be indispensable. There are, for example, no signs that identify the operations of arithmetic and no independent concepts of addition or multiplication. There is a general rejection of real numbers. There is the postsymbolic unification of syntax and semantics. There is in fact sufficient departure from modern symbolic mathematics to consider iconic form to be a different species of formal thought.

Treasures

Volume I focuses on visual and manipulable structures. Volume II takes an historical side trip to recount and compare the artifacts found by the first explorers of modern formal numerics about 140 years ago. Many of their discoveries have been canonized today as *what numbers are*, even though these artifacts were mined from cognitive environments that did not include vitally relevant experience with electrical machines, silicon computers, a global internet and a universe of software applications. Particularly absent from the cognitive artifacts of a century ago are modern knowledge engines such as *Mathematica* that can integrate sound, images, videos and databases within computational systems. Particularly absent from the mathematical artifacts of yesteryear is postsymbolic structure that reaches across the visceral territories of embodied thought.

Volume II explores iconic form with an emphasis on equivalence relations over patterns with a numeric interpretation. The conceptual artifacts brought back include void-equivalence, base-free exponents, dynamic objects and structural minimality. Figure 31-1 is repeated from Figure 16-1 of Volume II. It is the velvet cloth upon which are displayed both found treasures and cherished beliefs. The technical names of these structures are signposts installed along the way for others to follow. The new methods of iconic thinking are grounded by their *comparison* to well known methods of symbolic thinking. These new perspectives are the spoils of discovery. Their value is moot. Hopefully the iconic approach has sufficient value in its novelty, in its unexpected forms and in its anchors to symbolic concepts.

The Edges

Separated from the iconic forms of Volume I and from the contextualization of these forms in Volume II are the more exotic artifacts of this volume. Exotic conventional objects such as -1 and $\sqrt{-1}$ and ∞ have been studied for hundreds of years. Mathematicians now have excellent

Axioms and Theorems of James Algebra

Ground Interpretations

o = ( )　☞　1　　　　　　　　　(o) =*def*= #

<>　☞　0　　　　　　　　　　　<o>　☞　−1

[ ]　☞　−∞　　　　　　　　　　<[ ]>　☞　∞　　(*volume III*)

Unit Definitions

( ) ≠ *void*　　　　　　　　　**existence**

( ) ( ) ≠ ( )　　　　　　　　　**unit accumulation**

[ ] [ ] ⇒ [ ]　　　　　　　　　**unification**　(*volume III*)

[ ]<[ ]> ⇒ *indeterminate*　　　**indeterminacy** (*volume III*)

Pattern Axioms

([A]) = [(A)] = A　　　　　　　**inversion**　　*enfold/clarify*

(A [B C]) = (A [B]) (A [C])　　**arrangement**　*collect/disperse*

A <A> = *void*　　　　　　　　　**reflection**　　*create/cancel*

Interpretative Axiom　　　　(*volume III*)

(<[ ]>) = <[ ]> = [<[ ]>]　　　**infinite interpretation**

Theorems

( ) <( )> = *void*　　　　　　　**unit reflection**　*create/cancel*

([ ]) = [( )] = *void*　　　　　**void inversion**　*enfold/clarify*

(A [ ]) = *void*　　　　　　　　**dominion**　　　*emit/absorb*

A = ([A][o])　　　　　　　　　**indication**　　*unmark/mark*

A..$_N$..A = ([A][o..$_N$..o])　　**replication**　　*replicate/tally*

<<A>> = A　　　　　　　　　　**involution**　　*wrap/unwrap*

<A><B> = <A B>　　　　　　　**separation**　　*split/join*

<A <B>> = <A> B　　　　　　　**reaction**　　　*react/react*

(A [<B>]) = <(A [B])>
(A <[<B>]>) = <(A <[B]>)>　　**promotion**　　*demote/promote*

Figure 31-1: *Summary of definitions, axioms and theorems (Figure 16-1)*

strategies for dealing with, for example, complex numbers and infinite sequences. The three James pattern axioms were initially chosen to shed light upon natural numbers. From them arose two creatures that are so fundamental yet so unexpected that they deserved a volume of their own. The first, [<o>], labeled J, was discovered as a symbolic expression three hundred years ago and then lost in obscurity until now. This volume tells its story. The second, [ ], what we are calling the *square unit*, is non-numeric yet embedded at the very foundations of the iconic territory defined by the axiomatic belief system.

This volume also includes brief explorations of the derivatives of functions, the structure of trigonometric forms, the construction of imaginary numbers and the varieties of non-numeric form that we call infinity. These inquiries are experiments in the application of the James algebra to some well-known topics in elementary mathematics. The volume ends by returning to the visceral iconic dialects in Volume I.

The Structure of Numbers

Numbers are widely described as belonging to nested subsets. It is tempting to believe that natural numbers ($\mathbb{N}$) give rise to integers ($\mathbb{Z}$) which generate the rationals ($\mathbb{Q}$) which evolve into the reals ($\mathbb{R}$) which are somehow directly connected to the complex numbers ($\mathbb{C}$). Expressed symbolically as *containment relations*,

$$\mathbb{N} \subset \mathbb{Z} \subset \mathbb{Q} \subset \mathbb{R} \subset \mathbb{C}$$

Figure 31-2 provides the definitions of these double-struck symbols for number types.[5] There are certainly elements of group theoretic structure in these categories. Whole numbers are natural numbers with the additive identity 0 appended. Integers append the additive inverse –n. The multiplicative identity 1 is embedded as the foundation of natural numbers. Rational numbers append the multiplicative inverse 1/n. Irrational numbers have been

number type	includes	☞	James algebra
N *natural*	n		o o ≠ o
whole	0		*same as natural*
Z *integer*	−n		<N> = (J [N])
Q *rational*	1/n		(<[Z]>) = ((J [[Z]]))
R *real*	*order only*		[Q]
imaginary	bi		(J/2 [R])
C *complex*	a + bi		R (J/2 [R])

Figure 31-2: *The structure of conventional and James numbers*

Richard Dedekind
1831-1916

known since the ancient Greeks however until Dedekind defined the real numbers in 1888. Irrationals such as √2, π and e, were generally limited to numbers that had a distinct geometric meaning. **Algebraic numbers** are roots of polynomial equations, their category is uniquely linked to the historical evolution of algebra via a fascination with solving polynomial equations during the European Renaissance. Algebraic numbers are chimera, composed of incommensurable number types such as a natural number and an irrational, 1 + √2 for example. As mentioned in Chapter 27.2, the real numbers have the dubious distinction of being overwhelmingly composed of *lawless numbers* that are both indescribable and unknowable. The complex numbers, such as 3 + 4i, are a special type of algebraic number composed of two real numbers, one multiplied by the imaginary i.

Conventional numbers are an historical and evolutionary aggregation of concepts and design decisions. Each type is a *closure* that assures that operations on the type stay within the bounds of that type, with various exceptions of course like divide-by-zero. Figure 31-2 compares these traditional categories to the structures elicited by the James axioms. The James analogs are only examples and are not comprehensive. In particular James algebra does not include all real numbers. Since logarithms are transcendental irrationals, [Q] does include *describable* real numbers.

The James design decisions result in a completely different answer to the question: *What is a number?* James algebra trades our conventional diversity of notation for a minimal notation and much simpler operations, leading to a significantly more coherent design approach with

- *no zero*
- *one constant* J that is a focus of this volume
- *one operation*: containment
- *two types of container*: round and square[6]
- *three pattern axioms[7]*
- *one proof method*: pattern substitution
- *three exceptional rules* to handle non-numbers.

The James iconic pattern transformations cover all of elementary mathematics yet do not include the operations of addition, subtraction, multiplication or division.

31.3 Remarks

The many annotated demonstrations in this volume cover imaginary logarithms, differentiation, trigonometry and infinite forms. Collectively they support a primary observation that James forms are sufficient to construct almost all of elementary arithmetic. Harvey Friedman and many others who have recently developed **reverse mathematics** established that *arithmetic is sufficient* for constructive mathematics, a goal set by Hilbert as the **arithmetization of mathematics.**[8] The highly technical work on *computable foundations* suggests that the iconic exploration of diverse mathematical domains is of interest both theoretically and pragmatically. This volume is too primitive to make substantive contributions to either the theory or the pragmatics of computation. *Iconic Arithmetic* instead attempts to shine *first light* into iconic territories that are generally unexplored. We'll now step back to find the origin of J.

addition
$$A + B \ \text{☞} \ A \ B$$

subtraction
$$A - B \ \text{☞} \ A \ (J \ [B])$$

multiplication
$$A \times B \ \text{☞} \ ([A][B])$$

division
$$A/B \ \text{☞}$$
$$([A](J \ [[B]]))$$

power
$$B^A \ \text{☞}$$
$$(((([B]][A]))$$

root
$$B^{1/A} \ \text{☞}$$
$$((([B]](J \ [[A]])))$$

logarithm
$$\log_B A \ \text{☞}$$
$$([[A]](J \ [[B]]))$$

Endnotes

1. **opening quote:** J. Stillwell (2016) *Elements of Mathematics* p.8. Beginning with *almost everything*, the original is also in italics.

2. **boundary math resembles optimized computer architectures:** The RISC computational architecture is a Reduced Instruction Set Computer. The processing unit uses very few instructions but does them a lot of times.

3. **compute the square root of a number by hand:** As I did as an Australian 7th grader in the 1950s.

4. **large numbers are now hanging tenaciously by a thread:** Addition of columns of four digit numbers is still thriving, as is chanting the numeric matrices that structure digital addition and multiplication. Analogous content in English class would return us to the eighteenth century for memorization and recital of epic poems written in Middle English.

5. **definitions of these double-struck symbols for number types:** The origin of the double-struck typography appears to be very recent (within the last sixty years) as is the entire idea of agglomerating numbers into subsets. Retrieved online 7/20 https://mathworld.wolfram.com/Doublestruck.html

6. **types of container: round and square:** In this volume, the *angle-bracket* is taken to be an abbreviation for the constant J expressed within a J-frame, (J [A]). The two ensemble grouping axioms from Chapter 3.2 provide an additional type of bracket that pragmatically integrates into the James form a grouping notation for large accumulations of units that is the equivalent of adding columns to our conventional notation.

7. ***three pattern axioms:*** The pattern shared across these axioms is the James frame (A [B]), described in Chapter 35.1. Three additional axioms that characterize the behavior of the non-numeric square unit [ ] extend the James algebra into forms associated with the concept of infinity.

8. **by Hilbert as the arithmetization of mathematics:** Reverse mathematics asks which axioms are best suited for supporting the diversity of mathematical theorems. An excellent introduction to the field is J. Stillwell (2018) *Reverse Mathematics: Proofs from the inside out.*

Chapter 32

Invention

*In the end, one cannot help but feel that humanity is not
really clever enough to have 'invented' mathematics.[1]
— John Barrow (1992)*

In mathematics it is permissible to write down any
well-formed equation, and only well-formed equations
are permissible. Equations may be TRUE or FALSE but
sometimes apparently benign well-formed equations lead
to impossible, or at least unwelcome, structural consequences. When two valid expressions are placed on each
side of an equality symbol, valid transformation rules can
fail. The culprit, it appears, are the constraints embodied
in an assertion of equality. Although $x = 2$ may be taken to
be TRUE, declaring $x = x + 1$ is frowned upon. Both variables and the equations that contain them are inherently
constrained to a consensually agreed upon the domain of
discourse. What are most unwelcome are valid transformations that generate results outside of that predetermined
domain. This is why Peano's axioms of arithmetic (Volume
II, Chapter 22.2) carefully specify what qualifies to be
called a *number* and what is disqualified from being a
number. To qualify, a candidate for Peano numberhood
must be an already established number plus 1, that is $n+1$,
or it can be 1 itself. The disqualification is stated as an

1 is a number

$n+1 \neq 1$

algebraic inequality, n + 1 ≠ 1. That is, 1 itself is special, it is never a natural sum.

Here we will examine the consequences of violating symbolic restrictions, something that Peano apparently rigorously avoided. The hope is that James algebra might help to unify the monsters created when we elect to ignore the bounds implicit within well behaved equations. The conventional finesse is to define new types of numbers when equations generate creatures that escape the agreed upon limits imposed by a specific domain. An alternative is to suggest that the domain of discourse was ill conceived in the first place. It is also conventional wisdom to provide these new creatures with disparaging names: negative, irrational, imaginary, contradictory, surreal. What do these aberrations share in common? Are there more monsters lurking within the structure of valid equations? Why are some cherished (the imaginaries) and some despised (the negatives)?

32.1 Inventing Numbers

Embedded within the symbols of simple algebra and within our collective consensus of what they may mean are new and hidden worlds of numbers, each world extending the types of numbers that precede it. Figure 32-1 shows seven simple looking equations and their straightforward solutions. Each solution introduces *a new numeric domain*, highlighted by *quotation marks* in the figure. Each solution subsumes the inventions that precede it.

There are some remarkable patterns in this list. Each equation is equal to zero. The right-side of each equation declares that the expression on the left has no value. The left-side must manage to reduce to nothing. In James terms it must become *void*. And indeed that is what happens when we substitute a solution back into the equation that gave rise to it. Everything cancels. Each equation

equation	void-equivalent form	new concepts
$x + 0 = 0$	x	$x = \text{“0”}$
$x + 1 = 0$	x o	$x = \text{“–1”}$
$2x - 1 = 0$	x x <o>	$x = 2^{\text{“–1”}}$
$x^2 - 1 = 0$	([x][x]) <o>	$x = \text{“}\pm\text{”}\, 1$
$x^2 + 1 = 0$	([x][x]) o	$x = (-1)^{\text{“½”}} = (-1)^{\text{“}2^{-1}\text{”}}$
$2^x + 1 = 0$	(([[oo]][x])) o	$x = \text{“}\log_2 -1\text{”}$
$x + x = 0$	x x	$x = \text{“J”}$

Figure 32-1: *New concepts introduced by simple equations*

identifies a *new type of cancellation rule* for conventional notation and a new void-equivalent form within boundary notation.

An assertion of **structural equivalence** is fundamentally different than an assertion of **void-equivalence**. The void-based strategy of examining equations that equate expressions to zero places the inquiry outside of the Western *thesis-antithesis-synthesis* mode of discourse and squarely in the Eastern *creation-from-nothing* perspective.[2]

The solutions in the rightmost column of Figure 32-1 are a rouges' gallery of nightmares for school children. Negative numbers are the most error prone concept in arithmetic from third grade on up. **Negative one** is the arch-villain, it occurs in every solution but the first.[3] Negative one is the root cause of both our discoveries and our woes within numbers of all types. Negative one facilitates the invention of every new numeric type beyond the naturals.

In this chapter, we'll transcribe each of the equations on this list into James algebra. Since each asserts *is-equal-to-zero*, we'll use void-based thinking to arrive at an understanding of their solutions. We're heading toward a principled evolution of James forms that correspond to the stranger types of numbers we already know. In particular, we'll bring attention to the role of the James form J, [<o>], in the construction of novel numeric creatures, as groundwork for a more extensive exploration of J in the following chapters.

X + 0 = 0

The solution to the first (and the simplest) equation in Figure 32-1 is 0.

$$X + 0 = 0 \qquad\qquad X = \text{``0''}$$

In James notation, $X = void$. X is *void-equivalent*. Since every object in the equation is zero, perhaps we should also have written the equation as

$$X + X = X \qquad\qquad X = \text{``0''}$$

Indeed this equation has only one standard solution, $x = 0$.[4] In the spirit of the equations that follow we are looking for a solution that is not zero. The James form makes it clear that all of the left-hand forms are void-equivalent. There are also an unlimited number of illusory forms that by either Inversion or Reflection or Dominion are themselves void-equivalent.

void-equivalent

$$X = void = [(\,)] = A <A> = ([A][\,]) \ldots$$
☞ $\quad X = 0 = \log 1 = A - A = A \times 0 \ldots$

Thus of the unlimited number of different void-equivalent forms, any could be a solution to this equation.

X + 1 = 0

The solution is $x = -1$. This equation is not considered to be controversial in the 21st century but in the 16th century the idea of a "negative" number, a number that could not possibly have a real referent, seemed abhorrent. Although this equation appears to be straightforward, it requires us to invent something that was not present in the original equation, a type of number that cancels the positive unit. If we were living in a barter economy, negative numbers introduce the unpleasant, and undesirable, idea of exchanging our potatoes for symbols on a piece of paper because there are no negative potatoes.

Transcribing the equation into James form and solving for x using the cover and move operations of the Composition Principle (Chapter 18.1), we get

$$x + 1 = 0 \quad \text{☞} \quad x\ o\ =\ void$$
$$x\ \ \ =\ \text{<o>}$$

Unit cancellation provides an immediate answer, $x = \text{<o>}$. The invention in this case is already within James algebra as the angle-bracket defined by the Reflection axiom. The angle-bracket is not the same as -1, since negative one is one interpretation of the more general angle-bracket concept of Reflection. Reflection is intimately connected with the meaning of the equal sign as a mechanism to assert **identity**.

Composition Principle

$$A = B \Leftrightarrow \{A\ C\} = \{B\ C\}$$

cover

$$(A) = B \Leftrightarrow A = [B]$$

move

$$A\ C = B \Leftrightarrow A = B\ \text{<C>}$$

move

reflection

$$A\ \text{<A>} = void$$

identity

$$A = A$$

$2x - 1 = 0$

The solution is $x = 1/2$, or written in exponential notation, $x = 2^{-1}$. The new creature, 2^{-1}, is a *unit fraction*. Fractions have been around much longer than negative numbers so the solution does not come as a complete surprise. Both Babylonian and Egyptian math included unit fractions, the Egyptians embedding their unit fractions within the Eye of Horus. The concept of a fraction is not, however, to be found within the original equation to be solved. The structure of the fraction is fabricated to provide a solution. If we had been talking about cats, for example, fractions introduce the unpleasant, and undesirable, idea of half a cat. Fractions are the source of the second most common error made by school children. After a dozen years of schooling two out of three American adults remain incapable of accurately manipulating fractions.

Fractions (aka rational numbers) divide a unit into equal pieces. The denominator specifies both the size of the pieces and how many of the pieces constitute the whole. Unfortunately different denominators make different sized pieces so putting different fractions into the same container often creates a mess of incompatible fragments. Fractions are not well designed to be added together. They are totally at home being multiplied, cause after all that's what they do. Fractions divide single units into multiple pieces.

In James form, our current equation is

$$2x - 1 = 0 \quad ☞ \quad ([x][oo]) <o> = \quad void$$

move	$([x][oo])$	$= \quad o$
cover	$[x][oo]$	$= \quad [o]$
clarify/move	$[x]$	$= \quad <[oo]>$
cover	x	$= (<[oo]>) \quad ☞ \quad x = 1/2$

Finally, let's look at the boundary form of two equivalent expressions for unit fractions, the fractional and the exponential. A fraction is an unmarked exponential.

$$1/N = N^{-1} \quad ☞ \quad (<[N]>) = (([[N]][<o>]))$$

promote	$(<([[N]][o])>)$
unmark	$(< \quad [N] \quad >)$

$$x^2 - 1 = 0$$

The solution is ± 1.

$$x^2 = 1$$
$$x = \pm \sqrt{1} = \pm 1$$

Any solution must be a form of unity; whenever x is larger or smaller than 1, self-multiplication it does not return a unit. The surprise is that there are two solutions, the comfortable +1 and the difficult −1. Where does the negative solution come from? This question would not arise had we not inverted +1 in the first place. In other words, solving the equation x + 1 = 0 set us up for an inevitable *bifurcation of unity* that percolates through every numeric operation. How many unities are there? How many more will show up innocently as newly invented solutions to previously unsolved equations? Let's move forward by solving this quadratic equation using boundary methods.

```
x² - 1 = 0   ☞

    (([[x]][oo])) <o> =      void
    (([[x]][oo]))     =       o                          move
      [[x]][oo]       =    [[o]]                         cover
      [[x]]           =    [[o]]<[oo]>                   move
        x             = (([[o]]<[oo]>))    ☞ 1^(1/2)     cover
        x             = (([    ]<[oo]>))                 clarify
        x             = (              )   ☞ 1           absorb
```

The solution here is 1. There is no suggestion of −1 as a solution. Where is it? First let's demonstrate that −1 is a solution.

```
 x² - 1   ☞   (([[ x ]][oo]))   <o>     with   x = <o>
              (([[<o>]][oo]))   <o>                          substitute
              (  [<o>][<o>] )   <o>                          replicate
            <<(  [ o ][ o ] )>><o>                           promote
              (             )   <o>                          unwrap/clarify
                   void                  ☞ 0                 cancel
```

Compare the substitution of −1 as a solution above to the substitution of +1:

```
 x² - 1   ☞   (([[x]][oo]))<o>      with   x = o
              (([[o]][oo]))<o>                               substitute
              (([   ][oo]))<o>                               clarify
              (           )<o>                               absorb
                   void                  ☞ 0                 cancel
```

The primary difference is that substitution of −1 requires the use of the angle-bracket theorems Promotion and Involution. As well, the substitution of −1 as a solution introduces J into the solution path at the first substitution. For this we'll need the J-void theorem that is demonstrated in Chapter 34.4.

```
J J = void                                                   J-void
```

Here is the substitution of −1 again, this time with J made explicit. The reduction now mirrors the substitution of +1 above with the exception that J must be replicated to be voided.[5]

$$x^2 - 1 \quad \text{☞} \quad ((\,[[<o>]]\,[oo]))<o> \quad \textit{with} \quad x = <o>$$

substitute	$((\,[\quad J\quad]\,[oo]))<o>$
replicate	$(\quad J \quad J \quad)<o>$
J-void object	$(\qquad\qquad\quad)<o>$
cancel	$\textit{void} \qquad\qquad \text{☞} \quad \emptyset$

It is clear from substitution that −1 and +1 are both solutions. Rather than facing the prospect of no solutions this equation has an abundance of solutions. We have a choice. But if we had been talking about money, for example, square roots introduce the unpleasant, and undesirable, idea that giving money and getting money are both solutions to the same economic problem. But the question remains, how does taking a square root introduce multiple solutions? One possible resolution (suggested by Euler in Chapter 33.2) is to introduce a new type of unit, ±1, the superposition of +1 and −1.

In James notation, we can see that the two roots are generated by the symbolic replication of J.

$$([<o>]\,[<o>]) \quad \text{☞} \quad -1 \times -1$$

substitute	$(\quad J \quad J \quad) \quad \text{☞} \quad \#^{J+J}$
J-void object	$(\qquad\qquad) \quad \text{☞} \quad 1$

Approaching this equation from a different direction, the reentrant form of $x^2 - 1 = \emptyset$ is

$$x = 1/x \qquad \text{☞} \qquad x = (<[x]>)$$

In the reentrant equation x must still be a type of unit. If this were not the case then one side would be a number and the other side would be the reciprocal of that number. Could the two solutions be hiding another type of *unit* that is equal to its own inverse?

We are looking at these simple equations in detail to help understand why strange things happen in conventional arithmetic. What principled and fundamental logic (other than blind computation) underlies the idea that $\sqrt{1}$ has two values? To what extent have we invited trouble and confusion by introducing the imaginary idea of a negative unit? The intention here is not to explore new tools for high school algebra, it is to explore a different way of thinking about how and why high school algebra works. And why it sometimes doesn't work.

$x^2 + 1 = 0$

The solution is $\pm\, i$. The intrigue thickens and it is entirely reasonable to react with confusion. What is i? Where did it come from? Why does it too satisfy this equation with both positive and negative values? At first, before i was understood, some mathematicians of the 16th century were content to make up the imaginary creature. It solved certain technical problems they had with finding solutions to polynomial equations. Some rejected it as being too absurd. Euler wrote:

> Of such numbers we may truly assert that they are neither nothing, nor greater than nothing, nor less than nothing, which necessarily constitutes them imaginary or impossible.[6]

Several hundred years after its birth, this creature turned out to be fundamental to our understanding of the nature of light, electricity and magnetism. But if we had been talking about caring for a garden, for example, these imaginary numbers introduce the unpleasant, and undesirable, idea that it is possible to water the plants we are watching in a gardening video

i is a label for an actual numeric structure, $\sqrt{-1}$. Just like negative numbers and fractions, the form of i includes an operation, two operations in fact! We do not get to see an actual creature, only the instructions about how to generate it.

Here is where the current equation takes us.

$$x^2 + 1 = 0$$
$$x^2 = -1$$
$$x = \pm \sqrt{-1}$$

This type of solution is a finesse rather than an explanation. The symbol for the operation has just moved from one side of the equation to the other. But substituting i for x does satisfy the equation. And −i works just as well, there are again two solutions. The mechanism that generates two solutions is independent of the value of i itself.

We'll solve for x using James' transformations:

$$x^2 + 1 = 0 \quad ☞$$

	$(([[x]][oo]))$ o =	*void*
move	$(([[x]][oo]))$ =	$<o>$
cover	$[[x]][oo]$ =	$[[<o>]]$
move	$[[x]]$ =	$[[<o>]] <[oo]>$
cover	x	$= (([[<o>]] <[oo]>))$

$$☞ \quad \sqrt{(-1)}$$

This is the James form of the multiplicative imaginary i. And in the middle of it is J.

$$i = (([[<o>]] \ <[oo]>))$$
substitute $\quad (([\quad J \quad] <[oo]>))$

We'll engage in a little hybrid notation to show the relationship between i and J more clearly.

$$i = (J/2)$$

i is the result of dividing the more fundamental concept J in half. This observation will be a driving force behind Chapters 38 and 39.

Both +i and −i are solutions to our current equation. The hybrid James forms (J/2) and <(J/2)> both satisfy the boundary equation, which is to say that the structure of the boundary form, like the square root operation, is *sign-blind*. A **sign-blind** expression is equal to its own negation. 0 is the premiere example: +0 = −0.

The original equation can be rearranged to generate another perspective, the **reentrant** form.

$$x = -1/x = -x^{-1}$$

This reentrant equation shows that x must be some type of unit, on a par with −1 and +1. When x is named i, we have

$$i = -i^{-1} \quad ☞ \quad i = <(<[i]>)>$$

And we might again lose faith in formerly comfortable tools. If i is positive, then the polarity of the equation does not balance (one side is positive and the other side is negative). Similarly if i is negative. So i is a number that is neither positive nor negative. It is **bipolar**. Whatever it is, i is doubly self-negated by −1, both as an object and as a reciprocal operation. Each occurrence of the negative sign has a different conventional meaning, as negation and as division. In the boundary form both are the same operation of reflection.

$2^x + 1 = 0$

The solution is J. Now we have an exponential equation, one that is usually solved by taking a logarithm. We'll take the base-2 logarithm for convenience.

$$
\begin{aligned}
2^x + 1 &= 0 \\
2^x &= -1 \\
\log_2 2^x &= \log_2 -1 \\
x &= \log_2 -1
\end{aligned}
$$
base-2

What kind of creature is x? It is neither clearly positive nor clearly negative, since both positive and negative numbers as powers yield positive results. Since converting between logarithms involves multiplying by a constant, we can bravely borrow a technique from James algebra, the *base-free logarithm*.

$$
\begin{aligned}
\#^x + 1 &= 0 \\
\#^x &= -1 \\
\log_\# \#^x &= \log_\# -1 \\
x &= \log_\# -1 \quad ☞ \quad J
\end{aligned}
$$
base-free

When # is anchored by choosing a specific base, the base will come with a constant of proportionality that adjusts the general to the specific. But what is $\log -1$ in any base? It must be another imaginary creature, since logarithms of negative numbers do not exist. If we had been talking about the birth of a child, for example, negative logs introduce the unpleasant, and undesirable, idea that giving birth could leave you owing rather than having children.

The nonexistence of a number is, of course, not a barrier, we have already crossed that line with -1. So let's engage in the same subterfuge and accept $\log_\# -1$ as a legitimate numeric creature. We can continue by solving this equation using boundary methods.

$$\#^x + 1 = 0 \quad \text{☞} \quad (x)\ o\ =\ \textit{void}$$

move

cover

$$(x)\quad =\quad <o>$$
$$x\quad =\quad [<o>]$$
$$\text{☞}\quad x = \log_\# -1$$

There is a remaining consideration. Like self-multiplication, this equation also has two solutions.

$$x\ =\ \pm \log_\# -1 \quad \text{☞} \quad \text{J}$$

We can demonstrate this by substituting each into the original equation. In conventional notation,

positive solution		*negative solution*	
$\#^x$	$+1 = 0$	$\#^x$	$+1 = 0$
$\#^{\log_\# -1}$	$+1 = 0$	$\#^{-\log_\# -1}$	$+1 = 0$
-1	$+1 = 0$	$(1/\#^{\log_\# -1})$	$+1 = 0$
		$1/-1$	$+1 = 0$
		-1	$+1 = 0$

We can call upon boundary notation for an explanation. With clarification coming later, the two roots are due to the *sign-blindness* of J.

Using void-based reasoning:

positive solution	negative solution	
(x) o	(x) o	
(J) o	(< J >) o	substitute
<o> o	(<[<o>]>) o	substitute
void	<(<[o]>)> o	cancel--promote
	<(< >)> o	clarify
	<( )> o	void cancel
	void	cancel

The negative solution invokes *void reflection*, a perhaps dubious technique that allows us to eliminate the angle-bracket by reflecting nothing.

x + x = 0

It may be a bit premature, but let's sneak up on J as if we were solving an algebraic equation. As noted J is not 0, but by the *J-void* theorem it satisfies the equation

$$J \; J \; = \; void \qquad \text{☞} \qquad J + J \; = \; 0$$

One route to solve this equation is to solve a simpler puzzle, one that may not look simpler.

$$x + x + x + x = 0$$

This route goes through the imaginary i. We know by definition that

$$i^4 = 1$$

Take the logarithm of each side of this exponential equation. I'll use the natural logarithm, although any base will do.

$$\ln i^4 = \ln 1$$
$$\ln i^4 = 0$$
$$4 \ln i = 0$$
$$\ln i + \ln i + \ln i + \ln i = 0$$

And here is the solution to the simpler problem,

$$x = \ln i$$

Now the original problem of finding two identical forms that add to zero is easily within reach.

equation	*solutions*
$x^2 - 1 = 0$	$x = \pm 1$
$x^2 + 1 = 0$	$x = \pm i$
$2^x + 1 = 0$	$x = \pm \log_2 -1$
$x + x = 0$	$x = 0, \ x = \pm J$

Figure 32-2: *Simple equations with multiple solutions*

$$\ln i + \ln i + \ln i + \ln i = 0$$
$$2 \ln i \ + \ \ 2 \ln i \ \ = 0$$
$$J \ \ + \ \ \ J \ \ \ = 0 \qquad \textit{with } J = 2 \ln i$$

This can be rearranged to get to the simpler form of J.

$$J = 2 \ln i = \ln i^2 = \ln -1$$

Let's take the same approach to solve for J, but this time not calling upon i. Instead of taking the logarithm, we'll shift to the exponential space.

$$J + J = 0$$
$$e^{J+J} = e^0$$
$$e^J \times e^J = 1$$
$$(e^J)^2 = 1^2$$

We know that x^2 hides an alternative, $(-x)^2$ and this is where the alternative solution to our equation can be found.

$$x^2 = n \quad \Rightarrow \quad x = \pm \sqrt{n}$$
$$(e^x)^2 = 1 \quad \Rightarrow \quad e^x = \pm \sqrt{1} = \pm 1$$

There are again two solutions to the equation $(e^x)^2 = 1$:

$$e^x = +1 \qquad\qquad e^x = -1$$

Applying the logarithm transformation to both of these equations returns us from the exponential space and pro-vides two solutions to the equation $x + x = 0$,

$$\ln e^x = \ln +1 \qquad\qquad \ln e^x = \ln -1$$
$$x = 0 \qquad\qquad\qquad x = \ln -1$$

We have found three different solutions to this equation: *void* and the sign-blind ±J. To consolidate the observation of bipolar solutions, each of the equations shown in Figure 32-2 has (at least) two solutions.

32.2 Remarks

In the following chapters, we will explore the geometric interpretation of J as both bipolar and its own inverse, as well as several of its other unusual properties. We have foreshadowed the coming content by showing that J is intimately related to i. An intermediate objective will be to put a firm foundation under the various irregularities of arithmetic computation, including the sign calculus, the square roots of unity and the arbitrary restrictions on the transformation of exponential and logarithmic expressions.

Many different types of expressions stand in place of two or more values. For example, the absolute value function represents two different values:

$$|8| = 8 \quad and \quad |8| = -8$$

$$(\pm 3)^2 = 9$$
$$\sqrt{4} = \pm 2$$
$$\sqrt{-1} = \pm i$$
$$\log -1 = \pm J$$
$$\cos \alpha = \cos \pm \alpha$$

This feature, however, violates the uniqueness constraint on functions. The solution is to ignore the negative alternative, although it does exist. Thus we commonly say that $\sqrt{4} = 2$ rather than the more accurate $\sqrt{4} = \pm 2$.

We have introduced the concept of *sign-blindness* for these expressions. The concept plays a major role in current and past confusion about the meaning of the logarithm of negative numbers. But first we will examine the history of what we are here calling J, as it was debated and explored by the great mathematicians Leonhard Euler, Gottfried Leibniz and Johann Bernoulli.

Endnotes

1. **opening quote:** J. Barrow (1992) *Pi in the Sky* p.258.

2. **squarely in the Eastern creation-from-nothing perspective:** Hōsaku Matsuo emphasizes the difference between the holistic creative assertions that we are exploring and the synthetic logic of an algebraic equation:

> "1+2=3 is a form of a dialectic, a logic, but far more important than this is the reflection on (1+2)–3=0 which is another unique equation. Put another way, the zero-concept does not simply refer to nullity or nothingness but, most significantly, because of it, everything is possible and, contrarily, if it were not present nothing would materialize."

H. Matsuo (1987) trans. K. Inada. *The Logic of Unity* p.111.

3. **the arch-villain, it occurs in every solution but the first:** –1 is hidden within the abbreviation J in the last equation.

4. **Indeed this equation has only one standard solution, x = 0:** Non-standard solutions require new types of non-numeric "numbers". For example,

$$\infty + \infty = \infty$$

5. **the exception that J must be replicated to be voided:** Replication of J is intimately related to its void-based nature. As we will see in the following chapters (that incidentally trespass upon conventional concepts), it takes two replicas of J to reach *void*.

6. **which necessarily constitutes them imaginary or impossible:** L. Euler (1770) *Elements of Algebra* §144.

Chapter 33

History

From nothing I have created another entirely new world.[1]
— *János Bolyai (1823)*

Every mathematical object can be considered to be imaginary. There is no 1 in the physical world. We begin arithmetic with a construction in our imagination. We heap fantasy upon fantasy to construct −1, perhaps the most egregious imaginary. Then come fractions of unitary wholes, the self-contradictory 0, the affront of 1/0, infinitely complex real numbers, infinity itself, and of course the impossible $\sqrt{-1}$. Why has log −1 languished in relative obscurity? For that we will need to go back to the work of Leonhard Euler nearly three hundred years ago.

33.1 Historical Perspective

As you might expect, J is not really new. The concept of the logarithm of a negative number evolved along side the concept of the imaginary i during the early 18th century. Obviously complex numbers took center stage, relegating J to a footnote within the contributions of the mathematical genius Euler. A possible reason for the scarcity of the conventional use of J is the widely held belief that the imaginary i is the *simplest*, most fundamental imaginary.

Nonexistence

The prevalent view of log -1 is that it is undefined as a number. Just like we cannot divide by zero, we cannot find the logarithm of a negative number. But there are two kinds of nonexistence. A concept can be *imaginary* but completely real within the imaginary world. This kind of nonexistence is a simple disconnection from physical reality, not a disconnection from the conceptual abstractions that generate non-physical virtual realities such as mathematical objects. The other kind of nonexistence is a declaration that there are no virtual or physical realities within which the concept exists. Theoreticians who are enamored with physicality, for example, might deny the existence of all virtual realities, reserving the concept of *reality* for tangibles. Some folks enamored with mathematics might call real only those formal objects that connect to known abstractions, while denying the virtual reality of contradictions. For example, 5 = -5 would not exist in either real and virtual worlds. This unfortunate rejection, however, is also a rejection of the unifying concept of **absolute value**, for which |5| = ±5. The concept of sign-blindness also accepts that 5 = -5.

Some folks may suspend judgment to see if there is a deeper understanding that arises out of apparent contradiction. We could accept, for example 2 = 1, and see what happens. In this particular example we land within logic, as the expression of an idempotency law. A OR A = A. We also confirm Spencer Brown's Law of Calling with a numeric rather than a boundary interpretation.

calling

( ) ( ) = ( )

The distinction between types of existence differentiates the positions of the 18th century mathematicians who debated the nature of J. Some said it is real, some said it is imaginary, and some said it is neither real nor imaginary but instead absurd. I suspect the rejection of the logarithm of a negative number is based upon reasoning about meaning. Another more algebraic attitude is to accept log −1 *without meaning* but with strict rules of manipulation. For instance, the boundary form [<( )>] obeys the James axioms, occurs often, is stable, has unusual properties and can be interpreted as log −1. The structure of James algebra itself is sufficient, independent of whether or not we are comfortable with the interpretation. Within James algebra, J is certainly real in both a structural and an existential sense. If we accept the basic design decision that all James forms describe configurations of physical containers, then J can be physically real as well.

An Infinity of Logarithms

This chapter follows in the footsteps of Euler, who resolved the controversies surrounding J in 1747 by proposing that *every number has an infinity of logarithms*.[2] Positive numbers have exactly one real logarithm and an unlimited number of imaginary logarithms, while negative numbers lack the one real logarithm. The concept of an infinite number of logarithms comes directly from associating logarithms with the angles of rotation around a circle. Once around is 360° or 2π radians. But we can continue, twice around is 4π radians, three times around is 6π radians, without limit. Similarly logarithms are cyclic and increasing, with log 1 taking on the values 0, 2πi, 4πi, 6πi, ... It was the behavior of J that contributed to Euler's very creative idea that some expressions support an infinity of values.

For convenience in this section, let's standardize the base of logarithms to be e, since that's the way it was discussed three centuries ago. The **natural logarithm** is base-e, written as ln. The concept of base-free logarithms is new, so we revert to Euler's base-e for historical accuracy. Yes, the e stands for Euler and is often called **Euler's number**. And yes, Euler also named √−1 as "i", the first letter of the Latin word *imaginarius*.

33.2 The Great Mathematicians

The mathematicians Johann Bernoulli, Gottfried Leibniz and Leonhard Euler debated the meaning of ln −1 throughout the first half of the 18th century. Each was a world-class mathematician and each held adamantly to a different perspective. As Euler commented in 1749,

> This dissension seems all the more remarkable because it centers upon an article of the part of mathematics which we call pure, and which we do not ordinarily believe susceptible to any dispute.[3]

The letters shared among these three geniuses have been published. What stands out is that the discussion about ln −1 cannot be separated from a wide ranging and ongoing discussion about the meaning of both i and −1 in specific, about the meaning of various advanced aspects of calculus as context, and about metaphysics and philosophy as the ground of commitment. None of these men were exclusively mathematicians. This was a time when geniuses contributed to many different fields. Our three players are:

Leibniz (1646–1716) co-invented calculus (in international dispute with Newton). He is just as well known as a philosopher, a metaphysician and a logician. He also invented binary numbers.

Johann Bernoulli (1667–1748) came from a family of great mathematicians (thus we need his first name). He is a generally uncredited but foundational developer of the calculus and the most mathematically oriented of the three.

Euler (1707–1783) was also a physicist (mechanics, optics, astronomy, music) and clearly the most mathematically profound of the three. Euler often applied the methods of natural science to his exploration of mathematics.

I should also mention **Jean D'Alembert** (1717–1783), who participated in the discussion in support of Bernoulli. D'Alembert was a renowned physicist (fluid mechanics, music) and a philosopher as well as an important mathematician who made fundamental contributions to the theory of wave equations.

D'Alembert was born two days after Leibniz died at age 70. You can see from the age disparities that the debate over ln –1 was between student and teacher, between icon and upstart. Yet all were struggling to understand how negative numbers worked, in the context of logarithms, in the context of calculus, in the context of imaginary numbers and in the context of philosophy. Unlike the rapid pace of today's innovations, in the 18th century it sometimes took a century to reach consensual clarity about difficult mathematical issues. Eventually all accepted Euler's perspective which he published in 1751.

In the 1700s almost everybody in Western Europe (but not in China, India or Persia) was confused about how negative numbers worked, especially in relation to exponents and logarithms. It was Leibniz who first introduced the use of negative numbers into a specific mathematical system, the *infinitesimal calculus*.

Euler's position on logarithms of negative numbers provided both a single concept that resolved most of the confusion and a tightly reasoned rebuttal of the positions of his colleagues (and since Euler was one of Bernoulli's students, of his teacher). Here are the design decisions that each advocated.

- *Leibniz:* ln –a is imaginary and does not exist as a number.
- *Bernoulli:* ln –a is real and has the same value as ln a.
- *Euler:* there are an unlimited number of logarithms for each integer, all of them are imaginary for ln –a.

One central issue was to determine whether or not certain expressions were real or imaginary. Real expressions could be used to solve problems in the physical world. Imaginary expressions, those including the concept i, had the vexing property that although they did not have a specific physical metaphor, in combination they sometimes lead to real numbers and thus to real answers. i is purely imaginary, but i x i turns out to be −1. Well, negative one was at the time also dubious, was *it* real or imaginary? To short circuit that question, we know that i x i x i x i is equal to +1, the archetype of reality so far as numbers go. Hidden in the fourth power of i is a much more mundane conundrum, −1 x −1 = +1.

Impossible Numbers

Sixteenth century Italian algebraists focused primarily on the solutions to polynomial equations with the imaginary i occurring regularly and unavoidably. Most mathematicians got used to accepting imaginary numbers, at least as a tool for solving algebraic equations. Negative numbers, zero and algebraic notation lead the way, providing plenty of occasion for critical commentary on the absurdity of numbers with no imaginable interpretation in physical reality. No doubt there was also some political oppression from teachers and colleagues, so that many mathematicians would work with complex numbers while vehemently denying their existence.

Gerolamo Cardano, in 1545, is credited with first using complex numbers extensively. He wrote of their effect:

Gerolamo Cardano
1501-1576

> So progresses arithmetic subtlety the end of which, as is said, is as redefined as it is useless.[4]

Underlying almost all of the difficulty with imaginaries was a profound difficulty with the meaning and use of negative numbers. It was −1, not necessarily the square root of −1, that ran into severe resistance. As late as 1759

the Canadian mathematician Francis Maseres wrote that
negative numbers

Francis Maseres
1731-1824

> serve only, as far as I am able to judge, to puzzle the
> whole doctrine of equations, and to render obscure
> and mysterious things that are in their own nature
> exceedingly plain and simple.[5]

Maseres was an influential bureaucrat. The content of his
delightfully entitled 1758 book decrying negative numbers[6] found its way into textbooks well into the mid-19th
century. Maseres advocated that there are no negative
numbers, only the operation of subtraction. He wrote:

> If any single quantity is marked either with the sign
> + or the sign − without affecting some other quan-
> tity, the mark will have no meaning or significance,
> thus if it be said that the square of −5, or the product
> of −5 into −5, is equal to +25, such an assertion must
> either signify no more than 5 times 5 is equal to 25
> without any regard for the signs, or it must be mere
> nonsense or unintelligible jargon.[7]

Here we see the precursors to the concept of sign-blindness.
But Maseres' opinion was viable only for classrooms and
not for working mathematicians. The evolution of calculus
from 1670 to 1750 lead to widespread pragmatic acceptance of both negative and imaginary numbers, still with
profound misunderstandings of how to think about them.

Writing in 1831, the logician Augustus DeMorgan
remained adamantly opposed to negative quantities:

Augustus DeMorgan
1806-1871

> Above all, he [the student] must reject the definition
> still sometimes given of the quantity −a, that it is less
> than nothing. It is astonishing that the human intel-
> lect should ever have tolerated such an absurdity
> as the idea of a quantity less than nothing; above
> all, that the notion should have outlived the belief

in judicial astrology and the existence of witches, either of which is ten thousand times more possible.[8]

Multiplication of imaginaries remained unresolved one hundred years after Euler's assertion that *negative times negative is positive*, when DeMorgan observed

> The imaginary expression $\sqrt{-a}$ and the negative expression $-b$ have this resemblance, that either of them occurring as the solution of a problem indicates some inconsistency or absurdity. As far as real meaning is concerned, both are equally imaginary, since $0 - a$ is as inconceivable as $\sqrt{-a}$.[9]

To illustrate the depths of this confusion, many modern historians with excellent credentials write that Euler did not understand how to multiply imaginaries![10] This from Professor of the History of Mathematics Ivor Gratton-Guiness:

> Euler...gaffed in his algebraic handling of complex numbers, by misapplying the product rule for square roots $\sqrt{(ab)} = \sqrt{a}\,\sqrt{b}$, to write $\sqrt{-2}\,\sqrt{-3} = \sqrt{6}$ instead of $-\sqrt{6}$.[11]

Maybe a typo, maybe a misreading but not a gaff. In looking closely at context and interpretation, Alberto Martínez concludes that the source of misunderstanding is that Euler was referring to the dual values that the square root function generates:

$$\sqrt{a} = \pm b \quad \textit{where} \quad (\pm b)^2 = a$$

Euler wrote:

> The square root of a given number always has a double value, thus negative as well as positive can be taken...this holds also for the impossible numbers; and the square root of $-a$ is $+\sqrt{-a}$ as well as $-\sqrt{-a}$.[12]

In that sense $\sqrt{-2}\sqrt{-3}$ is equal to both $+\sqrt{6}$ and $-\sqrt{6}$. Euler not only supported but also thought in terms of a **bipolar**

unity, the sign-blind ±1. This perspective went out of style during the nineteenth century, in favor of defaulting to the positive root, just like we now refer to i rather than ±i as the value of $\sqrt{-1}$. Still, just like the resistance to negative numbers, the resistance to imaginary numbers was largely on philosophical rather than pragmatic grounds. In 1778 mathematician and Professor of Natural Philosophy John Playfair wrote

John Playfair
1748-1819

In algebra again every magnitude being denoted by an artificial symbol, to which it has no resemblance, is liable, on some occasions, to be neglected, while the symbol may become the sole object of attention. It is not perhaps observed where the connection between them ceases to exist, and the analyst continues to reason about the characters after nothing is left which they can possibly express: if then, in the end, the conclusions which hold only for the characters be transferred to the quantities themselves, obscurity and paradox must of necessity ensue.[13]

Playfair's critique is of algebraic structure itself. "The arithmetic of mere characters can have no place in a science which is immediately conversant with ideas."[14] He does not accept the validity of a symbolic representation that strays far from a concrete referent. Playfair's essential dilemma is then: "If the operations of this imaginary arithmetic are unintelligible, why are they also not useless?"[15] This conundrum is a precursor of Eugene Wigner's twentieth century dilemma: Why is mathematics so unreasonably effective in the natural sciences?[16]

Container based numbers embody a similar critique but with a twist that may have accentuated Playfair's dilemma. Imaginary quantities such as [<( )>] can take on a physical manifestation, demonstrating that the issue does not lay with the disconnect between symbolic and physical meaning, but at a deeper level, with the nature of abstraction itself.

Logarithms

Logarithms made their appearance early in the 17th century and quickly gained fame as a much easier way to compute multiplications. Astronomer and mathematician Pierre-Simon Laplace comments on logarithms toward the end of the 18th century:

Pierre-Simon Laplace
1749-1827

> An admirable artifice which, by reducing to a few days the labour of many months, doubles the life of the astronomer, and spares him the errors and disgust inseparable from long calculations.[17]

The groundwork of negative numbers and logarithms led to a correspondence between Johann Bernoulli and Leibniz in 1712-13 on the nature of complex numbers and in particular on the logarithms of negative numbers. They had been corresponding about the development and meaning of the calculus since 1693. Both Bernoulli and Leibniz relegated complex numbers to the impossible, readily using Descartes' word "imaginary" to indicate that they do not exist. Descartes and Leibniz agreed that complex numbers are *not* numbers and that whatever they are, their value is imaginary. Calling upon a rich analogy, Leibniz wrote:

> Imaginary numbers are a fine and wonderful refuge of the divine spirit, almost amphibian between being and not-being.[18]

But algebraic style values following rules more than it values making sense. The irony of algebra is that it is insensitive to what we humans would call *absurd*. Referring to i, Tobias Dantzig comments,

> But, as happened in the case of negative numbers, so here too the mere writing down of the impossible gave it a symbolic existence.[19]

Although i may be called imaginary, meaningless and impossible, the symbolic rules of algebra are designed to be free of interpretation and impervious to what we may think of its structures. Euler says of imaginary numbers:

> They exist in our imagination, and we still have sufficient idea of them; since we know that by √−4 is meant a number which, multiplied by itself, produces −4; for this reason also, nothing prevents us from making use of these imaginary numbers, and employing them in calculation.[20]

Bernoulli disagreed with Leibniz' position that i is imaginary, claiming (as D'Alembert and Maseres would later agree) that ln −1 does have a meaning as the value 0. He supported this position by claiming that the logarithm of a negative number is the same as the logarithm of a positive number. To Bernoulli, logarithms are sign-blind to their arguments.

$$\ln -a = \ln a$$
$$\ln -1 = \ln 1 = 0$$

These logarithmic equations correspond to the exponential equations

$$e^0 = -1 \quad and \quad e^0 = 1$$

which makes Leibniz' position appear to be most reasonable. Implicated within sign-blind logarithms is the idea that exponents can generate dual values, which is indeed the case for the power 1/2 (i.e. for the square root):

$$1^{1/2} = -1 \quad and \quad 1^{1/2} = 1$$

Euler agreed with Leibniz, at least until he had thought it over for a couple of decades. In the Introduction of *Analysin Infinitorum* (1748) Euler defined the logarithmic function *only* for positive numbers.[21] However his 1749 paper, *On the logarithms of negative and imaginary numbers*, provides his definitive resolution.

Euler's Definition

We'll return to the debate between Leibniz and Bernoulli in the 1720s after seeing Euler's resolution circa 1750. Euler was called in, as the acknowledged but much younger master, to adjudicate the positions of Leibniz and Bernoulli. His solution, which supported neither, was to define logarithms of negative real numbers as *complex numbers*. Euler proposed that ln −1 has both a real part and an imaginary part. The real part is the value 0, in support of Bernoulli; the imaginary part is the value iπ, in support of Leibniz.

The direct relationship between negative logarithms and complex numbers is *Euler's identity*. Here's a deconstruction of this relationship.

Euler's identity

$$e^{i\pi} + 1 = 0$$
$$e^{i\pi} = -1$$
$$\ln e^{i\pi} = \ln -1$$
$$i\pi \ln e = \ln -1$$
$$i\pi = \ln -1$$

Written as a complex number,

$$\ln -1 = 0 + \pi i$$

In providing a geometric interpretation for ln −a as a rotation in the complex plane, Euler constructed J upon a foundation of an orthogonal two-dimensional space structured by 1 and i. In this interpretation J, as iπ, is associated with a rotation of π radians or 180°. In the complex plane, a rotation of π/2 radians (90°) is associated with changing heading from along the 1-axis to along the i-axis. A 180° rotation of J is composed of two 90° rotations of i, so that the sum of two rotations indicated by i is equivalent to one rotation indicated by J. From this perspective, J is composite and i is fundamental.

complex plane

The issues discussed prior to Euler's resolution align closely to the development of the boundary concept J in the following chapters, so there is much to be learned from the great men. We'll present some of their arguments and transcribe their ideas into James notation as a way to highlight the comparison of i as the fundamental imaginary rotation (with J as a composition of two i rotations) to J as the fundamental imaginary reflection (with i as one-half of a single reflection).

33.3 Leibniz, Bernoulli and Euler

I'll restrict this account to examples that do not rely on calculus, if only to shorten the background needed to understand the differing positions. Each of these great men was motivated by figuring out what the Leibniz/Newton calculus would do with $\ln -1$. Bernoulli's style was to present copious examples to support his position. Leibniz' style was to refute them.

Here are Bernoulli's four arguments, each is delineated and clarified by Euler in his 1749 paper. Each highlights a structural property of J. None differentiate J from 0, the step necessary to legitimize J as a discrete additive imaginary number. Here are what Bernoulli exposed as TRUE statements about J while at the same time inaccurately identifying J with 0:

— *Reason 1:* $J = -J$
— *Reason 2:* $J + J = 0$
— *Reason 3:* $J + J \neq 2 \times J$
— *Reason 4:* $J = \ln i + \ln i$

J = 0, Reason 1

The development of mathematical thinking since the Greeks has often emphasized comparisons or ratios. Ratios have the advantage of being pure, they do not express a particular metric like time or distance because within a ratio the units of measurement cancel.

1 second compared to 30 seconds
is the same as 1 compared to 30

But a prominent conceptual problem arose when negative numbers were introduced into ratios.

$$1 \; compared \; to \; -1 = 1/-1 = -1$$
$$-1 \; compared \; to \; 1 = -1/1 = -1$$

The two ratios have the same value, −1. But the first compares greater to lesser and the second compares lesser to greater. How can the comparison be the same when what is being compared is opposite?

Historically, logarithms were thought to be measuring ratios. A ratio that has no logarithm is an impossible comparison. So Leibniz took the logarithm of these ratios,

$$\ln (1/-1) = \ln 1 - \ln -1 = -\ln -1$$
$$\ln (-1/1) = \ln -1 - \ln 1 = \ln -1$$

The philosophical conundrum was solved. Since $\ln -1$ does not exist, the comparisons themselves were impossible. Bernoulli thought otherwise (as you may expect).

$$\ln -1 = \ln (1/-1) = \ln 1 - \ln -1 = -\ln -1$$
$$therefore \; \ln -1 = -\ln -1$$

The only number that is equal to its own negation is 0. So $\ln -1$ does have a real value, it is not imaginary.[22]

Now we'll interpret this example as James forms to see the debate from a different perspective.

	$\ln (-1/1)$ ☞	[([<o>] <[o]>)]
substitute		[(J <[o]>)]
clarify		J < >
void cancel		J

	$\ln (1/-1)$ ☞	[([o] <[<o>]>)]
substitute		[([o] < J >)]
clarify		< J >

We arrive at J = <J>, but that *does not imply* that J = *void*. In particular, J is not void since it does not reduce to *void* via the James axioms. All that the form of J-self-inverse implies is that J is sign-blind. Indeed it belongs to the same tribe of bipolar numbers as do ±i, ±0 and |5|.

The heart of this debate is about division of different types of unit, not about logarithms, since we can eliminate the idea of a logarithm to arrive at similar structures.

```
-1/1 ☞                    1/-1 ☞
   ([<o>] <[o]>)             ([o] <[<o>]>)
   (  J   <[o]>)             ([o] <  J  >)      substitute
   (  J  <   >)              (   <  J  >)       clarify
   (  J      )               (  <  J  >)        void cancel
```

Bernoulli's argument gains its strength from the sign-blindness of 0. Arguing that ln −1 is equal to 0 is a form of begging the question. It's 0 because it is constructed to act like 0 with respect to signs. But that does not make ln −1 = 0, rather it identifies two apparently unequal forms both of which share the common property of being sign-blind.

J = 0, Reason 2

Euler thought that this example makes the strongest case for Bernoulli's position since none of the transformations could be criticized. Here is Bernoulli's reasoning.

$$(-a)^2 = a^2$$
$$\ln (-a)^2 = \ln a^2$$
$$2 \ln -a = 2 \ln a$$
$$\ln -a = \ln a$$

Euler especially encouraged maintaining the full generality of the algebraic rules that defined how exponents work. No one wanted to break or limit the known rules of exponents and logarithms, so the transformations above are sacrosanct. Let's look at each step of Bernoulli's demonstration as James forms.

```
(-a)² = a²  ☞
      ((([<a>]][2]))   = ((([a]][2]))
      ( [<a>][<a>] )   = (  [a][a]  )      replicate
    <<( [ a ][ a ] )>> = (  [a][a]  )      promote
      ( [ a ][ a ] )   = (  [a][a]  )      unwrap
```

Nothing unusual here. The negative signs reduce because self-multiplication allows two applications of Promotion, which set the stage for Involution. To continue,

$$\ln (-a)^2 = \ln a^2 \ \text{☞}$$

clarify
$$[((\lfloor[<a>]][2]))] = [((\lfloor[a]][2]))]$$
$$([[<a>]][2]) \quad = \quad ([[a]][2])$$
$$\text{☞} \quad 2 \ln -a = 2 \ln a$$

Application of the power rule for logarithms involves only Inversion, again nothing unusual. Next we'll divide by two.

$$(2 \ln -a)/2 = (2 \ln a)/2 \ \text{☞}$$

cancel
$$([[<a>]][2]<[2]>) = ([[a]][2]<[2]>)$$
clarify
$$([[<a>]] \qquad) = ([[a]] \qquad)$$
$$[<a>] \qquad = \quad [a]$$
$$\text{☞} \quad \ln -a = \ln a$$

The logarithm turns self-multiplication into multiplication by two, which is then canceled with a division by two. The form of doubling a negative logarithm ([[<a>]][2]) suppresses Promotion of the angle-bracket. It is this captured angle-bracket that is interpreted as the negative argument to the logarithm function. The seemingly innocuous final transformation of dividing by 2 can obscure the fact that Bernoulli's demonstration is *independent* of the value a.

Returning to the James form, we could apply Replication rather than division by 2.

$$([[<a>]][2]) = ([[a]][2])$$
replicate
$$[<a>][<a>] = [a][a]$$

Consider this addition equation from a conventional perspective.

$$\textit{Let} \ x = [<a>] \ \textit{and} \ y = [a]$$
$$x + x = y + y$$

Does this equation necessarily imply that x = y? The equation is independent of a so we can simplify by letting a = 1.

$$\textit{Let} \ x = [<o>] = J \quad \textit{and} \quad y = [o] = \textit{void}$$
$$J \quad J = \textit{void}$$
$$\text{☞} \ J + J = 0 + 0$$

The essential question is about the nature of J, not about the nature of all logarithms of negative numbers. To draw an analogy, $a \times 0 = 0$ regardless of the value of a. This property of zero is independent of a. Not only is multiplying by zero sign-blind, it is also magnitude-blind. Similarly, J is also both magnitude- and sign-blind. Euler was fully aware of this.

Only when we *presume* that J = 0, can we conclude that x = y above. J is not necessarily 0 because there is nothing in this example that requires J to be a real number. It could be imaginary.

J = 0, Reason 3

Bernoulli's reasoning here is intended to demonstrate that J = 0.[23]

$$\ln 1 \quad\; = 0$$
$$\ln (-1)^2 = 0$$
$$2 \ln -1 = 0$$

$2a = 0$ *implies that* $a = 0$, *therefore* $\ln -1 = 0$

If we presume that J ≠ 0, then at least one of the rules above must fail. *Or* we could question the final implication. And it is the implication that is the weakness in this example. If $\ln -1$ is something different than 0, then the way it might be different is that two of them add up to zero, but one of them does not. Multiplication by two as well as the value of J is in question. When we write $2a$, we construct and then tally two replicas. So underneath both addition and value there may be a fundamental difficulty with the act of replication.

Euler also recognized this surprising circumstance. He justifies this line of reasoning only in the case that a and $-a$ each have an infinity of imaginary logarithmic values.

We can trace the sequence of transformations within the James form:

	0 ☞ *void*	
void enfold	[( )] ☞	ln 1
substitute	[(([[<o>]][2]))]	ln (−1)²
clarify	([[<o>]][2])	2 ln −1
replicate	J J	ln −1 + ln −1

This construction leads directly to Bernoulli's conclusion, $2a = 0$ *implies that* $a = 0$ *where* $a = J$. Replication is the suspect point of failure in this logic:

$$2 \ln -1 = 0 \quad implies \quad \ln -1 + \ln -1 = 0$$

The reason for the failed logic is unexpected. A sum can cancel to zero, just as a product can cancel to one. The equation $2a = 0$ has two solutions: $a = 0$ and $a = J$. This situation is the same as $a^2 = 1$ implying both $a = 1$ and $a = -1$. The difference is that the imaginary solution for $a^2 = 1$ (i.e. −1) is constructed as a *multiplication*, while the imaginary solution for $2a = 0$ (i.e. J) is constructed as an *addition*. Multiplicative cancellation leaves the identity element for multiplication, which is 1. Additive cancellation leaves the identity element for addition, which is 0.

$a \times a = b \times b$
while
$a \neq b$

Here's a technical refinement from the James perspective. $2a = 0$ *does imply* $a = 0$. In the case of J however $a + a$ *does not imply* $2a$. We cannot arbitrarily accumulate void-equivalent forms because we cannot count them in the first place. Of course, we can count *symbols* that stand in place of void-equivalent forms. There are definitely three J tokens in "J J J". The issue is that within a void-based regime, *representation and meaning are not independent*. A belief that replication is free is built deeply into the mechanisms of symbolic mathematics. Once we change to the iconic form it is apparent that replication is not free. When we look closely at the ways that symbolic math fails, the assumption that the manipulation (particularly the replication) of symbolic representations maintains meaning so long as rules are followed is not strictly true. Colloquially, not responding to a question asked once is entirely different than not responding to the same question asked twice.

Can two identical forms cancel one another out? Reflection is the basic axiom that renders forms void-equivalent, but it requires a form A and the same form within angle-brackets <A>. The way out is to see that two *sign-blind* forms can add to zero without being zero. For example, the self-multiplication operation is sign-blind.

reflection

A <A> = *void*

$$(\pm 1)^2 = 1$$

Although $1 \neq -1$, it is the case that $(+1)^2 = (-1)^2$. We can apply the square root operation to expose the multiple solutions.

$$\sqrt{(\pm 1)^2} = \sqrt{1} = \pm 1$$

Although $1 \neq -1$, it is the case that $+\sqrt{1} = -\sqrt{1}$ so long as we choose one of the values of the square root to be +1 and the other to be −1. That is, it is possible to declare

$$\sqrt{1} + \sqrt{1} = 0 \qquad since \qquad 1 + -1 = 0$$

For this line of reasoning, we have to violate a **fundamental rule of substitution**: we cannot elect to use two different values of $\sqrt{1}$ in the same equation. But this violation does not implicate the actual value of $\sqrt{1}$, it instead violates a convention of substitution. Euler suggests that the symbol $\sqrt{1}$ means two things at the same time. It is the case that *both*

$$\sqrt{1} = -1 = -\sqrt{1} \qquad and \qquad \sqrt{1} = 1 \neq -\sqrt{1}$$

Sure there is an implicit understanding that we cannot choose two different values for the same symbol within the same equation, but that understanding rests upon the explicit understanding that symbols do not concurrently represent more than one single value. This is not the case for $\sqrt{1}$. Now if we take the logarithm of the contradictory result, we reach Bernoulli's conclusion.

$$\begin{array}{ll} -1 = & 1 \\ \ln -1 = \ln 1 & \end{array} \quad \text{☞} \quad [<o>] = [(\ )]$$
$$J = void$$

substitute/clarify

The source of the contradiction though has little to do with logarithms or with exponents. The problem is even deeper than permitting a square root to have two values. The root problem goes back to defining the product of two negatives to be positive. To refrain,

$$1 \times 1 = -1 \times -1 = 1$$

Although $1 \neq -1$, it is the case that $1 \times 1 = -1 \times -1$. Two values can *multiply* to 1 without both being 1. It is the *self*-multiplication operation that provides the dual solutions.

$$a \times a = 1 \qquad\qquad a = \pm 1$$

Now for the boundary forms. I'll show just the concrete version using unity,

$$1^2 = 1 \qquad \text{☞} \qquad ((\text{[[o]][2]})) = \text{o}$$

and

$$(-1)^2 = 1 \qquad \text{☞} \qquad ((\text{[[<o>]][2]})) = \text{o}$$

Let's simplify these two forms. The demonstration for −1 is substantively different than that for +1.

Positive

	$1^2 = 1$	☞	((\[\[o]]\[2]))
clarify			((\[ ]\[2]))
absorb			( ) ☞ 1

Negative

	$(-1)^2 = 1$	☞	((\[\[<o>]]\[2]))
replicate			(\[<o>]\[<o>])
promote			<<(\[o]\[o])>>
unwrap/clarify			( ) ☞ 1

In this demonstration the negative unit squared needs to be converted into a self-multiplication product,

$$((\text{[[<o>]][2]})) = (\text{[<o>][<o>]})$$

since the explicit exponential form does not structurally support Promotion.

When a function yields multiple values, somehow we need to erect a barrier that prevents us from beginning with the same form and deriving each of the different values from that form. This contradiction goes to the heart of what we mean by equality, in particular the transitivity of equality. In the case of $\sqrt{1} = \pm 1$,

$$A = B \quad \text{and} \quad B = C \quad \text{therefore} \quad A = C$$
$$1 = \sqrt{1} \quad \text{and} \quad \sqrt{1} = -1 \quad \text{therefore} \quad 1 = -1$$

It's easy to see why the evolution of function theory emphasizes *uniqueness*, that a function can map from an element in the domain to only one element in the range, something that the square root function fails to do.[24]

J = 0, Reason 4

An alternative version of Reason 3 calls upon i. Euler focused on this example.

$$\ln i = \ln (-1)^{1/2} = 1/2 \ln -1$$

Here we'll call upon a relation between i and J that is the primary content of Chapter 39. Briefly in hybrid notation

$$\ln i = 1/2 \ln -1 \quad \text{☞} \quad [i] = J/2$$
$$i = (J/2) \qquad \qquad \text{cover}$$

Euler reasoned: *if* J = 0 *then* ln i = 0 since above we have that ln i = J/2. This was unacceptable because ln i was known by other means not to be zero. From the James perspective, Reason 3 and Reason 4 are variants of the same underlying structure.

Reason 3 (linear)

$$((([<o>]] [2])) = o \quad \text{☞} \quad (-1)^2 = 1$$
$$([[<o>]] [2]) = void \quad \text{☞} \quad 2 J = 0 \qquad \text{cover/clarify}$$

Reason 4 (logarithmic)

$$([[<o>]]<[2]>) \qquad \text{☞} \qquad J/2 = \ln i$$

Euler (exponential)

$$((([<o>]]<[2]>)) \qquad \text{☞} \qquad e^{J/2} = i$$

J cannot equal 0 if we want to be able to take the log of J. Euler's approach is to assert that $e^J = -1$, whereas Bernoulli supported the idea that $e^J = +1$. Here is Euler's rather diplomatic comment:

If one wanted to insist that the formula e^x, in the case of $x = 1/2$, had a double value, and that $1/2$ were the logarithm of both $-\sqrt{e}$ and $+\sqrt{e}$, it would follow that the logarithms of imaginary numbers are also real.[25]

33.4 Euler's Solution

Euler responded to Bernoulli by carefully refuting his examples. He focused on one of Bernoulli's results from calculus. Bernoulli was working on one of the three classic geometric challenges of ancient Greece, how to construct a square with the same area as a given circle.[26] Bernoulli's finesse takes an excursion into complex conjugates:

$$a^2 + b^2 = (a + bi)(a - bi)$$

We'll transcribe the right-side of this equality to boundary form and then reduce it to the left-side:

```
(a + bi)(a - bi)    ☞
                ([a ([b][   i   ])] [a <([ b ][   i   ])>])
substitute      ([a ([b][(J/2)])] [a <([ b ][(J/2)])>])
clarify         ([a ([b]   J/2  )] [a <([ b ]   J/2  )>])
demote          ([a ([b]   J/2  )] [a  ([<b>]   J/2  ) ])
```

At this point we need to disperse the two subforms, what in conventional terms would be converting a factored expression into a polynomial expression via Distribution. Demote has prepared for the rearrangement of [a ([b] J/2)]. We are looking for the mechanism underlying Bernoulli's finesse. Thus far nothing imaginary has happened.

```
                  ([a ([b] J/2)] [a ([<b>] J/2)])
disperse/clarify  ([a][a]) ([a][b] J/2) ([a][<b>] J/2) ([b] J/2 [<b>] J/2)
promote           ([a][a]) ([a][b] J/2) <([a][b] J/2)> <([b][b] J/2 J/2)>
cancel            ([a][a])                             <([b][b] J/2 J/2)>
substitute*       ([a][a])                             <([b][b]   J   )>
J-transparent     ([a][a]) <([<([b][b])>] )>
clarify           ([a][a]) <  <([b][b])>   >
unwrap            ([a][a])    ([b][b])         ☞   a² + b²
```

Instead of symbolically self-multiplying i in the sub-expression +bi x -bi (marked by an asterisk) to reverse the polarity, we eliminate the imaginary J via J-transparency. **J-transparency** is a primary theorem of J that is demonstrated in the next chapter. This mechanism is also independent of b. Adding the two J/2 forms together sets the stage for J-transparency.

J-transparency

$[<(A)>] = A [<( )>]$

Bernoulli had provided an expression that can be factored into the product of two complex numbers. Bernoulli himself commented:

> One sees that imaginary logarithms can be taken for real circular sectors because of the compensation which imaginary quantities make on being added together of destroying themselves in such a way that their sum is always real.[27]

In responding to Bernoulli, Euler began with the definition of the area of a sector of a circle expressed in radian angles and polar coordinates.

$$area \ A = 1/2 \ r^2\alpha$$

Euler then integrated Bernoulli's expression to derive a different expression for the area of a sector of a circle.[28]

$$A = (r^2/4i) \ln ((\cos \alpha + i \sin \alpha)/(\cos \alpha - i \sin \alpha))$$

You might recognize Euler's equation in this formula,

$$e^{i\alpha} = \cos \alpha + i \sin \alpha$$

Now Euler noted that when $\cos \alpha = 0$ and $\sin \alpha = 1$, the formula provides the area of one quadrant of a circle. Setting α to $\pi/2$ radians and setting the two equations for area to be equal,

$$1/2 \ r^2 \ (\pi/2) = (r^2/4i) \ln (i/-i)$$
$$\pi = (1/i) \ln -1$$
$$i\pi = \ln -1$$

The logarithm of -1 is a special case of the logarithm of a complex number $a + bi$. Euler's general formula defines the logarithm function to be cyclic, holding not only for a specific angle α, but also for any *rotation* around a circle that returns to that specific angle.

$$\ln (a + bi) = i(\alpha \pm 2k\pi) \qquad \textit{with } k \textit{ in } \mathbb{N}$$

He then calls upon the trigonometric forms of a and b as cos and sin of a unit circle in the complex plane.

$$\ln (\cos \alpha + i \sin \alpha) = i(\alpha \pm 2k\pi)$$

Logarithms with no imaginary component have exactly one real value. In addition there are an unlimited number of complex values for any specific logarithm. Logarithms of negative numbers lack the one real value, and are thus entirely imaginary. Euler concluded:

> All the difficulties which might be encountered in this matter will disappear entirely, and the doctrine of the logarithms will be safeguarded from all attacks.[29]

Euler Constructs J

While wrestling with the apparent contradictions in both Bernoulli's and Leibniz' images of J, Euler explained:[30]

> I imagined that, just as a quantity always admits two square roots, three cube roots, four biquadratic roots, etc., in the same manner a quantity would be able to have a double half, a triple third, a quadruple fourth, etc. only one of which would be real, the others imaginary. In this way, setting $\ln y = x$ I was thinking that
>
> $$\ln \sqrt{y} = 1/2\ x \quad \textit{and} \quad \ln (-\sqrt{y}) = 1/2\ x'$$
>
> and that $1/2\ x$ and $1/2\ x'$ would be different, although the double of either would be the same, equal to x.[31]

Expressing in boundaries what Euler was exploring,

ln √y = x/2 ☞
        [(([[y]]<[2]>))]   ☞ x/2
        ([[y]]<[2]>)   ☞ x/2   clarify
ln (− √y) = x'/2 ☞
        [<(([[y]]<[2]>))>] ☞ x'/2
        J ([[y]]<[2]>)   ☞ x'/2   J-transparent

The difference between x/2 and x'/2 is the presence of J. And indeed, when both are doubled, x = x'. Doubling x/2,

   x = ([([[y]]<[2]>)][2])   double
     ([[y]]<[2]> [2])   clarify
     ([[y]]   )   cancel
      [y]   clarify

And doubling x'/2,

   x' = ([J ([[y]]<[2]>)][2])   double
    ([J][2]) ([([[y]]<[2]>)][2]) disperse
    ([J][2]) ([[y]]<[2]> [2]) clarify
    ([J][2]) ([[y]]   ) cancel
    ([J][2])   [y]   clarify
          [y]   J-void tally

In his seminal paper defining the logarithm as a **cyclic function**, Euler constructed all the logarithms of a positive number +a by solving the limit equation

$$y = \ln a = \lim_{n \to \infty} n\, a^{1/n} - n$$

With some algebraic manipulation, this equation becomes

$$\lim_{n \to \infty} (1 + y/n)^n = 1 \quad \textit{with} \quad y = \ln a$$

which you may recognize as the traditional definition of e when y = 1:

$$\lim_{n \to \infty} (1 + 1/n)^n = e$$

Euler's argument was somewhat informal since a rigorous theory of limits was not developed until the nineteen century, more than fifty years after his death. Euler separated the single real value of the logarithm of a positive number from its cyclic component, anchoring the infinity of imaginary values to the logarithms of 1.

$$\ln a = \ln 1a = \ln 1 + \ln a$$

The imaginary logarithms of 1 are $\pm 2k\pi i$, where $2k\pi$ corresponds to k revolutions around a unit circle. Denoting the real valued logarithm of a as A, the entirety of the logarithms of a is represented by the complex numbers

$$\ln a = A \pm 2k\pi i \qquad \textit{with } k \textit{ in } \mathbb{N}$$

and in particular

$$\ln 1 = 0 \pm 2k\pi i$$

$$\ln 1 = \{0, \pm 2\pi i, \pm 4\pi i, \pm 6\pi i, \pm 8\pi i, \ldots\}$$

The separation of the logarithms of +1 from the real valued logarithm A is of fundamental importance since it isolates the cyclic component of logarithms as a property of unity. This perspective also applies to –1, what we have identified as the J-transparency theorem.

$$\ln +a = \ln (+1 \times a) = \ln +1 + \ln a = 0 + \ln a$$

$$\ln -a = \ln (-1 \times a) = \ln -1 + \ln a = J + \ln a$$

Euler then applies the same logic to –1 as he did to +1, solving the equation

$$\lim_{n \to \infty} (1 + y/n)^n = -1 \qquad \textit{with} \quad y = \ln a$$

The result is the entirety of the logarithms of –1, which closely mimic those of +1;

$$\ln -1 = \pm(2k - 1)\pi i \qquad \textit{with } k \textit{ in } \mathbb{N}$$

More explicitly,

$$\ln -1 = \{\pm \pi i, \pm 3\pi i, \pm 5\pi i, \pm 7\pi i, \pm 9\pi i, \ldots\}$$

These values correspond first to rotating 180° (i.e. π radians) landing on –1 on the x-axis, and then rotating k full turns where k is a natural number. Since there is no real component to these imaginary values, there is no real logarithm of –1. Euler then points out that the logarithm of the square of –1 multiplies $\ln -1$ by 2,

$$\ln (-1)^2 = 2 \ln -1 = 2 \times \pm(2k - 1)\pi i$$

$$= \{\pm 2\pi i, \pm 6\pi i, \pm 10\pi i, \pm 14\pi i, \pm 18\pi i, \ldots\}$$

These values are a subset of the values of ln +1, thus:

> It remains true that 2 ln −1 = ln +1, even though
> · none of the logarithms of −1 occur among the log-
> arithms of +1.[32]

Euler reiterates this point several times over an entire page, making it clear that

> All the values of 2 ln −a, together with those of 2 ln +a,
> are included among those of ln a^2.... in this sense,
> we will be able to say that 2 ln −a = 2 ln +a , even
> though it is not the case that ln −a = ln +a.[33]

Euler then goes on to demonstrate that the same techniques apply to logarithms of complex numbers.

Expressing Euler's assertions in our current notation,

$$2 \times J = 2 \times 0 \quad \textit{even though} \quad J \neq 0$$

because what we mean by J and what we mean by 0 in these equations is an infinity of imaginary values. Later we will call this assertion *tally failure*. To be specific, Euler observed that

$$2 \times \pm(2k_1 - 1)\pi i = 2 \times \pm 2k_1 \pi i$$

even though $\qquad \pm(2k_2 - 1)\pi i \neq \pm 2k_2 \pi i$

thus

$$\pm(4k_1 - 2) = \pm 4k_1$$

even though $\qquad \pm(2k_2 - 1) \neq \pm 2k_2$

We cannot accurately divide the right-hand equation through by 2 because as it stands the values of $4k_1 - 2$ are limited to even numbers, while the values of $2k_2 - 1$ are limited to odd numbers. Division by 2 changes the domain of $4k_1 - 2$ from even numbers to odd numbers. To visually summarize Euler's construction,[34]

$$\ln 1 = \{0, \pm 2\pi i, \pm 4\pi i, \pm 6\pi i, \pm 8\pi i, ...\}$$
$$\ln -1 = \{ \quad \pm \pi i, \pm 3\pi i, \pm 5\pi i, \pm 7\pi i, ...\}$$

33.5 Remarks

From Euler's exploration we can begin to see that $J + J$, $(-1)^2$ and -1×-1 are intimately connected. Conventionally the well-known breakdown in the rules of logarithms is due to the generation of multivalued functions, which in turn arises from the primary design choice that $-1 \times -1 = 1$. However there is a yet deeper core. Underneath the multiplication of negative numbers is the additive fact $J + J = 0$.

Each of Bernoulli's four objections is algebraically *correct*. We'll provide them as theorems in the next chapter. As Euler gracious observes, it is Bernoulli's *inferences* that are incorrect. Bernoulli simply did not want to allow an imaginary with those characteristics. We will see in the next two chapters that J has all four characteristics, and that is OK since this creature opens new vistas in mathematical imagination.

The following chapters improve upon Euler's *infinite logarithms solution* by developing J as an independent value with discrete properties not reliant upon repeated rotation around a unit circle. An infinity of logarithms for each number is not necessary to define the behavior of J. Yes, J can be interpreted as an oscillating value, but it is not necessary to count the number of oscillations in order to come to an understanding of the **additive imaginary**. The three James pattern axioms are sufficient to define a sign-blind J that exhibits the behavior that Euler was exploring. J *emerges* out of the James axioms. Although the multiplicative imaginary i is cyclic, the additive imaginary J is not since J cannot be accumulated.

Endnotes

1. **opening quote:** J. Bolyai (1823) The quote is from a letter Bolyai sent to his father dated 11/3/1823 upon his excitement of discovering non-Euclidean geometry by assuming that a geometry can be constructed without Euclid's parallel axiom. Transcribed and translated by Péter Körtesi. http://mathsh-istory.st-andrews.ac.uk/DSB/Bolyai.pdf

2. *all numbers have an infinity of logarithms:* L. Euler (1747) On the controversy between Messrs. Leibniz and Bernoulli concerning logarithms of negative and imaginary numbers. *Berlin Academy of Sciences* [5] 1751 p.139-179.

Euler wrote two versions of this treatise, the first being the more conversational *On the Logarithms of Negative and Imaginary Numbers.* The *revised* version was first published in 1751. It presents a much more structured sequence of assertions and objections, followed by one central theorem establishing the infinity of logarithms for any number and then followed by problems and solutions determining specific values of logarithms.

3. **which we do not ordinarily believe susceptible to any dispute:** L. Euler (1747) On the logarithms of negative and imaginary numbers. *Actor. Acad. Berolinensis tomo V.A.* Number 807 §1.

This is Euler's first essay on J. It shares his path of discovery as he explores all the possible approaches to resolving the opinions of Leibniz and Bernoulli. He read it to the Berlin Academy in 1747, however it was not published until 1862.

4. **is as redefined as it is useless:** G. Cardano (1545) *The Great Art* p.220.

5. **things that are in their own nature exceedingly plain and simple:** F. Maseres (1759) *Complete Dictionary of Scientific Biography* 2008. Online 2/17 at http://www.encyclopedia.com. Also at http://www-history.mcs.st-and.ac.uk/Biographies/Maseres.html

6. **delightfully entitled 1758 book decrying negative numbers:** F. Maseres (1758) *A Dissertation on the Use of the Negative Sign in Algebra: Containing a demonstration of the rules usually given concerning it; and shewing how quadratic and cubic equations may be explained, without the consideration of negative roots. To which is added, as an appendix, Mr. Machin's quadrature of the circle*

7. **or it must be mere nonsense or unintelligible jargon:** Maseres' quote is in G. Baron (1804) *The Mathematical Correspondent* Volume 1 p.175.

8. **either of which is ten thousand times more possible:** A. DeMorgan (1831) *On the Study and Difficulties of Mathematics* p.71.

9. **both are equally imaginary, since 0 − a is as inconceivable as √−a:** DeMorgan p.156.

10. **write that Euler did not understand how to multiply imaginaries:** Examples of the misunderstanding show up in M. Kline (1980) *Mathematics: The loss of certainty* and in P. Nahin (1998) *An Imaginary Tale.* On page 12, Nahin states: "Euler was confused on this very point." To be fair, Nahin was probably relying on many prior authors who made the same claim.

11. **to write √−2 √−3 = √6 instead of −√6:** I. Gratton-Guiness (1997) *The Rainbow of Mathematics* p.334.

12. **the square root of −a is +√−a as well as −√−a:** Euler is quoted in A. Martínez (2007) Euler's "mistake"? The radical product rule in historical perspective. *Mathematical Association of America* 114 April 2007.

13. **transferred to the quantities themselves, obscurity and paradox must of necessity ensue:** Rev. J. Playfair (1778) On the arithmetic of impossible quantities. In Hutton, Shaw & Pearson (1809) *The Philosophical Transactions of the Royal Society of London* XIV p.356.

14. **a science which is immediately conversant with ideas:** Playfair p.357.

15. **are unintelligible, why are they also not useless:** Playfair p.357.

16. **Why is mathematics so unreasonably effective in the natural sciences:** E. Wigner (1960) The unreasonable effectiveness of mathematics in the natural sciences. *Communications in Pure and Applied Mathematics* 13(1).

17. **the errors and disgust inseparable from long calculations:** The quote by Laplace is in W. Bryant (1907) *A History of Astronomy* p.44.

18. **almost amphibian between being and not-being:** Leibniz' quote is in F. Kline (1932) *Elementary Mathematics from an Advanced Standpoint* p.56.

19. **writing down of the impossible gave it a symbolic existence:** T. Dantzig (1930) *Number* p.190.

20. **these imaginary numbers, and employing them in calculation:** L. Euler (1770) *Elements of Algebra* §145.

21. **the logarithmic function only for positive numbers:** G. Schubring (2005) *Conflicts between Generalization, Rigor, and Intuition: Number concepts underlying the development of analysis in 17-19th century France and Germany.*

22. **does have a real value, it is not imaginary:** Gratton-Guiness p.281.

23. **Bernoulli's reasoning here proves that** $J = 0$: Deepak Bal in *Leibniz, Bernoulli and the logarithms of negative numbers* (2006, p.8) observes:

> It would seem that Bernoulli himself would not have made this case. In his letter of June 7, 1713 to Leibniz, Bernoulli says that "Twice $\log(-n)$ is not $\log n^2$."

Online 7/19 at https://msuweb.montclair.edu/~bald/files/LeibBernLogs.pdf

24. **something that the square root function fails to do:** This also implies that square and square root are not inverses.

25. **the logarithms of imaginary numbers are also real:** L. Euler (1747) On the logarithms of negative and imaginary numbers §17

26. **how to construct a square with the same area as a given circle:** From antiquity, this problem was called the *quadrature of a circle.*

27. **in such a way that their sum is always real:** Quote in J. Fauvel & J. Gray (1987) *The History of Mathematics: A reader* p.439.

28. **derive a different expression for the area of a sector of a circle:** V. Katz (2009) *A History of Mathematics* p.597.

29. **the doctrine of the logarithms will be safeguarded from all attacks:** Katz p.598.

30. **Bernoulli's and Leibniz' images of** J, **Euler explained:** I have changed Euler's casual notation for the natural log from "l" to "$\ln$".

31. **although the double of either would be the same, equal to x:** L. Euler (1747) On the logarithms of negative and imaginary numbers §21.

32. **the logarithms of –1 occur among the logarithms of +1:** L. Euler (1747) On the controversy between Messrs. Leibniz and Bernoulli concerning logarithms of negative and imaginary numbers PROBLEM 2 SOLUTION.

33. **even though it is not the case that** $\ln -a = \ln +a$: Euler, PROBLEM 2 SOLUTION.

34. **To visually summarize Euler's construction:** Euler was a master of infinite series, so it is not surprising that he would suggest an infinite solution.

Chapter 34

Behavior

I am interested in mathematics only as a creative art.[1]
— Godfrey Hardy (1940)

Folks have become comfortable with the imaginary unit i, the square root of negative one.

$$i \times i = -1 \qquad i = \sqrt{-1}$$

To common sense, there is no unit that when multiplied by itself yields a negative. That just isn't how signed multiplication has been defined to work. One hint that something is quite strange is the central role of the origin of strangeness, –1. But the precedent established first by –1 and later by i is that a numeric object does not have to make sense. We can define what is sensible by *inventing special structures*, so long as any new transformation rules do not do serious damage to the structures that we have already defined.

negative numbers are imaginary

The imaginary i compounds two types of inverses. The square root inverts self-multiplication and the negative inverts the positive. The combination of two types of inverse operation appears to create a fracture in the structure of real numbers. Somehow, when you apply a square root to a negative number, the mixture explodes into a new realm of creativity.

I suspect that the educational emphasis on introducing negative numbers early in grade school contributes to the false impression that they are somehow more fundamental than operations such as multiplication and self-multiplication. They are not. As a general rule the sequence of evolution of mathematical concepts throughout history provides an accurate map of the sequence of developmental understanding in students. Exponents (circa 1350) predate negative numbers (circa 1500). The concept of self-multiplication certainly did not run into the extreme prejudice visited upon the concept of negative numbers from their introduction up until about two centuries ago.

multiplication is self-addition

34.1 Creation

Over the last several centuries we have come to realize that there are "numbers" that are completely independent of the integers we learn in grade school. Chapter 32 makes the case that these numbers are not mere flights of the imagination but are rather consequences of the construction of quite reasonable expressions combined with a statement of equality. In particular, when very simple well-formed algebraic expressions are equated to 0, the resulting equation gives rise to new numeric creatures. Traditionally we call these new numbers **inverses**, in recognition that they combine with the common operations of addition, multiplication and exponentiation to reverse the effect of those operations. That is, inverse objects reduce normal expressions to 0 in the case of addition, to 1 in the case of multiplication and to the *base* in the case of exponentiation. These inverses are intimately connected to James patterns containing angle-brackets:

$x + 1 = 0$

$2x + 1 = 0$

$x^2 + 1 = 0$

$2^x + 1 = 0$

— Conventional inverses are represented by an angle-bracket nested within a context.

reflection

A <A> = *void*

— Angle-brackets are defined by Reflection.

— Angle-brackets can block the reduction of forms to create unexpected stable structures.

J-conversion

<A> = (J [A])

— <A> is a shorthand notation for a J-frame (J [A]).

Systems of Units

Following strict formal rules of structure, other algebraic systems of imaginary numbers have been explored. In 1843 William Hamilton discovered a complex of four mutually defined imaginary units that he called **quaternions**. The four units {1, i, j, k} are related by these equations:

$$i^2 = j^2 = k^2 = i\,j\,k = -1$$

*William Hamilton
1788-1856*

The negative unit −1 breaks the connection of whole numbers to a concrete grounding in reality. The imaginary i breaks our understanding of self-multiplication. Quaternions break the rule of *commutativity*, the order in which they multiply inverts their polarity, in effect mixing transformation with bipolar imagination.

$$i\,j = -\,j\,i$$

Within a year Hamilton's college friend, John Graves, discovered the **octonions**, a complex of eight mutually defined types of imaginary unit, what might be called the algebra of eight dimensions. Octonions break the rule of *associativity*, changing the grouping of a sequence of binary operations changes the result.

*John Graves
1806-1870*

$$a\,(b\,c) \neq (a\,b)\,c$$

Alas the road seems to stop here. No more structural rules to break, no more well-structured imaginary algebras. However, all of these imaginary creatures address *multiplication of units*. We may not be able to find more contrary imaginary algebras, but perhaps we can imagine something simpler than i.

In this and the following chapters we will use James algebra to explore an **additive imaginary**, a form that breaks our understanding of addition. The form of J, [<( )>], occurs naturally and frequently in James algebra. Its two internal boundaries, <( )>, can be interpreted as −1, so J might provide some insights not only into i, but also into the root cause of why i is imaginary. We will indeed go farther, to use J to explain how −1 itself works.

FEATURES of J

* J is not zero.	$J \neq void$
J is a type of unit.	$<(J)> = o$
J supplants the concept of an inverse operation.	$<A> = (J \ [A])$
* J marks the presence of imaginary forms.	$i \ ☞ \ (J/2)$
* J is self-voiding.	$J \ J = void$
* Replicas of J do not accumulate.	$([J][oo]) = void$
* Js cannot be counted.	$J \ J \not\Rightarrow 2J$
* J does not respect polarity.	$J \ ☞ \ \pm J$
J is both object and operator.	$J = [<(\ )>]$
J is independent of and transparent to its contents.	$[<(A)>] = J \ A$
Being outside of J is the same as being inside.	$A \ [<(\ )>] = [<(A)>]$
Any base but 0 raised to the power of J is –1.	$\#^J \ ☞ \ <o>$
The analog of Euler's identity in the J domain:	$J \ e^J + J = 0$

Asterisks mark features identified by Euler (Chapter 33)

Figure 34-1: *Features of J*

We're examining the behavior of J from the perspective of mathematical foundations. J is most useful in helping to consolidate and explain the diversity of seemingly independent rules of arithmetic and algebra. As arithmetic matured over hundreds of years, new ideas were introduced more or less by accretion. A primary goal of 20th century mathematics was to discover the unifying themes that hold math together as a cohesive whole. Group theory, for example, has provided an integrated perspective on algebraic string structure. However since the Mathematics Subject Classification currently includes over 6000 different entries we might conclude that the goal of unification has not succeeded. Here we are not trying to organize the cornucopia, just trying to contribute to diversity by providing a different perspective on basic arithmetic.

J THEOREMS

J = [<o>]	**definition of** J
<A> = (J [A])	**J-conversion**
J J = *void*	**J-void object**
[<(J)>] = *void*	**J-void process**
([J][oo]) = *void*	**J-void tally**
J = <J>	**J-self-inverse**
[<(A)>] = A J	**J-transparency**
A (J [A]) = *void*	**J-occlusion**
J (J [J]) = *void*	**J-self-occlusion**
J = <[A]>[<A>]	**J-invariant**
[<J>] = J [J]	**J-absorption**
<(J/2)> = (<J/2>)	**J/2-toggle**

N *even* ([J][N]) = *void*	**J-parity**
N *odd* ([J][N]) = J	
N *even* J ([J]<[N]>) = ([J]<[N]>)	**J-parity**
N *odd* J ([J]<[N]>) = *void*	

Figure 34-2: J *theorems*

34.2 Features and Theorems

We begin with a summary of the features and theorems that define the structural meaning of J. Figure 34-1 identifies, in bumper-sticker format, many of the unusual features that characterize the J construct. We'll demonstrate their structural validity in this chapter, and examine them more closely in the next chapter.

Figure 34-2 lists the theorems that define the operational behavior of J. These theorems are the content of this chapter (J-parity is in the next chapter). No new axioms are introduced, each of these theorems is a simple and direct consequence of the interaction of the [<( )>] structure with the three James pattern axioms.

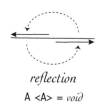

reflection

A <A> = *void*

cross

((A)) = A

NOT NOT A = A

double negation

A = A

identity

A simple physical model of how J works is *reflection*. J is the generic label for the space on the other side of the mirror within which an imaginary reflection resides.

Here is a geometric perspective. You are looking out in some direction, call that direction EAST = 0°. Turn around to look WEST, in the opposite direction. Turn around again and you are now looking EAST again. Ignoring time and effort, you have combined two identical actions (turning around 180°) to change nothing. This idea can be generalized to any operation that returns to its beginnings when repeated. Double negation in logic is a self-inverse operation. The archetype self-inverse within boundary logic is to cross. **Identity** requires replication but it does not require repetition. In contrast, both turning around and crossing a boundary do require sequential repetition. The difference is that J is a *self-inverse object* that denies its own existence when replicated. J is **self-voiding**.

34.3 The Nature of J

Since the creature called J does not show up in math textbooks it's appropriate to provide a comprehensive description. "J" is an abbreviated name for a particular James form consisting of three different nested boundaries.

$$J =label= [<o>]$$

Given the James pattern axioms, the form of J is stable, it does not reduce to something simpler. J can be interpreted as the base-free logarithm of –1.

$$[<o>] \quad ☞ \quad log_\# -1$$

J occurs naturally when we multiply by a negative number, although its form is certainly suppressed in conventional arithmetic. For example,

$$-1 \times 2 \quad ☞ \quad ([<o>][oo])$$

substitute

$$(\quad J \quad [oo])$$

Multiplying by a negative number implicitly enlists the logarithm of that number. The properties and theorems of J provide a new basis from which to understand how negative numbers work. J is our tool to vanquish the arch-villain −1.

The behavior of J is analogous to the behavior of 0. Conventional arithmetic simply declares *You may not divide by zero* but we are seeking to understand *why* we should not divide by zero and what happens if we do so anyway. Similarly we'll try here to figure out why J creates analogous difficulties. An immediate hint is the family resemblance:

divide by 0	☞	(<[ ]>)	*apparently non-numeric*
logarithm of −1	☞	[<( )>]	*apparently numeric*

These difficult forms are the same compound distinction viewed from different sides. The round unit is comfortable territory for numeric interpretation because ( ) has been identified with One. The square unit covers uncomfortable territory; [ ] has been identified with non-numeric Negative Infinity (explored in detail in Chapter 41). When the square-bracket is outermost, acting as an operator, negative contents lead us to imaginary logarithms. When the square-bracket is innermost, acting as an object, its emptiness leads us to the infinities.

Void Inversion asserts that *there is no privileged nesting perspective.*

$$([ ]) = [( )] = \textit{void}$$ **void inversion**

Clarifying ([ ]) or [( )] results in the same absence for either. When an angle-bracket intervenes between either inversion pair both void-equivalent forms become stable, they are no longer meaningless. [<( )>] occurs commonly within James forms. (<[ ]>) shows up rarely, in rather artificial circumstances. Another difference between these two forms is that Promotion of the angle-bracket can potentially apply to [<( )>] but not to (<[ ]>). This means that J is easier to deconstruct and work with than is divide-by-zero.

[()][()][()][()]
])([)([)([)([

inside & outside

[<()>][<()>][<()>]
]>)(<[]>)(<[]>)(<[

A New Unity

J is a *new type of numeric unit*, in the same category as 1, −1, ±1 and ±i. The *unit* J is a **pure object**, not an operation. It *defines* the angle-bracket as will be demonstrated in the coming J-conversion section. Without losing any descriptive power, James arithmetic then consists of *two* simple boundary types, ( ) and [ ], and one constant J.

J combines the three boundary types we have been considering. Here we are viewing J as a unit, a single form. J has an inside, just as all units do, but unlike the round and the square unit, J has an interior structure. We could create a new labeled boundary for J and define the others in terms of that boundary, just like Chapter 20 shows how to eliminate the angle-bracket without loss. This however tends to obfuscate the role of J as a process.

object	o
operator	( )
object	J
operator	[<( )>]

As are all boundary forms J can be seen to be *both object and operator*. Similar to the round unit J too has a different representation for each use.[2] We've identified the **object form** of J, formerly [<o>], by the single symbol J. The **process form** of J, [<( )>], is a compound boundary operating upon its innermost contents.

The unit 1 was formally defined first by Peano in 1889 as a singular object that accumulates. 1 + 1 generates a new number called 2. −1 gains its status when induction turns into recursion, permitting both accumulation up to infinity by incrementing in steps of 1 and de-accumulation down to the base of 1 by decrementing in steps of −1. These units can be converted into each other via self-multiplication, with 1 providing the irreducible basis:

$$1 \times 1 = 1 \qquad\qquad 1 = 1^2$$
$$-1 \times -1 = 1 \qquad\qquad 1 = (-1)^2$$

Self-addition of J yields not a unit, but *void*. Self-multiplication of J does not generate another unit type. In fact Euler defined J x J as a trigonometric value (discussed in Chapter 40).

$$J^2 = -\pi^2$$

J is the numeric logarithm operation on −1, just as i is the numeric square root operation on −1.

$$
\begin{array}{ll}
1 \quad \text{☞} \quad \text{o} & \textit{real unit} \\
-1 \quad \big| \quad \text{<o>} & \textit{imaginary unit} \\
\log -1 \quad \big| \quad [\text{<o>}] & \textit{imaginary logarithm}
\end{array}
$$

J can also be anchored in exponential space.

$$
\begin{array}{lll}
J = \log_{\#} -1 \quad \text{☞} \quad J = [\text{<o>}] & \textit{logarithmic unit} & \\
\#^{J} = -1 \quad \text{☞} \quad (J) = \text{<o>} & \textit{exponential unit} & \text{cover}
\end{array}
$$

J as a Fundamental Unit

The form of J can be deconstructed to express the real unit 1 in terms of J.

$$
\begin{array}{lll}
J \quad = [\text{<o>}] & & \\
\text{<}(J)\text{>} = \quad \text{o} \quad \text{☞} \quad -\#^{J} = 1 & & \text{cover}
\end{array}
$$

An alternative definition of the unit 1 in terms of J eliminates the angle-bracket:

$$
\text{<}(J)\text{>} = (J \ J) \quad \text{☞} \quad 1 = 1
$$

Raising a real base to the power of J yields −1.

$$
(J) = \text{<o>} \quad \text{☞} \quad \#^{J} = -1
$$

The analogous structure in the real domain is that raising a numeric base to the power of 0 yields +1.

$$
(\ ) = \text{o} \quad \text{☞} \quad \#^{0} = +1
$$

Since each common type of unit can be expressed as a form of J, we can experiment with the radical concept that J is an irreducible basis for arithmetic while the other types of unit are derivative:

$$
\begin{array}{lll}
\textit{void} \quad \text{☞} \quad 0 & \textit{nothing} \\
J \quad \big| \quad \log -1 & \textit{fundamental unit} \\
(J) \quad \big| \quad -1 & \textit{imaginary unit} \\
(J \ J) \quad \big| \quad 1 & \textit{real unit} \\
(J/2) \quad \big| \quad \sqrt{-1} & \textit{imaginary root}
\end{array}
$$

It is possible to consider J to be the ground upon which arithmetic is constructed. This requires shifting perspective from the numeric interpretation to the boundary structure. We begin with absence which yields to the unit J. Placing J within a round-bracket creates the first imaginary form. Placing two Js within a round-bracket converts the imaginary to the real. Placing one-half of one J within the round bracket generates a different kind of imaginary. The *only operator* is the round-bracket. The square-bracket inverts the round-bracket while the operation of inverting is represented by a inversion frame, (J [A]), which is abbreviated by the angle-bracket <A>.

Before considering the explanatory benefits of J as a fundamental numeric operator, we will need to establish three facets of the quite non-standard structural behavior of J. Even though J is a numeric unit, it is

— *independent* of other numeric forms
— *non-accumulating* and
— *sign-blind.*

Independence allows J to indicate an inverse transformation by its *presence* and a direct transformation by its absence. **Non-accumulating** allows J to escape the dominant presence of cardinality within arithmetic expressions. And **sign-blind** allows J to unite the schizophrenia of positive and negative values.

The behavior of J is a consequence of structural manipulation of forms following the pattern axioms. Appreciating J, however, may require learning to appreciate the desirability of building elementary arithmetic upon an independent, non-accumulating, sign-blind unit. Alberto Martínez observes that historically until negative numbers were introduced, all numbers were signless. Positive numbers came into being in order to differentiate the originally signless numbers from the new negative numbers. "Signs served to represent qualities while signless numbers represented quantities."[3] Sign-blind numbers convey the same idea, but emphasize a redesign well after numbers had become attached to their signs.

34.4 J is Non-accumulating

J does not accumulate, it is self-voiding and self-avoiding.
This is expressed by the *J-void object* theorem.

$$J \ J = void$$

J-void object

Here is a void-based demonstration:

void

`[ ([ o ][ o ]) ]`	enfold
`[<<([ o ][ o ])>>]`	wrap
`[ ([<o>][<o>]) ]`	demote
`[<o>][<o>]`	clarify
`J        J`	substitute

Let's let this sink in. We have interpreted multiple forms
within the same container as the form of addition. Now
we are putting two identical forms into a container and
the result is that the container becomes empty. That is,
the sum of two *identical* numeric expressions is zero.
Conventionally only 0 will do that but 0 is not numeric
and here we are putting two *numeric* forms together.
Notice the similarity to the behavior of the imaginary
i, which calls for the self-multiplication of one type of
unity to generate a different type of unity. The −1 result
of i x i is a *negated identity object* for unit multiplication.
The numeric unit i itself is generated by our imagination
when we define multiplication as capable of changing the
unit type of what is being multiplied. We have initiated
this type of conundrum by defining −1 x −1 = +1. The
same complexity also occurs within the imaginary unit
J. Rather than changing unit-type by self-multiplication,
J-void changes numeric to non-numeric by self-addition.

identity

A x 1 = A

not identity

A x −1 ≠ A

Another description of J is that it is an imaginary form
that does not support replication and it is not idempotent.
It makes no sense to count up how many infinities we
might be adding together or how many zeros we might
be adding and it makes just as little sense to count up
how many Js but for a different reason. Infinity does not

idempotent

A op A = A

self-voiding

A op A = void

support replication because it already incorporates all replicas. Zero does not support replication because there is nothing to replicate.[4] Neither ∞ nor 0 is numeric. J *is* numeric but does not support replication because of its unique structure.

By accepting J as a type of unit, we can now re-express the fundamental behavior of replicated units without the vacuous unit < >:

units that accumulate   ( )( ) ≠ ( )
units that do not accumulate   [ ][ ] = [ ]
units that self-void   J J = *void*

Self-inverse

J-void is curious, normally one of the two canceling forms exhibits a property and the other exhibits the inverse of that property. But both Js, being replicas, have the same property. J is its own additive inverse.

J-self-inverse

$$J = <J>$$

Here's a simple demonstration.

$$J \; J = \textit{void}$$

move

$$J = <J>$$

Self-inversion requires an **important caution** about working with J both computationally and conceptually. J *does not respect polarity*. Positive J is the same as negative J. Insensitivity to polarity goes hand-in-hand with the non-accumulating behavior of J.

±√–1 x ±√–1

= ±√(–1 x –1)

J itself is more accurately transcribed as ±J. As an analogy consider √1 = ±1. The shift in perspective is to see bipolar ±1 as *a new kind of unit*: both +1 and –1 at the same time. This approach follows Euler's preference described in Chapter 33.[5] In referring to functions with fractional powers (i.e. roots), John Stillwell states:

These functions have *branching behavior* at 0; they are *many-valued*, and hence they are not functions in a strict sense. The function $x^{1/2}$, for example, is two-valued because each number has two square roots, one the negative of the other.[6]

Declaring that J is sign-blind means that whenever the self-inverse theorem (and the theorems derived from it) is called upon, it will transfer the sign-blind property to the result. Contrary to expectation sign-blind behavior is a *goal* in order to remove the artificial limits placed upon conventional transformations.

J-void Process

J-void object transforms paired replicas of J into *void*, an object-oriented perspective. The operator-oriented perspective, *J-void process*, embeds J within itself to construct a form that is void-equivalent.

$$[<(J)>] = void$$

J-void process

The demonstration:

$$[<(\quad J \quad)>]$$
$$[<([<( )>])>] \qquad \text{substitute}$$
$$[< \quad <( )> \quad >] \qquad \text{clarify}$$
$$[\qquad ( ) \qquad] \qquad \text{unwrap}$$
$$void \qquad \text{clarify}$$

Solving the form of J-void process for J provides a void-based perspective. On its way to self-definition, J-void process passes through the conventional units of 1 and −1, as does self-multiplying i.

$$[<(J)>] = \quad void$$
$$<(J)> \ = \ ( ) \qquad \text{☞} \quad -\#^J = 1 \qquad \text{cover}$$
$$(J) \quad = <( )> \qquad \qquad \#^J = -1 \qquad \text{cover}$$
$$J \quad = [<( )>] \qquad \quad J \ = \log_\# -1 \qquad \text{cover}$$

Tallying J

There is a third way we might express the presence of two J forms within a boundary, by *tallying*. A tally multiplies a form by a cardinality, in this case the natural number 2.

	J J
mark	([J][o]) ([J][o])
collect	([J][oo])

J-void tally

$$([J][oo]) = \mathit{void}$$

This form however is deceptive. Just like it is a semantic error to attempt to tally *void* or to tally ∞, it is also an error to tally J. Due to J-void object we cannot collect replicas of J within the same container. Two replicas self-void rather than accumulate so two Js cannot coexist in order to be marked and tallied. It is possible that three or more J *tokens* from different sources could assemble all at the same place all at the same time, due to the promiscuity of symbol replication. We will need a policy to address the *imaginary presence* of multiple replicas of the token J.

Memory

J **without memory** means replicas never accumulate. J appears as one object that flashes on and off. J does not support being counted, to count past one is heresy. J does indicate *difference* via its presence, it is either there or not there. A form that does not include J as a subform can be directly interpreted as a conventional number. A form that includes J requires interpretation as imaginary, or more broadly *as an inverse*. Numerically, absence of memory can be expressed by the rule 2 ⇒ 0.

With memory provides a mechanism to count the number of pairs of J tokens that will self-void. The count of occurrences of the token J is a cardinality. Cardinality is sufficient as the memory mechanism. For the purposes of tallying J, *even* cardinality means no J is present while *odd* cardinality means J is present.

J-void tally can produce contradictory results as we'll see in Chapter 35. The appropriate design decision then is to **deny the application of J-void tally** since it is context sensitive.

$\exists n \quad n + n \ne 2n$

That is,

$$J \; J = ([J][oo]) \quad \textit{only sometimes}$$

$$J \quad J \quad = \textit{void}$$

and

$$([J][oo]) = \textit{void}$$

but

$$J \; J \not\Rightarrow ([J][oo]) \quad \textit{depending on context}$$

tally failure

The unexpected characteristic of J *tally failure* was recognized by Euler as described in Chapter 33.4.[7]

34.5 J is Transparent

The J-transparency theorem permits structural conversion between the process form of J and the object label form of J.

$$[<(A)>] = A \; J$$

J-transparency

In the following demonstration of J-transparency the angle-bracket is promoted out of $[<(A)>]$ and then used to build an independent J form.

$$[<(A)>]$$
$$[\; ([<(A)>][\; (\;) \;]) \;] \qquad \text{enfold}$$
$$[<([\; (A) \;][\; (\;) \;])>] \qquad \text{promote}$$
$$[\; ([\; (A) \;][<(\;)>]) \;] \qquad \text{demote}$$
$$A \quad [<(\;)>] \qquad \text{clarify}$$
$$A \qquad J \qquad \text{substitute}$$

J-transparency affirms that the operator/container J is *independent of its contents*. The contents of J can be freely moved into its context while forms within the context of J can be freely moved into its interior to become content. This makes J feel like a complex number with orthogonal real and imaginary components.

J-transparency provides a primary interpretation of the logarithm of a negative quantity as the logarithm of the positive quantity of the same magnitude with the unit marker J added.

$$\log{-A} \quad \text{☞} \quad [< \ A \ >]$$

enfold
$$[<([A])>]$$

J-transparent
$$[A] \quad J \quad \text{☞} \quad (\log A) \pm J$$

±J indicates that J is sign-blind, not necessarily that it is added or subtracted. Here then is a *definition* of the conventional imaginary logarithm, a definition that does not invoke Euler's infinity of imaginary values.

**imaginary
logarithm**

$$\log{-A} =\mathit{def}= \log A \pm J$$

The interpretation of J-transparency shows how logarithms convert multiplication to addition. I'll simplify the standard expressions by choosing base-e.

$$([A][<(\ )>]) = \ < \ A \ > \quad \text{☞} \quad A \times \ -1 = \ -A$$

cover/enfold
$$[A][<(\ )>] \ = [<([A])>] \quad | \quad \ln A + \ln{-1} = \ln{-A}$$

substitute/clarify
$$A \ [<(\ )>] \ = [<(\ A \ )>] \quad | \quad A + \ln{-1} = \ln{-e^A}$$

Notice how our conventional algebraic manipulation steps introduce redundant James transformations.

$$[< \ (A) \qquad >] \qquad \text{☞} \qquad \ln{-e^A}$$

J-convert/enfold
$$[([(A)][(J)])] \qquad\qquad \ln(e^A \times -1)$$

clarify
$$[(A)] \quad J \qquad\qquad \ln e^A + \ln{-1}$$

enfold/base
$$([\ A \ ][[((\ ))]]) \ J \qquad (A \times \ln e) + \ln{-1}$$

clarify
$$A \qquad\qquad J \qquad\qquad A \qquad + \ln{-1}$$

Permeability

Permeability is a boundary concept that does not exist within symbolic notation. *Transparent boundaries* are fully permeable. They allow their contents to flow freely between inside and outside, in effect making no distinction and thus behaving as though there is no boundary.[8] Permeable boundary forms are rare. Usually a transparent boundary has no effect and is therefore void-equivalent. The J boundary is special in that it is stable as a unit and transparent as a process, making its *presence* rather than its dynamics important. This qualifies J as a *unique* numeric unit.

$$[\ (A)\ ] = A\ [\ (\ )\ ]$$ *transparent and void-equivalent*
$$[<(A)>] = A\ [<(\ )>]$$ *transparent and numeric*

Composition on the outside generally differs from composition on the inside,

> $$A\ \{\ \} \neq \{A\}\quad \textit{but not always}$$

inside/outside

Here are some examples of the inside/outside difference.

$$A\ (\ )\ \neq\ (A)\qquad ☞\qquad A + 1\ \neq\ \#^A$$
$$A\ ((\ ))\ \neq\ ((A))\qquad\qquad A + \#\ \neq\ \#^{\#^A}$$
$$A\ (<[\ ]>) \neq (<[A]>)\qquad\qquad A + 1/0 \neq 1/A$$

The general pattern of a difference between inside and outside of a boundary is broken by the form of J.

$$A\ [<(\ )>] = [<(A)>]\quad ☞\quad A + \log_\# -1 = \log_\# -\#^A$$

Chapter 37 explores the unexpected result that asserting inside/outside equivalence for round units constructs a boundary equation that defines the constant e.

$$(A) = (\ )\ A$$

34.6 J-conversion

J is intimately connected to the Reflection axiom that defines the angle-bracket. From an operational perspective the angle-bracket is a *generic inverse*. In Chapter 20 the angle-bracket is shown to be a notational convenience that can be eliminated in favor of alternating odd/even levels of nesting. *J-conversion* is another method of associating nesting with natural and inverse spaces. *The conventional inverse operations can all be expressed by a J-frame.* In J-conversion J becomes a marker of inverse structure that unlike alternating odd/even nesting can occupy any depth and is thus *free of counting nesting levels*. J-conversion removes a residual numeric ordering from the structure of boundary forms.

> $$<A> =\textit{def}= (J\ [A])$$

J-conversion

operation	expression ☞	J form
negation	$-a$	$(J \ [a] \ )$
subtraction	$b - a$	$b \quad (J \ [a] \ )$
reciprocal	$1/a$	$(\qquad\qquad (J \ [[a]]))$
division	b/a	$(\quad [b] \ (J \ [[a]]))$
negative power	b^{-a}	$((J \ [[b]] \quad [a] \ ))$
base-b logarithm	$\log_b a$	$((J \ [[[b]]]) \ [[a]] \ )$
root	$b^{1/a}$	$((\quad [[b]] \ (J \ [[a]])))$

Figure 34-3: *The J form of common inverse operations*

Here is a void-based demonstration of the relation between the angle-bracket and J.

$$(\quad J \quad [A]) = <A>$$

move $\qquad A \ (\quad J \quad [A]) = void$

substitute $\qquad A \ ([<(\quad)>][A])$

J-transparent $\qquad A \ ([<([A])>] \quad)$

clarify $\qquad A \quad < \ A \ >$

cancel $\qquad\qquad void$

The reflection operator, <A>, is a bridge between standard numeric expressions and James forms. We can elect to read it conventionally as –A, or unconventionally as a *J-conversion frame* with A as the frame content. Here is J-conversion applied to each type of boundary. In each form the angle-bracket <{A}> is converted into a J-frame (J [{A}]).

$$< A > = (J \quad [A] \ )$$
$$<(A)> = (J \quad A \ )$$
$$<[A]> = (J \ [[A]])$$

J-void/clarify $\qquad <<A>> = <(J \quad [A] \ )> = (J \ J \ [A]) = A$

The bottom line shows that Involution is equivalent to J-void object.

J-conversion provides a more direct route to the demonstration of J-transparency:

operation	*symbolic expression*	*use of -1*	*exponential form*
negation	- A	(-1)A	$e^{J + \ln A}$
subtraction	B - A	B + (-1)A	$B + e^{J + \ln A}$
reciprocal	1 / A	A^{-1}	$e^{e^{J + \ln\ln A}}$
division	B / A	B x A^{-1}	$e^{\ln B + e^{J + \ln\ln A}}$
negative power	B^{-A}	$B^{(-1)A}$	$e^{e^{J + \ln\ln B + \ln A}}$
base-b logarithm	$\log_B A$	$\ln A \times (\ln B)^{-1}$	$e^{\ln\ln A + e^{J + \ln\ln\ln B}}$
root	$B^{1/A}$	$B^{A^{-1}}$	$e^{e^{\ln\ln B + e^{J + \ln\ln A}}}$

Figure 34-4: *Exponential form of common inverse operations*

```
[<   (A) >]
[(J [(A)])]          J-convert
 J   A               clarify
```

Figure 34-3 shows each standard operation that incorporates an inverse together with its corresponding J form. These operations exhibit a hierarchical structure based on the depth of the J marker. Instead of using odd/even nesting depths to express direct and inverse spaces, the depth of nesting of J identifies a *type* of inverse as indicated by this table:

depth of J	*standard operations*
1	negation, subtraction
2	reciprocal, division, negative power, logarithm
3	root

Figure 34-4 shows the conventional exponential notation for the James forms in Figure 34-3. For convenience the generic base is expressed as base-e in the figure. The primary reason for Figure 34-4 is to show that every inverse incorporates -1, the Mother of all inverses. The *location* of -1 as a multiplier, exponent or hyper-exponent identifies the type of inverse transformation. Figure 34-4 also illustrates another reason why patterns involving J have not yet been explored as fundamental mathematical structures. Standard notation for deeply nested exponents is, to put it mildly, not user friendly.

J-occlusion

J-occlusion is a restatement of the Reflection axiom written without angle-brackets. It is also the void-based form of J-conversion.

J-occlusion

$$A \ (J \ [A]) = void$$

The demonstration is succinct:

	A (J [A])
J-convert	A < A >
cancel	void

As an axiom

J-occlusion can replace Reflection as a **James axiom**, converting the angle-bracket into a notational convenience. The change in axiomatic basis can be achieved via structural assertion combined with definition.[9]

axiom	A (J [A]) = void
definition	(J [A]) =def= <A>
substitute	A <A> = void

Now we have reconverged with the basis used in Volume I and all demonstrations go forward unchanged while using the angle-bracket as an abbreviation. Since J *incorporates* an angle-bracket it feels rather circular to define J-conversion in terms of a J-frame,

$$<A> =def= ([<( )>][A])$$

However the angle-bracket within the structure of J is itself just shorthand for two applications of enfold.

	J
enfold	[(J [( )])]
J-convert	[< ( ) >]

Void-based identity

Reflection is the void-based form of an assertion of identity, so J-occlusion is also the form of *void-based identity*.

$$A = A \qquad ☞ \qquad A \ (J \ [A]) = void$$

Demonstration:

$$A \qquad\quad = A$$
$$A \ < \ A \ > \ = void \qquad\qquad \text{move}$$
$$A \ (J \ [A]) = void \qquad\qquad \text{J-convert}$$

reflection
$$A <A> = void$$

identity
$$A = A$$

Void-based equality

Beyond identity, J-occlusion is the void-based form of an assertion of *equality*.

$$A \ (J \ [A]) = void \qquad ☞ \qquad A = A \qquad\qquad \textit{identity}$$
$$A \ (J \ [B]) = void \qquad ☞ \qquad A = B \qquad\qquad \textit{equality}$$

The Reflection Bridge for equality then provides:

$$A \ (J \ [B]) = void = B \ (J \ [A]) \quad \textit{only when} \quad A = B$$

Self-occlusion

When we apply J-occlusion to J itself, we have *J-self-occlusion*. Setting A to J,

$$J \ (J \ [J]) = void$$

J-self-occlusion

J-self-occlusion is the **Euler identity for the J domain**.

$$J \ ([J] \ [(J)]) = void \qquad ☞ \qquad J + (J \times \#^J) = 0$$

The interpretation shows J being added, multiplied and exponentiated, all in one expression, resulting in zero. Here is a visual comparison to the Euler identity using standard notation.

$$1 \times e^{i\pi} + 1 = 0$$
$$J \times e^J \ + J = 0$$

Euler identity
J-self-occlusion

The rotational interpretation of $J = i\pi$ is explored in Chapters 39 and 40, bringing the similarity even closer. In hybrid notation,

$$1 e^J \ + 1 = 0$$
$$J e^J \ + J = 0$$

From the perspective of the pattern of the Euler identity, J is more inclusive than is 1. Whereas Euler's identity is notoriously exotic, in the J domain the Euler identity is immediately demystified since $e^{i\pi} = e^J = -1$.

$$(1 \times e^{i\pi}) + 1 = 0$$
$$(1 \times -1) + 1 = 0$$
$$-1\ + 1 = 0$$

Mystery still remains, but now it is showing its true colors as −1.

Invariance

Finally we will solve for the form of J within the J-occlusion theorem/axiom.

	A (J [A]) = *void*
move	(J [A]) = <A>
cover	J [A] = [<A>]
move	J = [<A>]<[A]>

☞ $J = \log_{\#} -A - \log_{\#} A$

The interpretation of this result reinforces the *definition* of $\log_{\#} -A$ for any numeric A.

$$\log_{\#} -A = \log_{\#} A + J$$

And due to J-self-inverse,

	<J> = [<A>]<[A]>
cover	J = <[<A>]<[A]>>
react	J = <[<A>]>[A]

☞ $J = \log_{\#} A - \log_{\#} -A$

This invariance relation is pretty enough to give a name.

J-invariant

$$J = [<A>]<[A]>$$

☞ $J = \pm(\log_{\#} -A - \log_{\#} A)$

When expressed in the more familiar exponential space, J-invariant transcribes to − A/A.

(J) = ([<A>]<[A]>)   ☞ $\#^J = -A\ /\ A = -1$

angle-bracket theorem	J-frame theorem
void reflection $< > = void$	**dominion** $(J\ [\ ]) = void$
reflection $A\ <A> = void$	**J-occlusion** $A\ (J\ [A]) = void$
involution $<<A>> = A$	**J-void** $(J\ J\ [A]) = A$
separation $<A><B> = <A\ B>$	**arrangement** $(J\ [A])(J\ [B]) = (J\ [A\ B])$
reaction $<A\ <B>> = <A>\ B$	**arrangement*** $(J\ [A\ (J\ [B])]) = (J\ [A])\ B$
promotion $(A\ [<B>]) = <(A\ [B])>$	**identity*** $(A\ J\ [B]) = (J\ A\ [B])$
J-transparency $[<(A)>] = A\ J$	**identity*** $J\ A = A\ J$
J-void process $[<(J)>] = void$	**J-void object** $J\ J = void$
J-self-inverse $J = <J>$	**J-conversion** $J = (J\ [J])$
J-reflection $J\ <J> = void$	**J-self-occlusion** $J\ (J\ [J]) = void$
J-invariant $J = [<A>]<[A]>$	**J-occlusion*** $J = J\ [A]\ (J\ [[A]])$

* Forms marked by an asterisk have been partially reduced.

Figure 34-5: *Angle-bracket theorems converted to J-frame theorems*

34.7 Axiomatic Structure Revisited

Every angle-bracket theorem can be expressed as a theorem that is free of angle-brackets. Figure 34-5 lists the James axioms and theorems that incorporate an angle-bracket, together with their form when angle-brackets are replaced by J-conversion.

Broadly J-conversion exposes frames (A [B]) as a primary conceptual structure from which to understand the operations of conventional arithmetic. Specifically each standard inverse operation is a J-frame.

The revised three frame-based axioms for James algebra are Inversion, Arrangement and J-occlusion. J-occlusion becomes essential for the demonstration of almost all theorems. Inversion becomes necessary for all theorems except J-conversion, while the role of Arrangement is expanded slightly to cover Separation. Most interesting is the shift of Promotion from the most complex demonstration in Volume I to an identity given Inversion. These comments of course come with the reservation that still more efficient demonstrations may be discovered.

34.8 Remarks

The angle-brackets that represent our standard inverse operations {−, ÷, √, log} can be converted into the form of J. We can thus explain the behavior of the algebraic inverses using the rules governing the behavior of J. We now have three different models of how arithmetic works — ensembles, angle-brackets and J-frames — that we can compare and contrast to our universal standard model.[10] In particular, we have alternative conceptualizations for addressing the unexpected structures that standard inverses introduce, such as signed multiplication, multiple values, divide-by-zero and the existence of the imaginary i.[11]

More fundamentally J can be seen to be an alternative to 1 as a basis for arithmetic, providing an extremely different perspective from which to understand the foundation of "numbers".

feature	example	concern
new unity	J	too extreme to be helpful
transparency	J [<( )>]	no parallel in standard notation
non-accumulating	J J	not a property of numbers
sign-blind	±J	loss of polarity information
tally failure	([J][oo])	contextual loss of confluence
self-inverse	<J>	restriction on composition
cyclic memory	2 x J	loss of distribution

Figure 34-6: *Some concerning features of* J

This chapter has introduced several worrisome structural features, at least from a conventional perspective. Figure 34-6 provides a partial list. These features include those enlisted by Bernoulli (Chapter 33) in support of his belief that J has the same value as the logarithm of positive one. They are also those justified by Euler in his correspondence with Bernoulli as demonstration of the existence of a unique J.

There are several occasions in which we encounter very unfamiliar properties of an arithmetic based on J (the complexity of the unit 1, transparency, uncountable forms, bipolar numbers, memory). These are part of the reason to explore iconic arithmetic in the first place.

In some circumstances J might lead to loss of confluence (sign-blindness, tally-failure). We have postponed discussion of the design decisions that constrain the occurrence of potential contradictions. There is also a choice of attitude about contradiction. Certainly from the conventional perspective contradiction is terminal. J is simply a bad idea if it generates unconstrained contradiction, or in computational terms, loss of confluence. From the perspective of this exploration however the unusual structure of J may be calling for unusual treatment of potential contradiction. An iconic notation may lead to a fuller conceptualization of arithmetic, one that includes forms with fractional polarity, non-distributive structures and new types of incommensurable units. Abandoning the semantics of value in favor of axiomatic structural substitution may soften the need for numeric consistency.

We'll next explore in detail the features and issues that J introduces into the structure of arithmetic. We'll try to come to an understanding about the relationship between constraints imposed on the behavior of J and the algebraic *restrictions* asserted within current conventional transformation rules.

Endnotes

1. **opening quote:** G. Hardy (1940) *A Mathematician's Apology* p.115.

2. **J too has a different representation for each use:** Keep in mind that within a boundary math a form is an object when viewed from the outside and an operator when viewed from the inside.

3. **while signless numbers represented quantities:** A. Martínez (2006) *Negative Math* p.191.

The relatively recent introduction of signed magnitudes was so influential that we now have a truly strange concept: *signed infinity*.

4. **does not support replication because there is nothing to replicate:** Replicating *tokens* is inherently meaningless. 0 + 0 is a semantic structure made of tokens, however "0" + "0" is a contradictory (i.e. meaningless) structure since the semantic plus sign does not apply to tokens. What the semantic structure means is quite ambiguous since we cannot *put together* (i.e. add) no cardinality and no cardinality.

5. **follows Euler's preference described in Chapter 33:** Many common functions require and construct sign-blind values, including both trigonometric and exponential functions.

6. **each number has two square roots, one the negative of the other:** J. Stillwell (2010) *Mathematics and its History 3rd Edition* p.191. Emphasis in original.

Stillwell explains that algebraic roots cannot be expressed as a power series, a primary tool for the development of the calculus. He observes that "many-valued behavior is typical of algebraic functions in general." (p.191.)

7. **J was recognized by Euler as described in Chapter 33.4:** Tally failure addresses the same issue as does Euler's infinity of imaginary logarithms but without introducing *memory* which in turn allows counting to infinity.

8. **behaving as though there was no boundary:** *Semipermeability* is the fundamental property that differentiates *logical* form from *numeric* form.

9. **via structural assertion combined with definition:** Asserting J-occlusion as an axiom of course implies that it cannot be demonstrated from the other two axioms.

10. **compare and contrast to our universal standard model:** Ensembles, in Chapters 2 through 4, rely only on *substitution* to achieve the operations of arithmetic.

11. `divide-by-zero`, **and the existence of the imaginary** i**:** In *On Numbers and Games* (1976) John Conway develops a different kind of imaginary, which he calls *, within the *surreal number system*.

$$* = \{0|0\} \qquad \qquad \textit{the imaginary surreal}$$

He shows that

$$\{n|n\} = n + *$$

which is the surreal analog of J-transparency. Although Conway states on page 7, "$\{0|0\}$ is *not* a number", it occurs extensively as a type of degenerate game in the latter half of the book. $\{0|0\}$ identifies an adversarial game in which Player A first chooses which side to play (with or against the wind in football, + or − in general) and then Player B goes first. In a $\{0|0\}$ game Player B has a winning strategy.

There is a connection here to sign-blindness. On page 4, Conway comments: "There is no property enjoyed by i which is not also shared by −i." The choice of side (i.e. which polarity) confers no differential advantage. From his (and Euler's) perspective i is sign-blind.

In Berlekamp, Conway & Guy (1982) *Winning Ways*, the authors provide the name * for $\{0|0\}$ since it is prevalent throughout the book. On page 40 we find

$$* + * = 0 \qquad \textit{while} \qquad * \neq 0$$

Thus * has the same non-accumulating behavior as J within a completely different iconic number system.

Chapter 35

Features

*I had a feeling once about Mathematics, that I saw it
all — Depth beyond depth was revealed to me — the Byss
and the Abyss. I saw...a quantity passing through infinity
and changing its sign from plus to minus...It was like
politics. But it was after dinner and I let it go![1]
—Winston Churchill (1930)*

Within the James arithmetic J is unavoidable. It is
especially entangled with the classical structural
issues such as the rules of negative numbers, multiple
solutions to roots, imaginary numbers, roots of the unit
1, breakdown in the rules of exponents and logarithms,
geometric operations of rotation and reflection, and even in
the precursors to complex analysis. Before tackling these
interesting issues in the next chapter, we'll have a closer
look at how J works, its oscillating and cyclic behavior,
sign-blindness, incommensurability with the integers,
ambiguities that must be managed, and the surprising
circumstance that J and angle-brackets are different
notations for the same concept. We have encountered one
particularly unusual behavior: the additive imaginary
seems to limit the application of multiplication and division
due to *tally failure*. We'll resolve the problem by taking
incommensurability seriously. To finish the chapter we'll
introduce **J-fractions** that add rational numbers to the J
domain while providing the behavior of complex numbers
without the constant i and without the complex plane.

conventional	*label*	*boundary structure*
2	2	oo
-1	-1	<o>
$\log_\# -1$	J	[<o>]
1/2	1/2	(<[oo]>)
$\log_\# i$	J/2	([J]<[oo]>)
$\sqrt{-1}$	i	(([J]<[oo]>)) = (J/2)
$^N\sqrt{-1}$	$i^{2/N}$	(([J]<[N]>)) = (J/N)
$2\pi/2$	π	([J] ([J]<[oo]>)) = (J/2 [J])

Figure 35-1: *Some special labels*

35.1 Special Structures

Figure 35-1 shows some useful abbreviations for specific boundary forms, particularly forms for imaginary and transcendental numbers. The labels will result in a **hybrid language**, one that predisposes us to regress into preexisting beliefs about creatures such as π, i and −1. But when 1, aka ( ), has an *inside* even the concept of unity comes into question. The use of special symbols is minimal, occurring only when specific observations about the structure of James numbers are useful. An abbreviation within a hybrid form is unlikely to open up into an operation unless there is a specific goal in mind. Thus it will be safe to consider these abbreviations to be convenience labels placed upon specific compound boundary forms, without an implied interpretation.

The boundary structure of i is substantiated by a direct transcription of the definition of i into James form.

hybrid	$i = \sqrt{-1}$ ☞	(([[−1]] <[2]>))
substitute		(([[<o>]] <[2]>))
substitute		(([J] <[2]>))
substitute/hybrid		(J/2)

$$i = (([J]<[oo]>)) = (J/2)$$

J *frames*

(J [A]) = <A>	**J-conversion frame**
(J [<A>]) = A	**J-involution frame**
(J <[A]>) = <(<[A]>)>	**J-angle frame**
(J [J]) = J	**J-self frame**

[J] *frames*

([J] [N])	J x N
([J]<[2]>)	J/2
([J]<[N]>)	J/N

Figure 35-2: *Frame-types incorporating* J

The form ([J]<[oo]>) has a special symbol, "J/2". It will also be useful to provide an abbreviation for unit fractions (<[N]>) as "1/N". The prevalence of the number 2 is more than coincidence. Were it not for canceling +2 and −2 and for adding 1/2 and 1/2, the fundamental concepts (1, π, i, J) would not exhibit simple relationships. Yet the 2 comes from several conceptually different sources:[2]

— the definition of i as a 1/2 power

— a full revolution of 2π radians

— the sign calculus square of units, (±1)^2 = 1

— two Js self-void, J J = *void*

— two 90° rotations achieve a reflection.

J Frames

Figure 35-2 shows some common inversion frames with the frame-type J. J-conversion, for example, converts the angle-bracket into a J-frame. J also occurs as [J] within a cardinality frame. The form [J] permits interpretation as multiplication by J and also as the addition of log J, both of which we will explore in later chapters. There is another way that J can participate in an inversion frame, as the frame-contents rather than as the frame-type. This is seldom the case since J is a unit marker and is not likely to be the dynamic contents of a frame.

35.2 J in Action

Before going further, I'll illustrate the use of J in computation. J provides alternative techniques for numeric computation, but its strength (so far as has been explored) is in exposing the unity underneath the diversity of rules for arithmetic and algebra. In particular, J helps us to understand −1. Consider the two versions of this demonstration that negative times negative is positive.

$$(-1) \times (-1) \quad \text{☞} \quad ([\text{<o>}][\text{<o>}])$$

```
promote            <<([ o ][ o ])>>
unwrap             ([ o ][ o ])
clarify            (          )  ☞  1
```

J provides a different perspective:

$$(-1) \times (-1) \quad \text{☞} \quad ([\text{<o>}][\text{<o>}])$$

```
substitute         (  J    J  )
J-void object      (          )  ☞  1
```

J is not implicated in the transformation that makes the self-multiplication of positive units positive.

$$1 \times 1 \quad \text{☞} \quad ([o][o])$$

```
clarify            (          )  ☞  1
```

Multiplying two negatives constructs a pair of self-voiding Js. The remaining empty container can be interpreted as +1. Seen from the minimal world of James axioms, J-void is *why* self-multiplying negatives makes a positive within a conceptual structure that is more fundamental: *unit plus unit is nothing.* This perspective may appear to be a bit perverse, but the important idea is *elegance.* We have not introduced the concept of polarity, we have not called upon −1 or +1 *within* the demonstration and the explanation does not differentiate between addition and multiplication. The result *emerges* when J-void is applied.

J-conversion

$$\text{<A>} = (\text{J [A]})$$

Constructing Js can offer a shortcut for symbolic manipulation. The shortcut itself is a different way of thinking about what is involved with specific transformation rules. The following examples illustrate basic numeric identities.

```
-(-1)    ☞    <   <   o > >
              (J [(J [o])])                        J-convert
              (J   J      )                        clarify
              (           )          ☞   1         J-void object
```

−1 can be read directly as (J):

```
-1/-1    ☞    ([(J)] <[(J)]>)
              (  J   <  J  >)                       clarify
              (           )          ☞   1          cancel
```

A negative unit power, A^{-1}, is conventionally defined to be a unit fraction, 1/A. At the level of exponents negative polarity specifies division. The J-frame form of a negative exponent, ((J [[A]])), is the *same* as the form of a unit fraction, (<[A]>), given J-conversion. Negative exponentials are not a *definition*, they are a structural consequence.

```
A^-1     ☞    (([[A]] [<( )>]))
              (([[A]]     J  ))                     substitute
              (< [A]         >)       ☞   1/A       J-convert
```

Here is the reciprocal of 1/A in exponential notation. For this example, it is easier to clarify directly rather than to go through the J form:

```
(A^-1)^-1   ☞   (<[ (<[A]>) ]>)                     clarify
                (<    <[A]>   >)                     unwrap
                (     [A]     )                      clarify
                      A               ☞   A
```

Here is an algebraic example that uses J as a computational shortcut.[3]

$$(A + 1)(A - 1) = A^2 - 1 \quad ☞$$

```
([A o][A <o>])
([A o][A (J)])                                       substitute
([A][A]) ([o][A]) ([A][(J)]) ([o][(J)])              disperse
([A][A])    A   ([A]  J  )        (J)                clarify
([A][A])                          (J)                J-occlude
                           ☞   A^2 - 1
```

To factor a simple polynomial, reverse the above steps, calling upon the construction of void-equivalent forms to provide the polynomial roots to the equation $A^2 = 1$.

Negative Base Logarithms

Negative numbers can be the base of an exponential. The constant i, $(-1)^{1/2}$, serves as an example. What kind of number is a logarithm with a negative base? Conventionally negative base logs are undefined. They can be managed by calling upon J.

We'll assume that the negative base <B> includes B as a natural number greater than one, partitioning the question of a negative base from the compound question of fractional negative bases. The explicit James form for a negative base is

$$\log_{-B} A \quad \text{☞} \quad (<[[<B>]]>[[A]])_\#$$

The problem is immediately apparent, there appears to be is no way to free the angle-bracket containing B. J-conversion provides a path.

$$\log_{-B} A \quad \text{☞} \quad (<[[< \ B \ >]]>[[A]])_\#$$

J-convert $\quad (<[[(J \ [B])]]>[[A]])$

clarify $\quad (<[\ J \ [B] \ ]>[[A]])$

$$\text{☞} \quad \log_\# A / (\log_\# B + J_\#)$$

Compare this result to the logarithm base-conversion formula for a positive base.

negative base $\quad \log_{-B} A = \log_\# A/(\log_\# B + \log_\# -1)$

positive base $\quad \log_B \ A = \log_\# A/(\log_\# B + \log_\# +1)$

Built into the logarithm conversion formula is an adjustment for the polarity of the base. This shared structure has been repressed probably because $\log_\# -1$ is not generally recognized as a legitimate expression.

It is also easier to see how to handle logarithms of negative numbers by applying the James form of the base conversion formula.

$$\log_\# -A = \log_\#(A \times -1) = \log_\# A + \log_\# -1 = \log_\# A + J$$

Combining these results gives us the form of a negative base logarithm of a negative number.

$$\log_{-B} -A = (\quad \log_{\#} -A) / (\log_{\#} B + J)$$
$$= (\log_{\#} A + J) / (\log_{\#} B + J)$$

The James form of this result can be constructed directly using J-conversion.

$$(<[[< \quad B \quad >]]>[[< \quad A \quad >]])$$
$$(<[[(J \quad [B])]]>[[(J \quad [A])]]) \qquad \text{J-convert}$$
$$(<[\quad J \quad [B] \quad]>[\quad J \quad [A] \quad]) \qquad \text{clarify}$$

When we let A = B

$$\log_{-A} -A = (\ln A + J) / (\ln A + J) = 1$$

The result is that $\log_n n = 1$ holds in all cases except $n = 0$ and $n = 1$, even when $n < 0$.

Roots of Negative Unity

J provides an elegant conceptual form for the roots of negative one, $^N\sqrt{-1}$.

$$^A\sqrt{B} \quad \text{☞} \quad ((([\quad B \quad]]<[A]>))$$
$$^N\sqrt{-1} \quad \text{☞} \quad ((([[<o>]]<[N]>)) \qquad \text{substitute}$$
$$((([\quad J \quad]<[N]>)) \qquad \text{substitute}$$
$$((([\quad J \quad][1/N])) \qquad \text{substitute}$$

For example, in hybrid notation the three roots of $^3\sqrt{-1}$ are

$$(([J][1/3]))_e \qquad \text{☞} \qquad e^{J/3}$$
$$(([J][2/3]))_e \qquad \text{☞} \qquad e^{2J/3}$$
$$(([J][3/3]))_e \qquad \text{☞} \qquad e^{3J/3}$$

J-fractions will be of central importance when we look at complex numbers and the trigonometry of the complex plane in Chapters 39 and 40.

35.3 Unconventional Behavior of J

We have identified incommensurability, sign-blindness and potential contradiction as behavioral problems that need to be addressed with design decisions. All are tightly connected. The reason for even considering such a potentially problematic concept as J is that it provides the ability to *replace the common inverse operators by a single constant* within the context of nested round- and square-brackets.

J Stands Alone

The incommensurability of J asserts that we cannot add or multiply numeric forms and Js together to achieve a single form. Unlike complex numbers, real numbers and imaginary J forms are held apart not by their inability to add together but by the topological separation of boundaries. The presence of J within a container marks that container as imaginary. Without J in the contents, the container refers to the world of real numbers. This situation is similar to that of *complex numbers* which are constructed by addition of two incommensurable worlds, $a + bi$. Stated in terms of a principle:

The Principle of Incommensurability
J does not interact with the other numeric forms within its container.

The Principle does not imply that J has *no* effect on other forms, but since J-occlusion is the only axiom that addresses the behavior of J, we can say that the only way that J does interact with other forms is by occluding replicas.

J-occlusion

A (J [A]) = *void*

The fundamental difference between i and J is that i supports accumulation. The b in bi is an arbitrary numeric multiplier, a cardinality measure of i. J without memory cannot be multiplied but it can, as we will see, be divided. J and i are within the same imaginary domain which is explored in Chapter 39.

J-transparency demonstrates that J is an independent numeric concept. J is often better conceived as an operator rather than an imaginary value. J *subsumes* the sign of negative numbers and their accompanying additive inverse. J-occlusion manages the inverse operations uniformly. In the case of addition, the frame-type J distinguishes positive from negative domains.

```
A - A      ☞     A <   A >
                 A (J [A])                        J-convert
            void           ☞    0                 J-occlude
```

In the case of division [A] rather than A is occluded.

```
A / A      ☞     ([A] <   [A] >)
                 ([A] (J [[A]]))                  J-convert
                 (    void    )    ☞   1          J-occlude
```

In the case of exponentiation the exponent is occluded.

```
1/n        ☞                      ((J [[n]]))
A^n                (((([A]][n]))
(A^n)^{1/n}   (((([    A^n    ]][  1/n    ]))   hybrid
              ((    [[A]][n]      (J [[n]])  ))  substitute/clarify
              ((    [[A]]                    ))  J-occlude
                        A                        clarify
```

J-occlusion then is the single structural concept that uni-fies the apparently different zeros and inverse operations of conventional numeric arithmetic.

Addition of negative numbers is implemented by Arrangement. For example:

```
-A + -B    ☞     (J [A]) (J [B])
                 (J [A B]))     ☞    -(A + B)     collect
```

Similarly for multiplication of fractions:

```
1/A x 1/B  ☞   ([ ((J [[A]])) ][ ((J [[B]])) ])
               (  (J [[A]])     (J [[B]])    )   clarify
               (  (J [[A][B]])                )   collect
```

Here are all the possibilities of adding *within* the J realm. For convenience we'll allow both sides of the interpretation finger to reference the J token.

```
J +  J     ☞    J J  = void                      J-void object
J + -J     |    J <J> = void                     cancel
-J + -J    |    <J><J> = <J J> = < > = void       join/J-void object
```

From the perspective of J = <J> the three boundary equations above are indistinguishable. However, we have formulated them as three different reduction rules (J-void, Reflection, and Separation).

Sign-blind

$$(\pm 1)^2 = 1$$
$$(\pm i)^2 = -1$$
$$\sin \pm \pi = \pm 0$$
$$e^{\pm J} = -1$$

J is insensitive to sign. Just like 0, positive J is the same as negative J. However unlike 0, the presence and absence of J does matter since the presence of J marks an inverse operation. Just how does a number that disrespects positive/negative polarity work? The situation is similar to the conventional concept of **absolute value**, which provides a notation equivalent to $\pm$.[4]

absolute value

$$|n| = \pm n$$

Here we will use the $\pm$ notation. Absence of an explicit $+$ or $-$ defaults to $\pm$ for J and for forms that inherit sign-blindness from interaction with J. A particularly surprising result is the apparent loss of the distinction between "negative" and "positive" when multiplying by J.

$$-A \times J \quad \text{☞} \quad ([<A>][J])$$

promote/demote

$$([A][<J>])$$

J-self-inverse

$$([A][J]) \quad \text{☞} \quad = A \times J$$

Multiplication by J transfers the sign-blind property of J to any form being multiplied. The operation is lossy, we lose the specific sign ($+$ or $-$) of the object A. This makes multiplying by J a quite special operation, not your common arithmetic.

$$([A][J]) \quad \text{☞} \quad \log_\# (-1)^A$$
$$([<A>][J]) \quad \text{☞} \quad \log_\# (-1)^{-A}$$

All void-equivalent forms are sign-blind. For example, the sign-blind property of the Reflection axiom is expressed directly as the Reaction theorem:

$$A < \quad A > = < \quad A < \quad A > > = void$$

J-convert

$$A (J [A]) = (J [A (J [A])])$$

J-occlude

$$(J [\qquad])$$

absorb

void

The Dominion theorem as well is sign-blind.

$$(A [ ]) = void = <(A [ ])>$$

Sign-blindness must be managed. Just like Dominion loses the magnitude information associated with the form A, it also loses the polarity. J joins self-multiplication and square root as *multivalued*. Here is an example, not sufficiently useful to be called a theorem, that illustrates the difficulties of applying J-self-inverse.

$$J [J] = [(J [J])] = [<J>] \Rightarrow [J] \qquad \text{ERROR}$$

Here's an erroneous demonstration:

void = J (J [J])	J-occlude
<J> = (J [J])	move
J = (J [J])	J-self-inverse ERROR
[J] = J [J]	cover

This result exposes an unmentioned **constraint on substitution**. Applying J-self-inverse to J on one side of the equation but not on the other side is an error. The difficulty is not within J-self-inverse itself but rather within the meaning of the equal sign when encountering bipolar forms. A different reduction path provides the correct result.

```
    J  [J]
    [<o>][J]                          substitute
  [ ([<o>][J]) ]                      enfold
  [<(     [J])>]                      promote/clarify
  [<      J  >]  ☞  log# −J = log# J + J   clarify
```

Louis Kauffman corrects this type of substitution error by the Flagg resolution.[5] We are not free to *partially substitute* one occurrence of a *sign-blind* token within an equation. This constraint disables the **replacement rule** of substitution since replacement permits partial substitution.

(substitute A for-any B in E) = E   *when* A = B   local replacement

The *global* substitution of J for <J> corrects the error. Even though J is sign-blind, when combined with an equality assertion, its change of sign must be for all contextual instances. For example, in the J-transparency theorem,

```
[<(A)>]  = A   J
[<(A)>]  = A <J>        NOT        substitution ERROR
```

Using Flagg substitution

```
[<(A)>]  = A   J
<[<(A)>]> = A <J>
```

Arrangement Inconsistency

Now we come to the form of rational numbers and division, both of which place angle-brackets in a location that cannot be promoted. Similar to divide-by-zero, here is where the conventional rules of arithmetic need to be extended.

To illustrate the problem here's a simple example: adding replicas of J/2. There are two different ways to express the sum of two half Js. The first example runs into no problems.

J/2 = ([J]<[oo]>)

```
        J/2 + J/2   ☞
            ([J]  <[2]>  ) ([J]  <[2]>  )
enfold      ([J][(<[2]>)]) ([J][(<[2]>)])
collect     ([J][(<[2]>)(<[2]>)])     ☞    (1/2 + 1/2) x J
tally       ([J][([(<[2]>)][2])])     ☞    (  2 x 1/2) x J
clarify     ([J]     <[2]> [2]  )
cancel      ([J]                )
clarify        J
```

Alternatively, we could elect to collect Js rather than 1/2s. In this case the fractional <[2]> is lost when the numerators cancel to nothing. Under Dominion, *any* multiplier will cancel.

```
              J/2 + J/2   ☞   ([J]<[2]>) ([J]<[2]>)
collect                       ([J J]<[2]>)
J-void object                 ([  ]<[2]>)
absorb                            void
```

The potential inconsistency occurs in this path when we attempt to tally J via collect. The diverging results arise from the *choice* of which form to collect, <[2]> or J. After collecting, either J-void object or Reflection applies, each leading to a different result.[6]

Tally Failure

In the first example the form ([J]<[2]>[2]) supports both J-void tally and cancellation. The design decision is to take numeric forms as applying to each other rather than applying to the cardinality of the indicator J. As mentioned in the previous chapter, this direct solution is the *tally failure restriction*.

$$J + J \neq 2J \qquad \text{☞} \qquad J \; J \not\Rightarrow ([J][2])$$

Euler resolved this quandary by declaring that logarithms have an infinite number of values with one and only one *real* value when the argument is positive. He was most reluctant to place restrictions on the general algebraic structure of exponents and logarithms, although the design decision to restrict certain exponential transforma-

$$\left(A^{1/2}\right)^2 \neq \left(A^2\right)^{1/2}$$

tions is today's consensus. Here we've adopted a different but benign restriction: since J is *incommensurable*, we'll *not* take numeric forms to refer to the cardinality of J. This choice is roughly equivalent to not allowing the real and imaginary components of a complex number to mingle.[7]

$$a+bi \neq (a+b)i$$

Tally itself is derivative of the *Arrangement axiom*, so the core idea is that J tokens cannot be arranged. We know at this point that a form may directly contain either one J or no J. Not collecting J is a design decision consistent with the intent that J itself is a specific type of indicator, one that signals presence or absence. It is in this sense a **type indicator** rather than a magnitude that accumulates. J-void object enforces the idea that a present/absent indicator does not support multiple presences. The situation would be analogous to collecting operator tokens rather than value tokens. For containers that contain J, the non-J numeric contents must be reduced together rather than being taken as the cardinality of J. After we know the magnitude of the numeric component, if it is exactly even (i.e. an even natural number) then the J-parity is zero. Otherwise the parity is one. Numeric forms tally, J forms do not. As a consequence, fractions of J add like conventional fractions.

We have seen that *void* cannot be collected since it cannot be indicated. In Chapter 41 we will see that the square unit cannot be collected as well. The next two sections continue to explore this unusual approach, one that seems unusual primarily due to the widely held symbolic assumption that replication is free.

replication

$$([A][o...o]) = A...A$$

35.4 Oscillation

J is an additive imaginary. Unlike i, J interacts with itself by addition instead of multiplication. Tallying expresses accumulation as multiplication by natural numbers, it is thus not an appropriate way to describe the behavior of J.

$$0 = J \times 0 \quad ☞ \quad ([J][\quad]) = \textit{void}$$
$$J = J = J \times 1 \quad | \quad ([J][\ o]) = J$$
$$J + J = 0 \neq J \times 2 \quad | \quad ([J][\ oo]) = \textit{void}$$
$$J + J + J = J \neq J \times 3 \quad | \quad ([J][ooo]) = J$$

The cardinality of J is modulo-2, but this inappropriately suggests two oscillating states. Since we cannot count J, we cannot count how "often" it is present. Counting Js is an inappropriate transfer of the natural number concept of cardinality into the algebra of an imaginary form that does not accumulate.[8]

Without Memory

The **without memory policy** establishes that the concept J does not support anything more than *presence* or *absence*. J is a reflection rather than a rotation. Without memory cardinality and accumulation are no longer available. For example, in conventional terms

$$J + J = 0 = 2 \times J \quad ☞ \quad J\ J = \textit{void} = ([J][2])$$

Without memory there is no transcription of 2 x J. Other void-equivalent forms, for example ([ ] A), may maintain symbolic existence over several transformation steps. The form J J can be *brought into existence* from void, however the form ([J][2]) cannot then be constructed since that requires that both J tokens support being marked.

indication

$A = ([A][o])$

Here is a comparison between the perspectives of modular cardinality, absence of accumulation and uncountable self-voiding. The primary difference is that a self-voiding J cannot be marked via the Indication theorem and thus cannot be tallied.

N mod 2	*modular cardinality*	
	J J J	
	([J][o])([J][o])([J][o])	mark
	([J][oo o])	collect
	([J][o])	delete oo
	J	unmark
tally J	*counted cardinality*	
	J J J	
	([J][o])([J][o])([J][o])	mark
	([J][o])([J][oo])	collect
	([J][o])	J-void tally
	J	unmark
J J = *void*	*self-voiding*	
	J J J	
	J	J-void object

Once we discover that J is self-voiding the design decision that it cannot be tallied is equivalent to Euler's constraint described in Section 33.4: some numbers legitimately invalidate a presumed relationship between addition and multiplication. That is, J is *non-distributive*.

$$J + J \nRightarrow 2 \times J \qquad ☞ \qquad J\ J \nRightarrow ([J][2]) \qquad\qquad appropriate$$

With Memory

Certainly the *token* "J" can be replicated indefinitely. And at times it may be beneficial to have a computational history of accumulated tokens rather than conceptual reflections. This way of thinking about accumulation subscribes to the **memory policy** that we can record the cycles of J. Memory permits J *indicators* to be replicated, collected and tallied. The overflow of J occurrences can be interpreted as a count of blinkings, of back-and-forth reflections, of bounces up and down, of cycles around a wheel, of waves passing by and of multiplications by −1. These counts are in any event *external* to the James calculus, they are a conceptual mechanism to *extend* James algebra into the natural numbers by introducing the concept of time as sequence.

Both computationally and conceptually *memory* requires mechanism. We can attach memory to a transformation, but only as an *independent* store. A **store** is any device that keeps track of accumulation. Serial counting requires more mechanism than does parallel counting. In particular, a **serial counter** must store the current total in order to know what it is adding 1 to. A **parallel counter** swaps memory for a plethora of concurrent operations. The trade is memory for process, object for operation. The advantage of the serial approach is that we can record the number of J reflections. Two reflections, 360°, is different than four reflections, 720°. This turns out to be crucial for Euler's infinity of imaginary values for a logarithm.[9]

35.5 Counting J Tokens

Cardinality is constructed when we apply Arrangement to collect indicators into the same container, thus giving that container a name, one that corresponds to the number of indicators that have been collected together. *Cardinality counts indications*, it does not matter what forms are being replicated and indicated.[10] *How many*, at this point, involves only natural numbers.

Cardinality can be generalized to permit negative accumulation, fractional accumulation, real accumulation and imaginary accumulation. These types of accumulation can be expressed by a form that can be interpreted as multiplication.

$$([replica] [occurrences])$$

Thus there are two symmetric aspects to the cardinality of J, counting occurrences *of* J and counting, so to speak, *by* J. By design we will not permit replicas of J to accumulate.[11] This is equivalent to not permitting cycles of rotation, frequency of waves, and infinities of imaginary values for logarithms. The intended nexus is simply to disallow accumulation by limiting J to one occurrence. Counting by J then is keeping track of presence or absence, with no explicit numeric component of cardinality.

J-parity

The self-voiding nature of J specifies that a *count* of the number of Js will be either 0 or 1. This leads to the J-parity theorem for *tokens*. When N is a natural number of J replicas,

N *even*	([J][N]) = *void*	
N *odd*	([J][N]) = J	

J-parity

This form of J-parity is not quite accurate since it suggests that replicas of J can accumulate.[12] If J is present in the context, an oscillation changes phase, starting at the contextual J rather than at *void*.

N *even*	J ([J][N]) = J	
N *odd*	J ([J][N]) = *void*	

J-parity

The demonstration of J-parity is straightforward. We partition the cardinality of J tokens into pairs that are void-equivalent. Here are the basic cases.

$$([J][]) = void \qquad \textit{dominion}$$
$$([J][\ o\ ]) = J \qquad \textit{indication}$$
$$([J][oo]) = void \qquad \textit{J-void tally}$$

Since J is sign-blind, accumulating positive or negative instances amounts to the same thing. Negative counts provide an extended version of J-parity.

N *even*	([J][N]) = ([J][<N>]) = *void*	
N *odd*	([J][N]) = ([J][<N>]) = J	

sign-blind
J-parity

When we consider negative counts, an entirely different boundary structure emerges, one that radically changes our interpretation of cardinality as a count.

$$-1 \times J \quad \text{☞} \quad ([<o>][J])$$
$$(\ J\ [J])$$
$$([(J)][J]) \quad \text{☞} \quad J \times \#^J$$

substitute
enfold

Negative accumulation has taken us directly to complex exponentials. We can, however recover the idea of counting by reinterpreting the form (J [J]) as using J as a counting unit, just like we have used −1. Counting by Js moves the concept of cardinality into the imaginary realm.

binary 0/1	odd/even	positive/negative	J-parity
addition			
0 + 0 = 0	even + even = even	pos + pos = pos	= void
0 + 1 = 1	even + odd = odd	pos + neg = 0	void J = J
1 + 1 = 0	odd + odd = even	neg + neg = neg	J J = void
multiplication			
0 x 0 = 0	even x even = even	pos x pos = pos	([ ][ ]) = void
0 x 1 = 0	even x odd = even	pos x neg = neg	([ ][J]) = void
1 x 1 = 1	odd x odd = odd	neg x neg = pos	([J][J]) = J^2

Figure 35-3: *Comparison of bivalent laws*

Figure 35-3 shows the rules for four different types of bivalence: binary 0/1, odd/even, positive/negative and J-parity. These patterns each have different shapes with some similarities. J-parity most closely resembles the pattern of binary 0/1 with 0 associated with *absence* and 1 associated with *presence*. Unlike 0/1, self-multiplication of J increases magnitude while magnitude is not available to the binary system. Although J-parity matches the numeric odd/even system, it does not accumulate magnitude in the other five cases. We could interpret *even* to mean 0, but then *odd* fails to align with the magnitude behavior of J. Fundamentally each of the four types of bivalence is unique.

Self-multiplication of Negatives

Negative bases such as $(-1)^5$ oscillate in polarity depending upon whether the exponent is odd or even.[13] James forms have no explicit representation to determine the difference, unlike natural numbers that permit an easy identification of parity by checking the last digit of a number. We can begin to explore the behavior of the powers of a negative numbers, i.e base--N, by observing some simple cases. We have already considered negative base

last digit
even {0,2,4,6,8}
odd {1,3,5,7,9}

logarithms to find that the magnitude and the polarity of a base can be separated and stored in the behavior of J.

What do the powers of –A look like?

$$(-A)^N \quad ☞ \quad ((\,[\,[<A>]\,]\,[N]\,))$$

Conventionally the polarity of A would oscillate between positive and negative depending upon the *parity* (odd/even) of N. When N is even, an even number of negative signs cancels to +1. When N is odd, pairwise canceling would leave one –1 remaining. Let's look first at N = 1, N = 2 and N = 3.

$(-A)^1$ ☞	`((([[<A>]][0]))`	
	`<A>` ☞ –A	clarify

$(-A)^2$ ☞	`((([[<A>]][2] ))`	
	`( [<A>][<A>] )`	replicate
	`( [ A ][ A ] )`	promote/unwrap
	`((([ A ]][2] ))` ☞ A^2	tally

$(-A)^3$ ☞	`((([[<A>]][3]      ))`	
	`( [<A>][<A>][<A>] )`	replicate
	`<( [ A ][ A ][ A ] )>`	promote/unwrap
	`<((([ A ]][3]      ))>` ☞ $-A^3$	tally

All generate the oscillating pattern as expected. The Involution theorem maintains parity by unwrapping paired angle-brackets. The same result can be achieved via J-void.

$(-A)^1$ ☞	`((([(J [A])]][0]))`	
	`( J [A]      ) ` ☞ –A	clarify

$(-A)^2$ ☞	`((([(J [A])]][2] ))`	
	`((( J [A] ][2] ))`	clarify
	`( J [A] J [A] )`	replicate/clarify
	`( [A] [A] )`	J-void object
	`(( [[A]][2] ))` ☞ A^2	tally

$(-A)^3$ ☞	`((([(J [A])]][3]) )`	
	`(J [A] J [A] J [A])`	clarify/replicate
	`(J ([[A]][3]) )`	J-void object/tally
	`(J [((([[A]][3]))] )` ☞ $-A^3$	enfold

Next, a variable power. $(-A)^N$ is the archetype unresolved oscillation.

$$(-A)^N \quad ☞ \quad ((([[<A>]][N])) \quad ☞ \quad \textit{does not simplify}$$

Here we have come across a class of non-reducing forms, which we'll revisit in Chapter 43. When N has an unspecified value, Arrangement cannot be applied because the number of replicas of $[<A>]$ is ambiguous. But we do have a technique to separate magnitude from polarity by calling upon J. Once separated, the polarity of whole number powers of a negative base can be determined by J-parity.

$$(-A)^N = (-1 \times A)^N = (-1)^N \times A^N$$

clarify/disperse
enfold

$$(-A)^N \quad ☞ \quad (([[(J\ [A])]][N])\ )$$
$$(\ ([J][N])\quad\ ([[A]][N])\ )$$
$$([((([J][N]))][((([A]][N]))])$$
$$☞ \quad (-1)^N \times A^N$$

35.6 J Unit Fractions

J departs from conventional parity functions when we extend to fractional counting, i.e. to division. The form $([J]<[N]>)$ does not reduce, regardless of the sign of N. Thus when J is divided by any integer, the form remains stable and unique. Rational fractions of J are discrete objects. There is however a subtle distinction to be made. What do we make of fractions such as 2/3 that have an even number in the numerator? 2/3 J might be considered as 2J/3, which would reduce to *void* by J-void. Or it might mean a legitimate fraction of a single J. Is $([J][2]<[3]>)$ void-equivalent since it appears that we have two replicas of J? Or does it indicate a 2/3 fraction of J?

Since the Principle of Incommensurability excludes numeric forms from interacting with J, the fraction 2/3 applies to one single J rather than two Js divided into three parts. The form of 2 x J is not equivalent to the form of J + J due to tally failure. This design decision supports any rational multiple of J. However we'll still have to eliminate multiples of exactly two Js under J-void. Thus,

```
2/3 J    ☞   ([J][2]<[3]>)                              stable
```

```
6/3 J    ☞   ([J]    [6]    <[3]>)
             ([J]    [2][3]  <[3]>)                     substitute/clarify
             ([J]    [2]          )                     cancel
                    void                ☞   0           J-void tally
```

```
8/3 J    ☞   ([J] [8] <[3]>)
             ([J][6 2]<[3]>)                            substitute
             ([J] [6] <[3]>)([J][2]<[3]>)              disperse
             ([J]    [2]    )([J][2]<[3]>)             substitute
                               ([J][2]<[3]>)            J-void tally
                                      ☞   2/3 J
```

J-Fractions

In the simplest case of a unit fraction, J-fractions consist
of the form [J] in the same container with a form <[N]>.

generic
J-fraction

$$J/N \quad ☞ \quad ([J]<[N]>)$$

An application of Inversion makes apparent the form
of multiplication ([...][...]) and the form of a unit
fraction (<[...]>).

```
J/N    ☞   ([J]   <[N]>  )
           ([J][(<[N]>)])   ☞   J × 1/N                enfold
```

Due to propagation of sign-blindness, J-fractions are also
sign-blind. J-self-inverse extends to include J-fractions.

$$J/N = <J/N>$$

Demonstration:

```
           ([ J ]<[N]>)
           ([<J>]<[N]>)                                J-self-inverse
           <([ J ]<[N]>)>                              promote
```

Here's the template for the sum of two arbitrary J-fractions.

```
J/M + J/N   ☞
  ([J]             <[M]>  ) ([J]            <[N]>)
  ([J]   [ N]<[N]><[M]>  ) ([J][M]<[M]><[N]>)       create
  ([J]   [M N]<[M]><[N]>  )                          collect/clarify
  ([J]   [M N]<[M]   [N]>  )                         join
  ([J][([M N]<[M]   [N]>)])  ☞  J × (M + N)/(M × N)  enfold
```

Unit Fractions

Unit fractions are an alternative way to view fractions with numerators greater than 1.

$$1/N \quad ☞ \quad (<[N]>) = ((J\ [[N]]))$$

Unit fractions were mastered by the Egyptian middle kingdom around 2000 BCE. It is known that any rational number can be expressed as the sum of unit fractions in multiple ways, so having only unit fractions is equivalent to having all rational numbers. For example,

$$4/7 = 1/7 + 1/7 + 1/7 + 1/7 = 1/2 + 1/14$$

4/7 ☞	([4]<[7]>)
create	(<[2]>[2][4]<[7]>)
substitute	(<[2]>[8] <[7]>)
substitute	(<[2]>[7 o] <[7]>)
disperse	(<[2]><[7]>[7])(<[2]><[7]>[o])
cancel/clarify	(<[2]>)(<[2]><[7]>)
split/substitute	(<[2]>)(<[14]>)
	☞ 1/2 + 1/14

J-fractions with even numerators can also be considered to be sums of fractions with the odd numerator 1. Expressions like 2/3 can be converted into sums that would not trigger J-void. The Principle of Incommensurability is supported by the idea that *every rational number is a sum of unit fractions,* in multiple ways. Numeric components apply to one J, not multiple Js divided into multiple parts.

2/3 = 1/3 + 1/3
     = 1/2 + 1/6

The *don't tally J constraint* still applies: numeric forms within a container do not refer to the "cardinality" of J itself. One way to make this design decision clearer in the notation is to maintain the structure of a frame whenever J or [J] is within a container.

structure of a J-frame   (J [...   ])
structure of a J-fraction   (J [([M]<[N]>)])

But let's be frank. J is the kind of unity that does not fragment well. The concept of division does apply and J forms are unique and irreducible for all rationals. But this requires a rather unnatural restriction, that any frame that contains J or [J] must remain as a frame until the numeric components are simplified. That is, numeric components are themselves enclosed in a numeric frame. In Chapter 39.7 we will see that J-fractions are a conceptual simplification of the idea of a complex plane. In Chapter 40 J-fractions will replace the concept of an angle in trigonometry.

35.7 Remarks

We have encountered unavoidable ambiguities that generate non-confluent transformations. We can suppress the ambiguity by partitioning real numeric forms from imaginary J forms and reduce the numeric forms independently of J. Yet even with these difficulties, J does contribute to an understanding of the myriad of contradictions peppered throughout conventional arithmetic, including

— multivalued functions (e.g. square root)
— functions that eliminate polarity (e.g. square)
— functions with an infinity of values (e.g. logarithm)
— contradictions in the rules of exponents
— manipulation of infinities
— restrictions on unusual values for bases and powers
— imaginary logarithms.

So J is a trade-off. It provides insight into the deeper mechanisms of arithmetic, at the cost of having to give up some of our conventional beliefs about how arithmetic should work. We'll next explore some of the symbolic transformation rules that generate contradictions in order to contrast the limits of standard arithmetic to the limits of James arithmetic.

Endnotes

1. **opening quote:** W. Churchill (1930) *My Early Life* p.41.

2. **comes from several conceptually different sources:** The full traversal of the circumference of a unit circle has been given a name, *tau*, the Greek symbol τ, where $\tau = 2\pi$. Several folks have made the argument that tau rather than pi should be used to describe the ratio of circumference to radius for a circle. Then $C = \tau r$, and for a unit circle, $C = \tau$. This modification of a convention would eliminate the prevalence of the number 2 in many trigonometric equations. Online 6/19, see https://www.scientificamerican.com/article/let-s-use-tau-it-s-easier-than-pi/

Reflective trigonometry in Chapter 40.6 is an innovative attempt to remove the multiplier 2 from trigonometric identities.

3. **using J as a computational shortcut:** Chapter 33.4 shows the James form of Bernoulli's clever use of complex numbers to factor $a^2 + b^2$.

4. **absolute value, which provides a notation equivalent to ±:** The concept of absolute value has only recently been confused with the idea of a positive number. Textbooks often say that the absolute value is a number with the minus sign deleted. When a signless magnitude $|n|$ is placed within an equation the symbolic form takes on two values as expressed by $\pm n$. However modern practice disassembles the bipolarity to yield two different values, $+n$ and $-n$, thus losing the critical insight that the variable n is *concurrently* multivalued.

5. **substitution error by the Flagg resolution:** L. Kauffman (2002) Time, imaginary value, paradox, sign and space p.2. (the original quotation is in capital letters). Online 7/19 at http://homepages.math.uic.edu/~kauffman/TimeParadox.pdf

> **The Flagg Resolution**
> You are not allowed to exchange "J" for "not J" anywhere unless you do so everywhere. There is one and only one expression "J". Substitution of "not J" for "J" (or vice versa) is therefore a global replacement. Other than this special treatment of "J", no rules of logic are changed from classical logic.

In this quotation from Kauffman, the Flagg resolution is applied to logic rather than to numerics and the letter J stands in place of a paradoxical statement such as "This statement is false". It is *not* the James imaginary so it is not presented here in Monaco font. For James algebra the Flagg resolution transcribes directly to

```
(substitute <J> for-every J in E) = E     globally
```

In logic the distinction is between *total substitution* and *partial substitution*. For **replacement**, in which an expression is replaced by an *equal* but different expression, partial substitution maintains equivalence. Total substitution maintains equivalence of numeric equations for any numeric substitution. Here is an example that emphasizes the difference:

global   (substitute 2x for-all x in x+x=2x) => 2x+2x=2(2x)

local   (substitute 2x for-any x in x+x=2x) => 2x+ x= 2x

The local case holds only when $x = 2x$, i.e. when $x = 0$.

6. J-void object or Reflection applies, each leading to a different result:

Here is the erroneous *generation* of J from *void*.

```
          void
        ([   ] <[2]>)              emit
        ([J J] <[2]>)             J-void object
        ([J]<[2]>)([J]<[2]>)      disperse
        (  [J]<[2]>  [2])         tally/clarify
        (  [J]            )       cancel
           J                      clarify
```

The particular problem with this construction is that the form <[2]> is *indeterminate*, which is the topic of Chapter 42.

7. real and imaginary components of a complex number to mingle: The

real and imaginary components of a complex number a+bi can of course be mingled using the Pythagorean relationship for determining the magnitude (the modulus) of a complex number, but it needs to be supplemented with the direction (the argument) of the complex number, again resulting in two incommensurable components. The modulus combines the real *magnitude* of each component so it is not a type violation. With Euler's exponential formulation, e^{a+bi} (Chapter 39), it becomes apparent that bi is an *angle*.

8. imaginary form that does not accumulate: Oscillating between two existent

states (turn light switch on, turn switch off) presupposes an object-oriented substrate (i.e. a switch) that has the property of binary oscillation. Oscillation between presence and absence is more like the light emanation that is turned on by the switch. It is either present or absent depending upon the state of the switch, but the emanation itself has one state, not two. Neither lightness nor darkness accumulates.

J is not a switch with two states. Accumulation of replicas supports the idea of a sequence of state changes. Accumulation of J replicas simply confuses time with space. Incidentally this same confusion permeates novice attempts to understand *Laws of Form*. A form has only one state, that of existence. *Void* is not a state.

9. Euler's infinity of imaginary values for a logarithm: Euler, and many other mathematicians no doubt, would say that $\ln -1 = \pm(2k - 1)\pi i$ is a single object and does not require unfolding over time. That's the difference between classical vs constructivist perspectives. Constructivist memory permits human visualization whereas comprehension of completed infinity requires training to believe in disembodied abstraction. J is self-voiding and in any event cannot reach infinity, it cannot even reach 2.

10. it does not matter what forms are being replicated and indicated: Chapter 9 describes the components of the cognitive activity of counting. Numbers (counts) are *not* a property of objects, they are a property of collections of indications. Indication is the cognitive act of putting essentially unique objects into categories that identify only a specific selected property of an object. Similarly, **sets** are not collections of objects, they are collections of indications that identify a common property across unique objects.

11. we will not permit replicas of J to accumulate: This decision differs from Euler's, who elected to count an infinity of Js. Should we permit J to accumulate, we would encounter the same multiple value difficulties as the sine and the log functions. The sine of 0 is equal to the sine of 2π is equal to the sine of $2k\pi$ for any natural number k. As we travel around a circle, by symmetry we return to our starting place every 2π radians. Euler effectively constructed a memory function, a counter, that keeps track of the number of revolutions.

12. suggests that replicas of J can accumulate: Counting the token J by units results in behavior that is reminiscent of both the Kronecker delta function and the Dirac delta function. Both indicate specific numeric circumstances by taking on discrete values of either 0 or 1.

13. depending upon whether the exponent is odd or even: Some powers of negative numbers can take us into the imaginary realm since $i = (-1)^{1/2}$. In fact all non-integer powers of a negative base generate complex numbers. Fractional powers of negative numbers lead to complex numbers which are explored in Chapter 39. Fractional powers as roots are a central topic in Chapter 40 and powers of exotic bases like negative infinity are the subject of Chapter 43.

Chapter 36

Revision

In mathematics you don't understand things.
You just get used to them.[1]
— John vonNeumann (c.1950)

We have been exploring the consequences of taking the second step into numeric abstraction, the introduction of the negative unit <( )> , which can also be expressed as (J). (The first step is the accumulating unit ( ) which leads to the concepts of counting and cardinality.) The purpose here is not to discover new relationships but rather to expose existent relationships within the new language of boundary forms. The extremely small set of axioms and concepts within James algebra, the **purely structural algebraic** methods of proof and the inherently visual iconic notation may shed some light on some puzzling aspects of simple arithmetic. And we have been exploring the stable form J = [<( )>]. A thesis is that the introduction of negative one, –1, about 500 years ago is the root cause of deviant numeric structures such as the self-multiplication of negative units, the occurrence of multiple valued functions, the struggle to maintain universal rules of exponents and logarithms, the behavior of exotic forms such as negative infinity and finally the role of bipolar numbers in arithmetic.

The empty round-bracket, ( ), is the fundamental unit that we call one. The angle-bracket converts one into negative one, <( )>. The axiom that defines angle-brackets is Reflection

reflection

$$A \quad <A> = void$$

Applied to one, Reflection becomes Unit Reflection

unit reflection

$$o \quad <o> = void$$

We have also seen that J is equivalent to the angle-bracket, permitting a different form of Unit Reflection that replaces the angle-bracket with a J-frame and the Reflection axiom with the J-occlusion axiom.

unit J-occlusion

$$o \quad (J \ [o]) = void$$

This new form of unit reflection now lets us explore the behavior of negative one from a different perspective. In particular J converts the angle-bracket into an *imaginary constant*, resulting in a new form of –1 ☞ (J). When J is carried into the interpretation as an innovation we find that negation, subtraction, division and logarithms are no longer necessary as *operators*.

36.1 Sign Calculus

Why is –1 x –1 = +1? In his *Elements of Algebra* Euler says

> Since negative numbers may be considered debts, because positive numbers represent real possessions, we might say that negative numbers are less than nothing....It is of utmost importance through the whole of Algebra, that a precise idea should be formed of those negative quantities.[2]

Euler argues that the product of two negative units must be a unit, either +1 or –1. If we accept

$$+1 \ x \ -1 = -1$$

then there is no alternative but to accept that –1 x –1 must be +1. This is not a particularly strong position since the product could be a new kind of unit, just like the invention of the imaginary unit i.

Euler's Rationale

In a footnote, Euler appends an algebraic argument for the idea that multiplication of two negatives yields a positive. Euler examines the expansion of the product $(a - b)(c - d)$ with all variables assumed to be positive. His strategy is to closely examine the necessary polarity of each of the four product terms to determine which of these two cases is true:

$$(a - b)(c - d) = ac - bc - ad + bd$$
or $\quad (a - b)(c - d) = ac - bc - ad - bd$

Here is the James form of Euler's logic. He begins by distributing a to determine the sign of two of the product terms.[3]

a x (c – d)	☞	([a][c <d>])
a x c		([a][c])
a x –d		([a][<d>])
ac – ad		([a][c])<([a][d])>

therefore

$\quad$ a x –d = –(ad) $\quad$ ☞ $\quad$ ([a][<d>]) = <([a][d])>

From this distribution he makes an assertion: the product of a with something *less than* c, i.e. c – d, must be less than ac, so we must *subtract* ad. Similar to Euler's axiomatic use of Distribution, the James version disperses via the Arrangement axiom. Euler's conclusion is an application of the Promotion theorem. In the James form we have not introduced an interpretation of the angle-bracket and conceptually the idea of subtraction does not exist. Promotion is a natural consequence of the Reflection axiom.[4] Thus there is no need to appeal to the nature of quantity, real possessions or debt. Euler continues by distributing a – b:

$\quad$ (a – b)(c – d) $\quad$ ☞ $\quad$ ([a <b>][c <d>])
$\quad$ (a – b) x c – (a – b) x d
$\qquad\qquad$ ☞ ([a <b>][c]) <([a <b>][d])>

By subtracting the expression $(a - b)$ x d, Euler combines Arrangement and Promotion into a single rule based on the same argument as above, that a – b must be less than a.

The sign of d is transferred outward so that

$$(a - b) \times -d = -[(a - b) \times d]$$

Another distribution yields the four product terms. Euler considers the sign that would properly annex the product of the two negatives to the three other established product terms.

$$(a - b) \times c \quad \textit{is} \quad ac - bc \quad \text{☞} \quad ([a][c])<([b][c])>$$
$$-[(a - b) \times d] \quad \textit{is} \quad -(a \times d) \quad \textit{annex} \quad -b \times -d \quad \text{☞}$$
$$<([a][d])> \textit{annex} \ ([<b>][<d>])$$

Assembling the four product terms,

$$ac - bc - ad \quad \textit{annex} \quad -b \times -d \quad \text{☞}$$
$$([a][c])<([b][c])><([a][d])> \textit{annex} \ ([<b>][<d>])$$

Euler reasons,

> Now we have seen that from the product $ac - bc$ we must subtract the product of $(a - b) \times d$, that is, we must subtract a quantity less than ad; we have therefore subtracted already too much by the quantity bd; this product must therefore be added; that is, it must have the sign + prefixed; hence we see that $-b \times -d$ gives $+bd$ for a product; or − minus multiplied by − minus gives + plus.[5]

This convoluted argument is essentially that we can promote twice, and then apply Involution,

$$([<b>][<d>])$$

promote $<<([\ b \ ][\ d \ ])>>$

unwrap $([\ b \ ][\ d \ ])$

The conclusion is that *annex* must mean add.

$$(a - b)(c - d) = ab - ac - ad + bd \quad \text{☞}$$
$$([a <b>][c <d>]) =$$
$$([a][b])<([a][c])><([a][d])>([b][d])$$

In the James form, there is no need to postulate different types of annexation, all we have of that nature is putting things into a container. Involution allows us to remove double angle-brackets without the bookkeeping of adding

involution

$<<A>> = A$

and subtracting quantities. Euler concludes with a statement of the Involution theorem:

> The taking of a negative quantity negatively destroys the very property of negation, and is the conversion of negative into positive numbers. So that if $+ \times - = -$, it necessarily follows that $- \times -$ must give a contrary product, that is, $+$.[6]

Euler immediately introduces a sign calculus, separating the meaning of the signs + and − from the quantities that they might be attached to. A **sign calculus** defines axioms for operators rather than objects. Euler: "Like signs, multiplied together, give +; unlike or contrary signs give −."[7]

An Algebraic Rationale

It may seem strange to revert to work that is centuries old in order to describe the multiplication of signs, however Euler's *Algebra* is the seminal text that not only defines how symbolic algebra works but also provides the descriptive language of algebra that is still in use today.

A more modern description of the same process that Euler considered semantically is purely algebraic. By collecting the same expression in different ways, distribution provides the desired result.[8]

$$
\begin{aligned}
E &= (a)(b) + (-a)(b) + (-a)(-b) \\
&= (a)(b) + (-a)((b) + (-b)) \\
&= (a)(b)
\end{aligned}
$$

$$
\begin{aligned}
E &= (a)(b) + (-a)(b) + (-a)(-b) \\
&= ((a) + (-a))\,(b) + (-a)(-b) \\
&= \qquad\qquad\qquad (-a)(-b)
\end{aligned}
$$

Therefore $\qquad (a)(b) = (-a)(-b)$

This logic assumes the Reflection axiom. The multiplication rules for signs can also be demonstrated by the Arrangement of void-equivalent forms. The void-based sequence that follows is rather inescapable: Emit a void-equivalent context, fill it by creating forms that cancel and then disperse them across the remaining forms.

$$E = \quad void$$

emit $\quad$ ([$\quad$][b])

create $\quad$ ([<a> a][b])

disperse $\quad$ ([<a>][b]) ([a][b])

$$E = \quad void$$

emit $\quad$ ([<a>][$\quad$])

create $\quad$ ([<a>][<b> b])

disperse $\quad$ ([<a>][<b>]) ([<a>][b])

Therefore by void-equivalence

$$([<a>][b]) \ ([a][b]) = ([<a>][<b>]) \ ([<a>][b])$$

decompose $\quad$ ([a][b]) = ([<a>][<b>])

☞ $\quad$ a x b = −a x −b

By choosing structures that interact with each other, the dispersed forms can lead to useful structural theorems. The feeling is very much like cross-multiplication, except you are free to choose the objects being multiplied. Of course, this example of void-based thinking is simply a copy of how we would think within symbolic notations. There is a simpler approach using Promotion and Involution that is illustrated in Figure 36-1.

A Distributive Rationale

Mathematician Barry Mazur asks the very same question: "So, why does minus times minus equal plus?"[9] He naturally rejects the answer "By definition". His why is that the sign calculus must be so in order for distribution to continue to work for all numbers.

> The distributive law is a fundamental characterization of the operation of multiplication (of positive whole numbers).[10]

Mazur is entirely correct. Distribution is implicated in the way of thinking introduced earlier when we considered

$$(a - b)(c - d) = ac - bc - ad \ \textit{annex} \ (-b \ x \ -d)$$

o ☞ + <o> ☞ −

combine signs ☞ ([ ][ ]) ☞ *multiply*

+ x +	☞	([o][o])	
is +		( )	clarify

+ x −	☞	([o][<o>])	
		([<o>])	clarify
is −		<o>	clarify

− x −	☞	([<o>][<o>])	
		<<([o][o])>>	promote
		([o][o])	unwrap
is +		( )	clarify

Figure 36-1: *The conventional sign calculus*

Euler assumed distribution and deduced − x − = +. Mazur argues that to do otherwise would violate the Distributive axiom. But it is not Distribution that defines the behavior of signs. The sign calculus is embodied within the introduction of −1, in the form of Unit Reflection.

$$o \ <o> = \textit{void} \qquad\qquad \textit{unit reflection}$$

Unit Reflection leads directly to Unit Involution via move.

$$o = <<o>> \qquad\qquad \textit{unit involution}$$

The core transformation in James algebra is Promotion, which is derivative of both Reflection and Arrangement.

$$([<o>][<o>]) = <<([o][o])>> \qquad \text{unwrap}$$

Now we can explain why two negatives make a positive. In its simplest form, it is an application of Involution.

$$-(-1) = 1 \quad ☞ \quad <<o>> = o$$

The −(−1) format suppresses the coefficient 1 from the leading minus sign in favor of defaulting to a unary sign calculus rather than a binary self-multiplication, as in

natural substitution	failed substitution	
⟦ o o o ⟧ = o		
⟦ o ‹o› ‹o›⟧ = o	⟦‹o› ‹o› o ⟧ = o	*commutes*
⟦‹o› o o ⟧ = ‹o›		
⟦ o o ‹o›⟧ = ‹o›	⟦ o ‹o› o ⟧ = o	*contradiction*
⟦‹o› ‹o› ‹o›⟧ = ‹o›	⟦‹o› o ‹o›⟧ = ‹‹o››	*to-be-decided*

Figure 36-2: *Options for substitution of signed units*

(–1)(–1). For self-multiplication we must introduce Promotion. Promotion uses the multiplication template ([ ][ ]) as the *context* of sign calculus, not as the operation of multiplication. The role of Distribution is passive.

$$(-1) \times (-1) = 1 \quad ☞ \quad ([‹o›][‹o›]) = (\ )$$

An Ensemble Rationale

⟦a b c⟧
substitute a *for* b *in* c

The ensemble rationale is independent of a numeric interpretation and depends solely upon the definition of valid substitution. Chapter 2.3 derives the sign calculus from the behavior of *substitution as multiplication*. Figure 36-2 closely corresponds to Figure 2-7 in Volume I. The notation in the figure is

$$o \quad ☞ \quad 1 \qquad ‹o› \quad ☞ \quad -1$$

⟦a b c⟧ = d   means   *substitute* a *for* b *in* c *yields* d

The interpretation of multiplication as substitution is

$$⟦a \quad b \quad c⟧ = d \quad ☞ \quad d = (a \times c)/b$$

Of the eight possible combinations of unit substitutions five are natural substitution instances that confirm three multiplication rules,

$$1 \times 1 = 1 \qquad 1 \times -1 = -1 \qquad -1 \times 1 = -1$$

Of the three substitutions that fail, two do so because there is nothing that matches the structure of the substitution instance b. Conventionally such a substitution attempt does not result in a change in the form c being substituted into. One of the two failures to match is a commutative variant of a matching substitution. The other non-substitution contradicts the confirmed multiplication rules by asserting

$$(\!(o\ \ <o>\ \ o)\!) = o \qquad ☞ \qquad 1 = (1 \times 1)/\!-\!1$$

The third "failed" substitution does find a match and does make a substitution but it generates a new form, <<o>>, that needs a design decision for interpretation.

$$(\!(<o>\ \ o\ \ <o>)\!) = <\!<o>\!> \qquad ☞ \qquad new = (-1 \times -1)/1$$

Of course we do not want to introduce a new kind of unit here, the result should be either 1 or −1. That is,

Option A: <<o>> = <o>   ☞   −(−1) = −1
Option B: <<o>> = o   ☞   −(−1) = 1

Option B can resolve the contradictory substitution:

Option B: $(\!(o\ \ <o>\ \ o)\!) = (\!(o\ \ <o>\ \ <\!<o>\!>)\!) = <o>$

as well as provide a consistent interpretation

$$(\!(o\ \ <o>\ \ o)\!) = <o> \qquad ☞ \qquad -1 = (1 \times 1)/\!-\!1$$

Option A requires that we give up both commutativity and associativity of multiplication to maintain consistency. Here *Option B* is more appealing. As well, it is consistent with the definition of the angle-bracket as Reflection:

<<o>>

<<o>> <o> o   create

o   cancel

A James Rationale

Calling upon J, we can eliminate the angle-bracket and its representation of the concept of a negative number. Since J is sign-blind, this rationale is not a sign calculus but rather a journey into imaginary logarithms. First, here is Unit Involution expressed in terms of J.

	−(−1) ☞	`<  <  o > >`
J-convert		`(J [(J [o])])`
clarify		`(J    J      )`
J-void object		`(              )`

J-conversion is derivative of the Arrangement axiom, so that even here we are building from a base of all three axioms. Next, Unit Reflection:

	1 − 1 ☞	`o <   o >`
J-convert		`o (J [o])`
J-occlude		*void*

And finally the more explicit form of signed multiplication,

	(−1) × (−1) ☞	`([<o>][<o>])`
substitute		`(  J    J  )`
J-void object		`(             )`

We have reached the goal. The sign calculus aligns with the J calculus. The two are connected by a fundamental structural relationship with a rather simple transcription.

$$o \ (J) = \textit{void} \quad ☞ \quad 1 + \#^{\log_\# - 1} = 0$$

36.2 Martínez' Experiment

In *The Cult of Pythagoras*[11] Alberto Martínez eloquently demonstrates that the axioms of our number system and its consequent behavior are to some extent arbitrary design decisions, a position that as a computer scientist I take as given.

> To treat numbers as unique, eternal, and unchangeable is a kind of number mysticism reminiscent of the legendary Pythagoreans. But there is not reason for it.[12]

Martínez describes his experiment with signed numbers, exploring the possibility that *negative times negative is negative*. The non-conventional but still sensible Martínez rules for multiplication match the behavior of the addition of negative numbers. We will need to agree to put the larger magnitude number first for addition. Magnitude doesn't matter for multiplication, but sequential position does. The *first argument* determines the polarity of the result for both addition and multiplication.

pos + pos = pos	*pos × pos = pos*
pos + neg = pos	*pos × neg = pos*
neg + pos = neg	*neg × pos = neg*
neg + neg = neg	*neg × neg = neg*

Here's an example. Unfamiliar yes but also consistent. The Martínez sign calculus writes algebraic forms quite differently but be aware that the way we do it now is the result of painstaking memorization, not the necessity of logic.

$$(n - 1) \times (n - 1)$$
$$(n \times n) + (-1 \times n) + (n \times -1) + (-1 \times -1)$$
$$n^2 + -n + n + -1$$
$$n^2 - 1$$

For **non-commutative** multiplication it matters which argument comes first. Non-commutative operators should not come as a shock. Subtraction, division and exponentiation are all non-commutative. To determine the sign of any binary operation, look at the first argument. Since both arguments of -1×-1 are negative, the product is also negative. In the case of $+1 \times -1$, the product is positive. And in the case of $-1 \times +1$, the negative product makes the operation of multiplication *anticommutative* when signs differ.

In the Martínez system, *the imaginary number* i *does not occur!*

$$\sqrt{-9} = -3 \qquad \text{since} \qquad -3 \times -3 = -9$$

This design decision reverberates through the rules of exponents, gallantly removing the conventional contradictions and confusions. For example,

conventional $\qquad \sqrt{-1} \times \sqrt{-1} \neq \sqrt{(-1 \times -1)}$
$$\qquad or \qquad (\sqrt{-1})^2 \neq \sqrt{(-1)^2}$$

Martínez $\qquad \sqrt{-1} \times \sqrt{-1} = \sqrt{(-1 \times -1)} = \sqrt{-1}$
$$\qquad or \qquad (\sqrt{-1})^2 = \sqrt{(-1)^2} = \sqrt{-1}$$
$$\qquad where \qquad \sqrt{-1} = -1$$

The self-multiplication operation, n^2, is no longer lossy. It no longer hides the Bipolar One, ± 1. The square root operation is no longer multivalued, it no longer needs $\pm\sqrt{}$. Here are some other advantages:

$$(-1)^n = -1 \qquad \textit{when n is odd or even}$$
$$- \sqrt{x} = \sqrt{-x}$$
$$x^n = 1 \qquad \textit{has one rather than n roots}$$

The point is this: *how algebra works is a design decision.* Design choices provide "rules" which more properly should be called definitions. Some design decisions lead to simplicity, others lead to complexity. What seems to be overlooked is that "discovered" complexity is not necessarily a natural aspect of arithmetic but is rather a perhaps unexpected consequence of a design preference.

Non-commutative Containment

Container arithmetic has no concept of ordering, so a non-commutative calculus is quite unnatural for James containers. Here we'll take a short excursion into Martínez' binary non-commutative multiplication. Addition is not affected since Reflection manages the resulting sign of an addition. For multiplication, we could label the leading FIRST square-bracket with an asterisk.[13] This finesse eliminates the idea of putting arguments in a sequential order in favor of nominating one container that is special. The asterisk is intended to remove the linguistic connotations of FIRST as a textual ordering concept. Consistent with the principles of void-based reasoning, when there are two choices only one needs to be indicated; the other is unambiguously unlabeled. If a labeled square-bracket is alone within a container, discard the label as irrelevant.

$(*[\ ]_{FIRST}[\ ]_{REST})$

In Figure 36-3 a leading asterisk, $*[...]$, serves as a *mark of priority*. The cost of introducing a new type of bracket is having to apply a different reduction rule for the specially marked square-brackets. To help to formulate this behavior as a replacement rule we'll convert o ☞ +   <o> ☞ −

combine signs ☞ (*[ ][ ]) ☞ *multiply*

signs		angle-brackets	J	
+ x +	☞	(*[o][o])	(*[o][o])	
		([o][o])	([o][o])	bode
is +		( )	( )	clarify
+ x −	☞	(*[o][<o>])	(*[o] J)	
		([o])	([o])	bode
is +		o	o	clarify
− x +	☞	(*[<o>][o])	(*J [o])	
		([<o>][o])	(J [o])	bode
is −		<o>	(J)	clarify
− x −	☞	(*[<o>][<o>])	(*J J)	
		([<o>][o])	(J)	bode
is −		<o>	(J)	clarify

Figure 36-3: *A James version of the Martínez sign calculus*

angle-brackets to J forms using J-transparency. This
shifts the mark of priority to J. In particular:

$$[<a>] = \quad\quad J\ [a]$$
$$*[\ a\ ] = \quad\quad [a]$$
$$*[<a>] = *[<([a])>] = *J\ [a]$$

The new transformation rule is bode.[14]

To Bode:
Delete all asterisks and all Js.
*Keep the J when *J is present.*

*J maintains the desired J-parity. Thus in the Martínez'
algebra

$$(*[\ a\ ][\ b\ ]) = (\ \ *[a]\quad [b]) = (\ \ [a][b])$$
$$(*[<a>][\ b\ ]) = (*J\ [a]\quad [b]) = (J\ [a][b])$$
$$(*[\ a\ ][<b>]) = (\ \ *[a]\ J\ [b]) = (\ \ [a][b])$$
$$(*[<a>][<b>]) = (*J\ [a]\ J\ [b]) = (J\ [a][b])$$

Abstractly	*	= *void*
	*J	= J
	* J	= *void*
	*J J	= J

Converting non-commutative multiplication into labeled containers by introducing a special asterisk notation is expensive. By incorporating the Martínez sign calculus into initial design decisions (rather than grafted it on at this late date) we might construct something more elegant. In contrast, the mechanism introduced by Euler's solution to the conundrum of log –1 includes imaginary numbers that turn exponentiation into a host of complexities: rotation, multivalued and lossy functions, rule inconsistencies and violations, and branch cuts and cyclic functions with infinitely many values.

36.3 The Square Root of Unity

The square root of one is *multivalued*, the operation yields two values: +1 and –1. We have identified this specific feature as *bipolar*. In general,

$$A^{1/2} = \pm B \qquad and \qquad (\pm B)^2 = A$$

Euler elegantly summarized this circumstance as

$$A^1 = A^{2/2} = (A^2)^{1/2} = \pm A$$

This relationship also holds in the case of imaginary units. The imaginary component of the square root of a negative number can be extracted from the expression so that

$$\sqrt{-A} = \sqrt{(+A)} \times \sqrt{(-1)} = \pm\sqrt{A} \times \pm i$$
$$where \qquad (\pm i)^2 = -1$$

Euler's analogy that positive refers to ownership while negative refers to debt makes an arbitrary distinction. Everything works out fine when positive refers to debt and negative refers to ownership. Consider for example, the perspective of the holder of a debt's promissory note. The negative amount indicates a positive wealth. That is, the semantic argument for the behavior of negative values is not particularly sound.

Multivalued functions create tears, or at least folds, in the fabric of the Cartesian plane. You might say that they require a third dimension to display. The usual patch is to restrict the range of the square root function to only one of the possible polarities. In the case of i, for example, it has been virtually forgotten that $\sqrt{-1}$ has two values. Moreover, *there is no principled way that we can distinguish between* +i *and* −i. Here is Barry Mazur again:

> There is no intrinsic (algebraic) way of distinguishing $+\sqrt{-1}$ from $-\sqrt{-1}$. Each of them, of course, is a square root of −1.... These entities, +i and −i, are twins, and the only breaking of their symmetry comes from the way in which we name them.[15]

In general the Nth root of unity, $^N\!\sqrt{1}$, has been defined to have N different values. This circumstance is due to Gauss' work on the construction of regular polygons. We will examine these cyclotomic numbers more closely in Chapter 40.6. For now it suffices to observe that bipolar numbers are the tip of the iceberg. Multivalued functions are the rule rather than the exception within exponential and logarithmic space.

Sign-blind Self-multiplication

Square roots introduce multiple values even when we begin with a single positive value. However, the conventional practice is to apply the numerator of a fractional power first. Power has precedence over root which results in

$$(A^2)^{1/2} \neq (A^{1/2})^2 \quad \textit{since} \quad \pm A \neq +A.$$

Let's look at the relationship between ± 1 and J to try to find the origin of −1 as a value that satisfies $\sqrt{1}$. In general the form of a square root is

$$\sqrt{A} = \pm B \quad \text{☞} \quad ((\lbrack\lbrack A\rbrack\rbrack<\lbrack 2\rbrack>)) = B \; \textit{and} \; <B>$$

Our problem is to show that taking a square root yields a sign-blind result. Conventionally, we know that

$$(\;B)^2 = \;B \times \;B = (\;1 \times B) \times (\;1 \times B) = (\;1 \times \;1) \times B^2$$

$$(-B)^2 = -B \times -B = (-1 \times B) \times (-1 \times B) = (-1 \times -1) \times B^2$$

The square of a number can be decomposed into the square of a sign-free (i.e. "positive") number and the self-multiplication of a unit, either 1 or –1. The source of the negative solution to a square root appears to be tied to the self-multiplication of a negative unit being defined as the *positive unit*. We'll thus consider operations on units only.

$$A = 1^2 \qquad \textit{has two solutions} \quad A = \pm 1$$

$$1^2 \qquad ☞ \quad ((\text{[} \text{[o]][2]}))$$

and $\qquad (-1)^2 \qquad ☞ \quad (([\text{[<o>]][2]}))$

We will first assume that $1^2 = (-1)^2$

$$(([\text{[o]][2]})) = (([\text{[<o>]][2]}))$$

But a complexity arises:

$$(([\text{[o]][2]})) = (([\text{[<o>]][2]}))$$

decompose $\qquad\qquad [\text{[o]][2]} \quad = \quad [\text{[<o>]][2]}$

decompose $\qquad\qquad\quad [\text{[o]]} \quad = \quad [\text{[<o>]]}$

decompose $\qquad\qquad\qquad\quad\; o \quad = \quad <o>$

The bifurcation of units leads to a numeric contradiction. The sign-blindness of the self-multiplication operation creates a sign-blindness in unity itself. The result that 1 is its own additive inverse is the same structure we found for J in the previous chapter. The sign-blindness of 1^2 transfers to 1 itself by application of decomposition only. However this issue does not arise if we replicate first, that is, if we express the form as 1 x 1 rather than as 1^2. In the retry below we use the J notation to replace the angle-brackets inside [<o>].

$$(([\text{[o]][2]})) = (([\text{[<o>]][2]}))$$

substitute $\qquad (([\text{[o]][2]})) = (([\quad J \quad][2]))$

replicate $\qquad\quad ([o] [o]) = (\quad J \qquad J \quad)$

clarify/J-void $\qquad (\qquad\quad) = (\qquad\qquad\qquad)$

Replication, replacing an exponential expression by a multiplication in conventional terms, avoids the contradiction. Might Replication introduce the multiple values? Let's step back a bit and rewrite the algebraic James reduction prior to the application of Replication.[16]

```
(([[o]][2])) = (([   J   ][2]))
(([    ][2])) = (([   J   ][2]))          clarify
(            ) = (([   J   ][2]))          absorb
(            ) = (                )        J-void tally
```

To see how −1 shows up as a root of 1^2, we need only look at J-void. The form of positive one, ( ), can accommodate a void-equivalent form inside. By placing J-void within ( ), we convert +1 into −1 x −1, and thus provide the source of the negative solution.

```
1²  ☞  (([[ o ]][2]))
       (([     ][2]))                      clarify
       (           )                       absorb
       (  J   J    )                       J-void object
       ( [<o>][<o>] )  ☞  −1 x −1          substitute
       (([[<o>]][2]))  ☞  (−1)²            tally
```

The multiple values of the square root function come directly from the design decision that minus times minus is plus.[17] Although this decision has a side benefit of maintaining the applicability of Distribution for both positive and negative numbers, the core reason that − x − = + is to maintain the essential nature of −1 as a unit that cancels +1.

We can also approach the issue of multivalued exponential functions by solving the two algebraic equations

$$\sqrt{A} = 1 \quad and \quad \sqrt{A} = -1$$

Both equations should yield the same value of A.

```
√A = 1  ☞  (([[A]]<[2]>)) =      o
           [[A]]<[2]>     =   [[o]]        cover
           [[A]]          =   [[o]][2]     move
               A          = (([[o]][2]))   cover
                            (([   ][2]))   clarify
                            (          ) ☞ 1   absorb
```

$$\sqrt{A} = -1 \ \text{☞} \ (([[A]]<[2]>)) = \ <o>$$

cover/substitute	([[A]]<[2]>)	=	J
cover	[[A]]<[2]>	=	[J]
move	[[A]]	=	[J][2]
cover	A	=	(([J][2]))
J-void tally	(	)	☞ 1

The two solutions are structurally the same except for the presence of J in the second solution, introduced by <o>.

Multiple Values

We still need to explain how the multiple values of the square root come into existence. It is usually taken as given that a square root yields two values of the same magnitude but different polarity. We can however trace the James form to expose the source of divergent polarities. We'll consider four paths during the pattern-reduction of $\sqrt{(-1 \times -1)}$. *Path 1* calls upon J-void immediately.

$$(-1 \times -1)^{1/2} \ \text{☞}$$

Path 1:	((([[([<o>][<o>])]] [(<[2]>)]))
substitute	((([[(J J)]] [(<[2]>)]))
J-void object	((([[( )]] <[2]>))
clarify	((([ ] <[2]>))
absorb	( ) ☞ 1

The critical subform is J J. Applying J-void renders <[2]> indeterminate. This is a problem since a fractional power 1/N of 1 creates N roots. *Path 2* shows that tallying J suppresses J-void and facilitates Reflection:

Path 2:	((([J J] [(<[2]>)]))
tally ERROR	((([([J][2])] [(<[2]>)]))
clarify	(([J][2] <[2]>))
cancel	(([J]))
clarify	(J) ☞ -1

Although this reduction returns the missing −1 result, we must elect to suppress tallying J. Consider next Promotion, for which we will need the operator form of J.

Path 3: `((([  ([<o>][<o>])  ]][(<[2]>)]))`
`((([<<([ o ][ o ])>>]][(<[2]>)]))`   promote
`((([  ([ o ][ o ])  ]][(<[2]>)]))`   unwrap
`((([            ] <[2]> ))`   clarify
`(                        ) ☞ 1`   absorb

Path 3 effectively self-multiplies −1 first, eliminating any chance to locate the source of the negative root. Finally *Path 4* first disperses the two Js.

Path 4: `(([J J][(<[2]>)]))`
`(([J J]  <[2]> ))`   clarify
`(([J]<[2]>)([J]<[2]>))`   disperse
`(  J/2      J/2  )`   substitute
`(      J      ) ☞ −1`   substitute

The two one-half Js suppress Dominion and thus preserve the negative result.[18]

We have shown four different reduction paths, two result in +1 and two in −1. This result is not entirely inappropriate because $\sqrt{1}$ does have two values, ±1. We can also trace the source of the divergence. J-void and Promotion lead to +1, while Replication (as tallying) and Arrangement lead to −1. *Transformation of angle-brackets gives the positive result, while replication of forms gives the negative result.*

Path 4 introduces a new concept, *a fraction of* J, here in the form of J/2. In Chapter 39.1 this fraction is shown to define i, the imaginary unit. *Path 4* thus suggests that the source of bipolarity may reside within complex numbers.

These non-confluent reductions are initially disturbing, since they suggest an inconsistency in the algebra. We are at the crossroads of contradiction. How can we know which subforms to gather together to transform? In *Path 4* we call upon the free replication of J. One villain in this story is the *indiscriminate use of symbolic replication.* Yes, it does matter how many replicas are created during transformation. And in particular it is Arrangement (and only Arrangement) that generates replicas.[19]

Bipolar Values from J Replication

To find the two values of $\sqrt{1}$, why is it necessary to introduce -1×-1 instead of working directly with $\sqrt{+1}$? We can construct the demonstration from $\sqrt{1}$ however it takes us through the undesirable J void tally:

$$1^{1/2} \quad \text{☞} \quad ((\text{[} \quad \text{[o]} \quad \text{][(<[2]>)]))}$$

clarify	$(([\quad\quad\quad\quad\quad] <[2]>))$
J-void tally	$(([[([J][2])] <[2]>))$
clarify	$(([J][2] <[2]>))$
cancel	$(([J]))$
clarify	$(J) \quad \text{☞} \quad -1$

It is Dominion that suppresses sign divergence. And it is Dominion that allows the introduction of J-void tally to generate -1. The underlying mechanism though is the construction of two replicas of J/2 by converting the fractional power (as <[2]>) into a fraction of J. Here we have done without the comfort of the imaginary $\sqrt{-1}$ only to be pushed in the direction of J/2, a fraction of an imaginary logarithm. In the following chapters we will follow the form of J on its inevitable collision course with the form of i.

36.4 When Exponents Break

$(\pm 1)^2$ also causes problems for the rules of exponents. If we distribute square root over multiplication of negative numbers, we encounter an ugly contradiction.

$$\sqrt{-1} \times \sqrt{-1} \neq \sqrt{(-1 \times -1)}$$

The problem is with the Distributive rule for exponents, which no longer works for any even root of a negative number. The even/odd parity of roots corresponds to the positive/negative polarity of the expression.

The generic rule for distribution of multiplication over exponents is

$$A^N \times B^N = (A \times B)^N$$

Since we can partition the negative sign from the magnitude of the number, we can simplify the generic rule by addressing only units.

When $A = B = -1$ and $N = 1/2$

$$(-1)^{1/2} \times (-1)^{1/2} \stackrel{?}{=} (-1 \times -1)^{1/2}$$
$$i \quad \times \quad i \quad \stackrel{?}{=} \quad 1^{1/2}$$

The key is that $1^{1/2}$ is equal to both $+1$ *and* -1. The equality is incorrect only if we fail to treat square roots as multivalued. That is,

$$\pm i \times \pm i = \pm(1^{1/2})$$

Alternatively, we can express like terms as squares rather than as self-multiplications.

$$\sqrt{-1} \times \sqrt{-1} = (\sqrt{-1})^2$$
$$\sqrt{(-1 \times -1)} = \sqrt{(-1)^2}$$

This rewriting shifts the problem to a different exponential rule. The rule in question is no longer Distribution of exponential forms, it is now multiplication of stacked exponents.

$$(A^{1/2})^2 \neq (A^2)^{1/2}$$

Taking M and N to be natural numbers, in general

$$(A^M)^N = A^{M \times N} = A^{N \times M} = (A^N)^M$$

The problem shows up whenever M or N is a unit fraction, i.e. a fractional exponent. This effectively changes multiplication into division in the exponential space.

$$(A^M)^{1/N} = A^{M \times 1/N} = A^{1/N \times M} \neq (A^{1/N})^M$$

Here's an example that keeps track of multiple values. When $\pm N$ is squared it becomes positive. The square root, in contrast, maintains its dual sign.

$$(\sqrt{+4})^2 \neq \sqrt{(\pm 4)^2}$$
$$(\pm 2)^2 \neq \sqrt{+16}$$
$$+4 \neq \pm 4$$

Magnitude is maintained but sign is confounded. Squaring looses information about polarity while the square root generates that information. The two solutions are *lost* when self-multiplication is the final operation, but *gained* when the square root is the final operation.

Were we to multiply exponents, the original sign of the base is preserved.

$$(A^{1/2})^2 = (\pm\sqrt{A})^2 \quad = +A$$
$$A^{1/2 \times 2} = +A^1 \quad = +A$$
$$A^{2 \times 1/2} = +A^1 \quad = +A$$
$$(A^2)^{1/2} = (A \times A)^{1/2} = \pm A$$

The claim that it is Distribution that fails is not entirely accurate since self-multiplication also fails in the same circumstances. The expressions show overtly that exponential powers can be non-commutative. Stepping through this observation using James forms:

For $((-1)^{1/2})^2$,

substitute $\qquad (-1)^{1/2}$ ☞ $(([J]<[2]>)) = (J/2)$

$(-1)^{1/2} \times (-1)^{1/2}$ ☞ $([(J/2)][(J/2)])$

clarify $\qquad\qquad (\quad J/2 \qquad J/2 \quad)$

substitute $\qquad\qquad (\qquad J \qquad)$ ☞ -1

For $((-1)^2)^{1/2}$,

J-void object $\qquad -1 \times -1$ ☞ $([<o>][<o>]) = (J\ J) = (\ )$

$(-1 \times -1)^{1/2}$ ☞ $((([( )]]<[2]>))$

clarify $\qquad\qquad (([\qquad]<[2]>))$

absorb $\qquad\qquad\qquad (\qquad\qquad)$ ☞ 1

The first result, -1, maintains the negative sign because the J-fraction $J/2$ suppresses J-void. The second reduction does not take the form of a J-fraction and thus has lost the negative result. This is the same process that was observed in the previous section when we attempted to locate the lost bipolar result of a square root. Reintroducing $J\ J$ and dispersing recreates the $J/2$ forms. The broken rule is

$$(-1 \times -1)^{1/2} \neq ((-1)^2)^{1/2}$$

Under a root (or under a log), we may not convert $+1$ into -1×-1, and we may also not convert -1×-1 to $(-1)^2$.

$$+1 \neq -1 \times -1 \neq (-1)^2 \quad \textit{sometimes}$$

Both expressions converge to the same James form, so long as we do not invoke J-void. To suppress J-void we need to *tally* J, a process that we have actively avoided.

For $((-1)^2)^{1/2}$

$\quad$ −1 x −1 $\quad$ ☞ $([<o>][<o>]) = (([J][2]))$ $\qquad$ tally

$(-1 \times -1)^{1/2}$ $\quad$ ☞ $((([[(([J][2]))]]<[2]>))$

$\qquad\qquad\quad$ $((\quad [J][2] \quad <[2]>))$ $\qquad$ clarify

$\qquad\qquad\quad$ $((\quad [J] \qquad\qquad))$ $\qquad$ cancel

$\qquad\qquad\quad$ $(\quad J \qquad\qquad\quad)$ ☞ −1 clarify

This time we have localized the problem as converting self-multiplication, which is known to be lossy, to the squaring operation. Once the multiplication is carried out, we do not know whether we started at +1 or at −1. Unless, of course, we install a memory mechanism into multiplication. The sole objective of *multiplicative memory* would be to retain the specific objects that were multiplied together. This memory can also be implemented by treating multiplication of unit fractions as explicitly non-commutative.

Tallying (as Arrangement) is essentially the Distributive rule. The polarity of the result depends upon whether or not forms are tallied first then reduced or reduced first so that tallying would not occur. The change in sign however occurs in the imaginary realm, not in the mechanism of distribution. There is no right or wrong polarity in the way we have set up the behavior of multivalued functions. These two expressions are both equal and unequal, depending upon when we apply abstraction (i.e. tallying, counting).[20]

$$\sqrt{-1} \times \sqrt{-1} \quad \neq and = \quad \sqrt{(-1 \times -1)}$$

Martínez suggests that *this contradiction did not exist for Euler* because he saw the square roots of units to be multivalued.[21]

$$\sqrt{1} = \pm 1 \qquad and \qquad \sqrt{-1} = \pm i$$

Thus,

$$\sqrt{(-1 \times -1)} = \sqrt{-1} \times \sqrt{-1}$$
$$\sqrt{\quad 1} = \pm i \times \pm i$$
$$\pm 1 = (\pm i)^2 = \pm(-1)$$

Yet another route to eliminate the breakdown of the rules of exponents is to multiply stacked exponents first while holding the base constant, even if the base is a compound expression. Here is an example

$$(A^{1/2})^2 = A^1 = (A^2)^{1/2}$$

and

$$((-A)^{1/2})^2 = (-A)^1 = ((-A)^2)^{1/2}$$

In the James form

	$(A^{1/2})^2$	☞	`(([ (([[A]]<[2]>)) ]][2]))`
clarify			`(( [[A]]<[2]> [2]))`
cancel			`(( [[A]] ))`
clarify			`A` ☞ `A`

	$((-A)^{1/2})^2$	☞	`(([ (([[<A>]][2])) ]]<[2]>))`
clarify			`(( [[<A>]][2] <[2]>))`
cancel			`(( [[<A>]] ))`
clarify			`<A>` ☞ `−A`

36.5 When Logarithms Break

Bipolar J poses a similar choice for the rules of logarithms but with better consequences. We'll consider the logarithm of $(-n)^2$ when it is replaced by $-n \times -n$. First the ground case.

	0	☞	*void*
void inversion	log 1		`[( )]`
J-void object/enfold	log (−1 × −1)		`[[[(J)][(J)]]]`
clarify	log −1 + log −1		`J      J`
J-void object	0		*void*

Now here are two distinctly different transformation paths for log $(-n)^2$. The first uses the power law for logarithms, the second uses self-multiplication.

	log $(-n)^2$	☞	`[(([ <n> ]][2]))]`
clarify	2 log −n		`([ <n> ]][2])`
J-convert	2 log (−1 × n)		`([[(J [n])]][2])`
clarify	2 (log −1 + log n)		`([ J [n] ][2])`
disperse	2 log −1 + 2 log n		`([J][2])([[n]][2])`
J-void tally	2 log n		`([[n]][2])`

The logarithm rule accepts the imaginary logarithm of -1 and then applies J-void tally. Self-multiplication however bypasses J via the application of Promotion.

$\log (-n)^2$	☞	`[((([<n>]] [2])) ]`	
$\log (-n \times -n)$		`[ ([<n>][<n>]) ]`	replicate
$\log --(n \times n)$		`[<<([ n ][ n ])>>]`	promote
$\log\ \ \ (n \times n)$		`[ ([ n ][ n ]) ]`	unwrap
$\log n^2$		`[((([ n ]][2])) ]`	tally
$2 \log n$		`([[ n ]][2])`	clarify

The two paths maintain confluence by arriving at the same result. In passing through J-void tally, the logarithm power rule endows the logarithm of a negative number with the sign-blindness of J. This in turn blocks a smooth transition from logarithms to powers. We can see this dynamic by taking the logarithm of supposedly equal squares.

$\log n^2 = \log (-n)^2$ ☞

`[((([<n>]][2])))]`	=	`[((([n]][2])))]`	
`([[<n>]][2])`	=	`([[n]][2])`	clarify
`[[<n>]][2]`	=	`[[n]][2]`	decompose
`[[<n>]]`	=	`[[n]]`	decompose
`<n>`	=	`n`	☞ $-n = n$ cover

From this perspective the restriction that removes the contradiction appears to be appropriately placed on logarithms of negative numbers (as Euler suggested), rather than on the logarithms of powers. The analysis however indicates that the two are equivalent when J is employed.

This then returns us to a theme: -1 is never trouble-free. Should we add, multiply, raise to a power, or take the logarithm of -1, it will look as though the rules of addition, multiplication, exponentiation and logarithms do not work unconditionally. The strangeness arises directly from the non-standard behavior of the additive imaginary, $J + J = 0$, which shows up most clearly in logarithmic rather than exponential space.

36.6 Loss of Confluence

In a rewrite system, only rules that match specific patterns apply, so the idea of violating the structural rules of an operation (e.g. the rules of exponents) does not occur. Rule failure simply means that a rule does not match the template pattern and thus does not get applied. Substitution of equals for equals is sufficient to generate the rules of an operation as emergent properties of a usually small number of axiomatic patterns. Violation of equality takes the form of a **failure of confluence** in which a specific pattern supports two different rules while applying each separately leads to two forms that are not equivalent.

What we call rule violation in algebra becomes the dynamic unfolding of branches of a process that generates a path from an initial form to a final form. The final form is usually the simplest, or *canonical*, form. This process is called computing the value in arithmetic, solving for the unknown in algebra and deductive proof in logic.

The introduction of indeterminate forms, for example, can generate arbitrary results. Here are two different substitution paths starting from ( ) that diverge in value.

	(	)
emit	((⟦ ⟧<[2]>))	((⟦ ⟧<[4]>))
J-void object	((⟦ J J ⟧<[2]>))	((⟦ J J ⟧<[4]>))
tally ERROR	((⟦(⟦J⟧[2])⟧<[2]>))	((⟦(⟦J⟧[2])⟧<[4]>))
clarify	((⟦J⟧[2] <[2]>))	((⟦J⟧[2] <[4]>))
cancel	((⟦J⟧))	((⟦J⟧ <[2]>))
substitute	(J)	(J/2)
	☞ –1	☞ i NOT

The first step uses Dominion to construct two different *indeterminate* forms. We then violate the tally restriction on J by creating and tallying two replicas of J. The tallies then interact with the indeterminate forms via cancellation to construct divergent results. This example can be read bottom up as well, obscuring the generation of indeterminate forms and leaving the tally of J as the source of error.

Independent of the J tally error, the inequality does not occur until a choice is made inconsistently. In this case, two structurally different indeterminate forms are constructed. Should we enforce a single choice, usually achieved by asserting a rule restriction, then no contradiction arises because the non-confluent choice point has been removed. We then live with the consequences of making that one specific choice.

Confluence then is an ideal that may require compromise. It is most desirable not to have particular restrictions on rules, allowing them to apply whenever their pattern has been matched. Restrictions make axioms clumsy, effectively admitting that they are not really axioms but instead simply special conditions. It is also most desirable not to have divergent paths in a reduction leading to two different reduced forms. This type of contradiction risks the stability of the equivalence classes within a system.

A contrasting perspective is that branches in reductions and contradictions in rules are entirely natural aspects of a symbolic technique that supports multivalued functions. Allowing $\sqrt{1}$ to have two values, ± 1, assures branching and contradiction. There is nothing wrong with the axioms, the problem originates with the separation of a bipolar object into two halves and then giving one of those halves priority.

A similar issue challenges imaginary numbers, however their sheer imaginariness allows contradiction to be packed neatly into two additively incommensurable number systems, 1 and i. Loss of confluence echoes this compartmentalization of units as decision points in a reduction sequence.

Conventional algebra bars structural rules specifically in those circumstances where a wrong choice can generate variety. When you get to $\sqrt{(-1 \times -1)}$ do not take the path to $\sqrt{-1} \times \sqrt{-1}$! This admonition can also be read as: Do not step over from real numbers to imaginary numbers, keep both worlds separate. The only path between real and imaginary is through $i^2 = -1$.

36.7 Remarks

The global perspective is that each of these vexing issues is a viewpoint on one single source, the design decision to put -1 on the same number line as $+1$. As benign as that may appear, polarity is put at risk whenever multiplication of two identical units yields a different kind of unit. At the foundation of the arithmetic of signs is a **type error**.

type error

$$1 + -1 = 0 \qquad ☞ \qquad o <o> = \mathit{void}$$
$$-1 \times -1 = 1 \qquad ☞ \qquad (J \; J) = (\;)$$

Structurally addition places the object and its inverse into the same container, resulting in nothing. Multiplication, perversely, places bounded replicas of the same negative unit (as [<o>]) into the same container, resulting in a positive unit. We can see from the James forms that the positive unit is the container of the replicas which themselves have become void-equivalent. J-void captures this transformation explicitly.

Having explored J in these last four chapters, we will now return to a variety of applications of James algebra. The upcoming chapters have unfortunately been postponed until now, although several of them were intended to be included at least in Volume II. They represent attempts to test the capabilities of James algebra as it was being developed. None are intended to contribute to abstract mathematics, rather they evolved as separate experiments applying James form to the fields of calculus derivatives, complex numbers, trigonometry and types of infinite expressions.

Endnotes

1. **opening quote:** J. von Neumann is quoted in G. Zukav (1979) *The Dancing Wu Li Masters: An overview of the new physics* (1979) p.208 footnote.

According to F. T. Smith of Stanford Research Institute, the quote was von Neumann's reply to a physicist friend who had said "I'm afraid I don't understand the method of characteristics."

2. **should be formed of those negative quantities:** L. Euler (1770) *Elements of Algebra* §18, §20.

3. **to determine the sign of two of the product terms:** Euler mixes the use of juxtaposition, e.g. ab, to represent multiplication without regard to sign with the use of the times symbol x to represent multiplication of compound quantities, e.g. $(a - b)$ x c.

4. **Promotion is a natural consequence of the Reflection axiom:** This is demonstrated in Chapter 10.1.

5. **or − minus multiplied by − minus gives + plus:** Euler §33.

6. **follows that − x − must give a contrary product, that is, +:** Euler §33.

7. **multiplied together, give +; unlike or contrary signs give −:** Euler §34.

The idea of a sign calculus, or an *operator calculus*, has been removed from elementary math education, possibly because learning about how processes might interact was seen to be less desirable than learning about how objects interact.

8. **distribution provides the desired result:** This demonstration can be simplified by using $a = b$. It can also be simplified using a sign calculus:

$$E = (+)(+) + (-)(+) + (-)(-)$$
$$= (+)(+) + (-)((+) + (-))$$
$$= (+)(+)$$

$$E = (+)(+) + (-)(+) + (-)(-)$$
$$= ((+) + (-)) (+) + (-)(-)$$
$$= \qquad\qquad (-)(-)$$

Therefore $\quad (+)(+) = (-)(-)$

9. **minus times minus equal plus?:** B. Mazur (2003) *Imagining Number* p.102.

10. **multiplication (of positive whole numbers):** Mazur p.102.

11. **In *The Cult of Pythagoras*:** A. Martínez (2012) *The Cult of Pythagoras* Chapter 12 Inventing Mathematics.

12. **But there is not reason for it:** Martínez Chapter 12.

13. **the leading FIRST square-bracket with an asterisk:** Labeling a bracket with a special symbol is equivalent to introducing a new type of container.

14. **The new transformation rule is bode:** *To bode* is to provide a sign of things to come, to foretell or presage. The bode operation gives a special power to the first argument of a binary operation. In the Martínez arithmetic of signs the first argument foretells, or determines, the sign of the entire operation.

15. **symmetry comes from the way in which we name them:** Mazur p.216.

16. **prior to the application of replication:** The algebraic reduction assumes that there are no multiple value expressions and no indeterminate expressions.

17. **decision that minus times minus is plus:** The use of J in this demonstration is evidence that the squared form harbors computational difficulties.

18. **and thus preserve the negative result:** Here is the detail of adding J/2.

```
J/2 + J/2   ☞   ([J]   <[2]>  ) ([J]   <[2]>  )
                ([J][(<[2]>)]) ([J][(<[2]>)])   enfold
                ([J][  (<[2]>) (<[2]>)])         collect
                ([J][([(<[2]>)][2])   ])         tally
                ([J]     <[2]>  [2]    )         clarify
                 J                               cancel/clarify
```

19. **it is Arrangement (and only Arrangement) that generates replicas:** Our primary source of replicas, the Replication theorem, derives its validity from Arrangement.

20. **when we apply abstraction (i.e. tallying, counting):** This observation highlights a theme: *replication is not free.*

21. **because he saw the square roots of units to be multivalued:** A. Martínez (2007) Euler's "mistake"? The radical product rule in historical perspective. *Mathematical Association of America* 114, April 2007.

Chapter 37

Derivative

But how is one to make a scientist understand
that there is something unalterably deranged
about differential calculus...?[1]
— Antonin Artaud (1947)

Our primary exploration is the arithmetic of numbers, however the James square unit has lead us
to non-numbers such as divide-by-zero. To address the
challenges of the non-numbers 0 and ∞ conventional
technique moves on to calculus and to numeric analysis.
In calculus symbolic form meets geometric form. Calculus
courses often begin with the idea of a functional derivative, the study of *infinitesimal* changes in the trajectory
of a function. Derivatives are invariably described with
reference to the graph of a function. Computing the derivative of a function skitters to the edge of the non-numbers,
often tickling the dragon of the indeterminates and the
infinite exotics of Chapters 42 and 43.

In this chapter we will examine the definition of a
derivative applied to James forms. An initial goal is to
construct the derivative of the three James brackets so
that we can explore how boundary differentiation handles limit processes, non-numeric forms and the absence
of familiar functions such as addition and multiplication.

Another compelling motivation is to examine the structure of differentiation from the foundational perspective of round- and square-brackets. Calculus presumes the wide-ranging infrastructure of the whole of algebra. A student of calculus is expected to have mastered the manipulation of algebraic expressions particularly as it has developed over hundreds of years within the theory of polynomials. Must we consider this evolution to be inevitable, or is what is taught as essential mathematics one path among many?

Our motivation is not to compare the *efficiency* of boundary and algebraic techniques.[2] Algebra has evolved to make the manipulation of string expressions relatively simple. The boundary patterns for differentiation achieve the same computational objectives without introducing additional iconic mechanism. The derivatives of the common algebraic functions can be computed from the James axioms using simple pattern-matching and substitution. We'll also suggest that the conceptual structure of James algebra provides a natural framework for understanding derivatives, without calling upon limits, tangents at-a-point, infinitesimal movement in space, or geometric visualization. The tools that fill every calculus textbook are of course vital, both historically and conceptually. The objective here is not to deconstruct but rather to explore the possibility that iconic tools might provide new perspectives on the nature of differentiation within the calculus. Some useful techniques not accessible using symbolic tools include

— differentiation frames
— base-free exponents and logarithms
— independence of contents
— boundary transparency
— explicit absence of addition, multiplication and function inverses
— void-based techniques including void-equivalence and void substitution.

boundary	limit rule
round	L(f) = (Lf)
square	L[f] = [Lf]
angle	L<f> = <Lf>
contents	L f g = Lf Lg

Figure 37-1: *Limit rules for boundaries*

37.1 Form Limits

Our interpretation of round- and square-brackets is within the exponential/logarithmic domains. Differentiation of these functions is famously simple when the base is the constant e. The purpose of a **limit variable** is to be able to *approach* but to not actually become non-numeric, to get as close to *void* or one of the forms of infinity [ ] and <[ ]> as desired while still remaining numeric. Figure 37-1 briefly outlines the behavior of limits for James brackets. The three brackets are *transparent to limit processes*, a feature that lets us identify limit variables solely by attaching a warning label to specific numeric variables that might misbehave. James boundaries are transparent because the variables they contain are independent. Since all three brackets can be interpreted as continuous functions, and since no other functions are involved, we will bypass the intricate logic that evolved over hundreds of years to ground calculus in **delta-epsilon limit theory**. Instead we'll adopt the expedient of labeling any limit variable with a limit process token L and consider only approaches to *void*.

$$\lim_{n \to 0} n \quad \text{☞} \quad Ln$$

To lay a foundation we'll consider a *definition* of the irrational number e that includes a limit variable approaching *void*.

$$e =_{def} \lim_{n \to 0} (1 + n)^{1/n}$$

☞ $\lim_{n \to void}$ ((([n o]][(<[n]>)]))   hybrid

$\lim_{n \to void}$ ((([n o]] <[n]>))   clarify

((([$\lim_{n \to void}$n o]] <[$\lim_{n \to void}$ n]>))   transparent

The limit percolates through the transparent James brackets. When it reaches the limit variable it is abbreviated as L.

constant e

$$e =_{def} ((([Ln \ o]] <[Ln]>))$$

Form of the Base

$e_{base-10} = 2.71828...$

$e_{base-2} = 111.110...$

$e_{base-e} = 1.$

The boundary definition of e is *base-free*. The numeric constant e is itself almost always expressed in base-10, as are all constants in numeric expressions. The *definition* of e is in the form of an exponential, with a varying base equal to Ln o. In preparation for base conversion here is the reciprocal relationship between base-10 and base-e:

$$\log_{10} e = 1/\ln 10$$

The demonstration is straightforward

$$\log_b a \ ☞ \ (< \ [[b]]>[[a]] \ \ \ \ \ )$$

react

enfold

$$(< \ [[b]]<[[a]]> \ >)$$

$$(<[(([[b]]<[[a]]>)]>) \ ☞ \ 1/\log_a b$$

The James **generic base** # has a specific form:

generic base

$$\# = ((\ ))$$

The round unit ( ) can be interpreted as $\#^0 = 1$, while the form of the base (( )) becomes $\#^1 = \#$. When # is assigned a specific base, the form of that specific base is *defined* to be (( )).[3] In general, a base-free numeric n requires an **additive conversion factor**, $[[\#]]_b$, to convert to base-b.

$$[[n]]_b = [[n]]_\# \ [[\#]]_b$$

When forms remain base-free, the conversion factor is $[[((\ ))]] = void$. This technique is unconventional, we will soon see it in action.

37.2 Form Derivatives

Rather than introducing another type of boundary, a *differential boundary*, we'll use Leibniz' notation of a small d in front of the form being differentiated. There is no risk of confusion here, since dA is the derivative of

name	derivative	☞	interpretation
constant	dc = *void*		dc = 0
variable	dx = ( )		dx = 1
round	d(u) = (u [du])		d#^{u} = #^{u} (ln #) du
square	d[u] = (<[u]>[du])		d(log$_#$ u) = 1/(u ln #) du
angle	d<u> = <du>		d(–u) = –du
contents	d(u v) = (du dv)		d(u+v) = du + dv

Figure 37-2: *Derivatives of boundaries*

the form labeled A, while d{A} is the derivative of the outer bracket with contents A, whatever either may be.

We'll derive the bracket derivatives d(u), d[u] and d<u> from the conventional definition of a derivative and then use the unit forms to determine d( ), d[ ] and d< >. We'll use these forms to demonstrate conventional derivative formulas of product, quotient and power. Then we'll show how derivatives can be constructed from *void* and that they inherently incorporate the form of the constant e. We'll show that the chain rule for differentiation is built into the nesting of boundary forms, and close the chapter with the development of a single substitution template for differentiation of any well-behaved function.[4]

Differentiation Frame

Figure 37-2 previews the derivatives of the James brackets under our interpretation of exponents and logarithms. The derivatives of round- and square-brackets are in the form of James *frames*. The shape of a generic frame is

$$(frame\text{-}type \ [framed\text{-}form])$$

generic frame

The *frame-type* for the round-bracket derivative is its contents, while the *frame-content* is the derivative of the contents.

$$d(contents) = (contents \ [d \ contents])$$

d round frame

The frame-type for the derivative of the square-bracket is <*[contents]*> while the framed-form is again the derivative of the contents.

d square frame

$$d[contents] = (<[contents]> \; [d\,contents])$$

Although standard differentiation itself is algorithmically simple, the boundary forms expose an extreme simplicity that addresses common functions by introducing a single new concept, a **generic template** for converting the form of a function into the form of its derivative.

The **differentiation frame template** is

$$d\{contents\} = (frame\text{-}type \; [d\,contents])$$

with the frame-types

$$d(contents) \quad \Rightarrow \quad contents$$
$$d[contents] \quad \Rightarrow \quad <[contents]>$$

The derivative of a bracket transfers the derivative operation to all contents of that bracket independently. As well we are working in a base-free system, so that the constant e does not have a conceptually special status. Its role is to provide a pattern that simplifies a differentiated form at the cost of abandoning base-free computation. The many examples that follow demonstrate that the three James pattern axioms are sufficient to define and reduce differentiation templates.

Definition

The definition of the derivative is conceptualized both geometrically and algebraically as the ratio of a small change in a function compared to that small change. It is defined by a limit process as the small change approaches zero. For simplicity we'll consider only single variable derivatives.

$$df(x) =_{def} \lim_{h \to 0} \; (f(x + h) - f(x)) / h$$

hybrid ☞ $\lim_{h \to void} (\; [\{x \; h\} < \{x\}>] \; <[h]> \;)$

The **curly-brace** stands in place of any James bracket. We'll percolate the limit process into the boundary form and shorten its label. Again the definition is *base-free* while the variable x stands in place of a numeric value.

$$d\{x\} =_{def}= (\ [\{x\ Lh\}<\{x\}>]\ <[Lh]>\ )_\#$$

generic James
derivative

This form can be modified slightly by an application of Arrangement.

$$d\{x\} =_{def}= ([\{x\ Lh\}]\ <[Lh]>)\ ([<\{x\}>]\ <[Lh]>)$$ disperse

Finally we'll preemptively apply J-convert to eliminate the angle-bracket containing {x}. Another way to phrase this transformation is that we are building an imaginary space to temporarily store polarity in.

```
d{x} = ([{x Lh}] <[Lh]>) ([<    {x} >] <[Lh]>)
       ([{x Lh}] <[Lh]>) ([(J [{x}])] <[Lh]>)    J-convert
       ([{x Lh}] <[Lh]>) (  J [{x}]    <[Lh]>)    clarify
```

By assuming that all functions of interest can be expressed by James brackets, we need only to derive from this definition the structure of the derivative of each fundamental bracket type.[5]

Round Derivative

The form of the round derivative is constructed directly from the boundary definition of derivative expressed as base-free iconic structure.

$$d\#^x = \lim_{h\to 0} (\#^{x+h} - \#^x)/h \quad ☞$$

```
d{x}# = ([{x Lh}] <[Lh]>) ([{x}] <[Lh]> J)    template
d(x)# = ([(x Lh)] <[Lh]>) ([(x)] <[Lh]> J)    substitute
        (  x Lh   <[Lh]>) (  x   <[Lh]> J)    clarify
```

An intermediate objective is to reduce this form so that there is only one occurrence of the variable x. We'll immediately collect the replicas of x <[Lh]>.

$$(x \; <[Lh]> \quad Lh \;) \; (x \; <[Lh]> \quad J \;)$$

enfold $$(x \; <[Lh]> \; [(Lh)]) \; (x \; <[Lh]> \; [(J)])$$

collect $$(x \; <[Lh]> \; [(Lh)(J)])_{\#}$$

$$☞ \; \lim_{h \to 0} \#^x \; (\#^h - 1)/h$$

We'll next construct the definition of e within this form. Here is where a clever but visually apparent relabeling of the limit variable pays dividends.

Let Ln = (Lh)(J) and solve for Lh.

relabel $$Ln \quad = (Lh)(J) \quad ☞ \quad \lim_n n = \lim_h \#^h - 1$$

move/substitute $$Ln \; o = (Lh)$$

cover $$[Ln \; o] = Lh \qquad ☞ \quad \lim_n \log(n+1) = \lim_h h$$

We have not lost track of the limit process. Here Ln approaches 0. To check, let Lh =*def*= *void*,

$$Ln = (Lh)(J)$$

substitute $$Ln = (\;\;)<o>$$

cancel $$Ln = void$$

Now substitute the new limit variable Ln.

$$(x \; < \qquad [\; Lh \;]> \; [(Lh)(J)] \qquad\qquad)$$

substitute $$(x \; < \qquad [[Ln \; o]]> \; [\; Ln \;] \qquad\qquad)$$

react $$(x \; < \qquad [[Ln \; o]] \; <[\; Ln \;]> \qquad >)$$

enfold $$(x \; <[[\; (([[Ln \; o]] \; <[\; Ln \;]>)) \;]]>)$$

Recalling the definition of e, we can identify a substitution instance of the label e:

$$e =*def*= ((([Ln \; o]] \; <[Ln]>))$$

$$(x \; <[[((\; [[Ln \; o]] \; <[\quad Ln \quad]> \;))]]>)$$

substitute $$(x \; <[[\qquad\qquad\qquad e \qquad\qquad]]>)$$

Unexpectedly the form of e has obviated concern about the limit of n. We'll later demonstrate the construction of the form of e from *void*.

$$d(x)_{\#} = (\; x \quad <[[e]]>)$$

enfold $$([(x)] \; <[[e]]>) \qquad ☞ \quad \#^x \; / \log_{\#} e$$

We are still in an arbitrary base; the substitution of the pattern labeled e does not necessarily imply base-e.

To shift the derivative to base-e, we'll assign e to the generic James base: e = # = (( )). The form <[[e]]> is the *additive conversion factor* mentioned earlier that converts from base-free to base-e.

$$d(x)_\# = (x \ <[[\quad e \quad]]>)_\#$$
$$d(x)_e = (x \ <[[((\ ))]]>)_e \qquad \text{substitute}$$
$$(x \qquad\qquad)_e \quad ☞ \quad e^x \qquad \text{clarify/void cancel}$$

e *is* fundamental not because it is "natural", but because the pattern of the definition of e is contained within the pattern of the definition of the derivative. It is the *location* of the label e that suggests converting the token e to the generic base (( )). e itself is simply a convenient label for a particular boundary form that can be associated with our choice for the definition of *either* "derivative" or "e". What is fundamental is the relation between two limit functions:

$$\lim_{h \to 0} (\#^h - 1)/h \quad \sim \quad \lim_{n \to 0} (1 + n)^{1/n}$$

The substitution of the limit variable Ln on the previous page results first in the "natural" form

$$(x \ <[[Ln \ o]]> \ [Ln])$$

while the special location for the form of e is the additive conversion factor constructed by building additional structure via react and enfold.

$$(x \ <[[((\quad [[Ln \ o]]<[Ln]> \quad))]]> \ ) \qquad \text{react/enfold}$$

This suggests that the natural communality between the definitions of the round derivative and e lies in the void-equivalence of these forms

$$[(Lh)(J)] \ <[Lh]> = void = [[Ln \ o]] \ <[Ln]>$$

This derivation closely follows those found in calculus textbooks. We have called upon the boundary definitions of derivative and of e and that is all. No symbolic algebra, no geometry, no appeal to base-e except as an after-thought for further structural simplification. In the case of the round-bracket the metalanguage stories that allow us to visualize df and to visualize e are essentially the same story.

Square Derivative

To construct the form of the square derivative we'll use the boundary derivative form prior to dispersal.

$$d(\log_{\#} x) = \lim_{h \to 0} (\log_{\#}(x+h) - \log_{\#} x)/h$$

template	☞ $d\{x\} =_{def}= ([\{x \ Lh\}<\{x\}>] <[Lh]>)$
substitute	$d[x]_{\#} = ([[x \ Lh]<[x]>] <[Lh]>)$

The structure of the square derivative is the same as that of the round derivative except for the substitution of a square-bracket for { } in the template. The substitution of [ ] results in structural differences in the method of reducing replicas of the variable x and will suggest a new choice for relabeling the limit variable.

	$d[x]_{\#} = ([\ [x \qquad\qquad Lh]<[x]> \ ] <[Lh]>)$
enfold	$([[([x \qquad\qquad Lh]<[x]>)]] <[Lh]>)$
disperse	$([[([x]<[x]>)([Lh]<[x]>)]] <[Lh]>)$
cancel	$([[(\qquad\qquad)([Lh]<[x]>)]] <[Lh]>)$

The square-bracket allows disperse to reduce the occurrence of x replicas by eliminating a replica via cancel rather than via collect as was the case for the round-bracket. We'll continue with relabeling. Let $Ln = ([Lh]<[x]>)$ and solve for Lh.

	$Ln \qquad = ([Lh]<[x]>)$
cover	$[Ln] \qquad = [Lh]<[x]>$
move	$[Ln][x] \ = \ [Lh]$
cover	$([Ln][x]) = \ Lh$

Here's the limit check: Lh is *void*. Solving for Ln,

	$Ln = ([Lh]<[x]>)$
substitute	$Ln = ([\ ]<[x]>)$
absorb	$Ln = \qquad void$

Continuing with the substitution of the relabeled form:

	$d[x]_{\#} = ([[o \ ([Lh]<[x]>)]] <[\qquad Lh \qquad]>)$
substitute/clarify	$([[o \qquad Ln \qquad]] < \ [Ln][x] \ >)$

Again x is isolated, again the form of e has been exposed:

split	$(\qquad [[Ln \ o]]<[Ln]> \qquad <[x]>)$
enfold	$([[\ (([[Ln \ o]]<[ln]>)) \ ]] <[x]>)$
substitute	$([[\qquad\qquad e \qquad\qquad]] <[x]>)$

The deeper communality is between

$$[[Ln\ o]]<[Ln]>\ and\ [[o\ ([Lh]<[x]>)]]<[Lh]>$$

but here the variable x is entangled with the limit structures. By taking a void-based perspective, the section that follows will permit us to explicitly disentangle the variable x and the constant e. Continuing for now, the square derivative in the generic base-# is

$$d[x]_{\#} = (<[x]>[[e]])_{\#}\ ☞\ (log_{\#}\ e)/x = 1/(x\ ln\ \#)$$

In base-e with e = (( )):

$$d[x]_e = (<[x]>\qquad\qquad)_e\ ☞\qquad\qquad 1/x$$

Angle Derivative

The angle-bracket is the simplest case, it is transparent to the derivative process. d<x> = <dx>

d{x} = ([{x Lh}<{x}>] <[Lh]>)	template
d<x> = ([<x Lh><<x>>] <[Lh]>)	substitute
([<x Lh <x>>] <[Lh]>)	join
([< Lh >] <[Lh]>)	cancel
<([Lh] <[Lh]>)>	promote
<( )> ☞ −1	cancel

The derivation converts x into −1, the negative polarity associated with the interpretation of the angle-bracket. This directly suggests that the derivative of a positive variable is +1. Canceling [Lh] above requires Lh to re main numeric. If Lh = *void* the form would then be indeterminate.[6] This historical conundrum can be bypassed by computing the angle derivative directly from the form of J-conversion.

d<x> = d(J [x])	J-convert
(J [x] [dJ d[x]])_e	d(.)
(J [x] [(<[x]>)]])_e	dc/d[.]
(J [x] <[x]>)_e	clarify
(J)_e ☞ −1	cancel

Now it's easy to go back to demonstrate the two degenerate cases: the derivative of a constant and of a variable.

Variable and Constant Derivatives

In the case of a constant function $f(x) = c$, the James bracket { } is transparent; the operator does not change the argument. We will simply delete the generic boundary from the definition. As well the value of a constant is *constant*, adding Lh does not change it, so that $c + Lh = c$.

template	$dc = (\ [\{c\ Lh\}<\{c\}>]\ <[Lh]>\ )$
substitute	$(\ [\ c\quad\ <\ c\ >]\ <[Lh]>\ )$
cancel	$(\ [\quad\quad\quad\ ]\ <[Lh]>\ )$
absorb	*void* ☞ 0

Immediately we can see that the indeterminate result of letting $Lh = 0$ has been finessed by absorbing it before it becomes 0. Rather than demonstrate the derivative of a variable since that was shown to be 1 when we differentiated the angle-bracket, we'll go directly to the derivative of a linear expression $mx + b$ to illustrate differentiation of a simple expression. More generally the curly braces in the generic form of the derivative stand in place of the entire function being differentiated, while the variable x is replaced by x Lh.

With $\{x\} \Rightarrow ([m][x])\ b$

$d([m][x])b =$

template	$([\{\quad\ x\ Lh\ \}\quad\quad <\{\quad x\quad \}>]\ <[Lh]>)$
substitute	$([([m][x\ Lh])\ b\quad\quad <([m][x])\quad b>]\ <[Lh]>)$
split	$([([m][x\ Lh])\ b\quad\quad <([m][x])><b>]\ <[Lh]>)$
cancel	$([([m][x\ Lh])\quad\quad\quad <([m][x])>\quad]\ <[Lh]>)$
disperse	$([([m][x])([m][Lh])\ <([m][x])>\quad]\ <[Lh]>)$
cancel/clarify	$(\quad\quad\quad [m][Lh]\quad\quad\quad\quad\quad\quad <[Lh]>)$
cancel	$(\quad\quad\quad [m]\quad\quad\quad\quad\quad\quad\quad\quad)$
clarify	m

Differentiation of the linear form comes down to multiple applications of Reflection, which cancels the constant b, the scaled variable $([m][x])$ and finally $[Lh]$. If the limit variable Lh remains numeric, $[Lh]$ can be safely canceled.

Figure 37-3 collects the base-free derivatives and the base-e derivatives of James brackets for arbitrary forms, for variables and for units.

form	derivative	☞	interpretation
d(u)$_\#$	(u <[[e]]> [du])		$(1/\log_\# e)$ $\#^u$ du
d[u]$_\#$	(<[u]> [[e]] [du])		$(\log_\# e)(1/u)$ du
d<u>$_\#$	<du>		−du
d(x)$_\#$	(x <[[e]]>)		$(1/\log_\# e)$ $\#^x$
d[x]$_\#$	(<[x]> [[e]])		$(\log_\# e)(1/x)$
d<x>$_\#$	<dx> = <o>		−1
d( )$_\#$	(<[[e]]>[ ]) = *void*		0
d[ ]$_\#$	(<[ ]> [[e]] [ ])		*indeterminate*
d< >$_\#$	*void*		0
d(u)$_e$	(u [du])		e^u du
d[u]$_e$	(<[u]> [du])		$(1/u)$ du
d<u>$_e$	<du>		−du
d(x)$_e$	(x)		e^x
d[x]$_e$	(<[x]>)		$1/x$
d<x>$_e$	<dx> = <o>		−1
d( )$_e$	([ ]) = *void*		0
d[ ]$_e$	(<[ ]>[ ])		*indeterminate*
d< >$_e$	< > = *void*		0

Figure 37-3: *Derivatives of boundary forms in* base-# *and* base-e

37.3 Void-based Differentiation

The limit equation that defines e just happens to fit the forms generated by the definition of a derivative, at least for the round- and square-brackets. There is a void-based alternative approach. Consider the form of the round derivative prior to preparing to match the definition of e by substituting the label Ln.

$$d(x)_\# = (x \ [(Lh)(J)] \ <[Lh]>)$$

The limit as h→0 cannot be resolved by direct substitution since Lh is inside a square-bracket, so we'll consider the conditions necessary to eliminate Lh. Basically we want all forms containing Lh to be void-equivalent, so we'll construct a hypothetical void-equivalent assertion that eliminates Lh.

hypothesis	[(Lh)(J)] <[Lh]>	=?=	*void*
move	[(Lh)(J)]	=	[Lh]
decompose	(Lh)(J)	=	Lh
move/substitute	(Lh)<Lh><o>	=	*void*

Since Lh is no longer within a square-bracket, it is safe to let its value approach *void*.

substitute	( )< ><o>	=	*void*
cancel	*void*	=	*void*

And indeed the hypothesis of void-equivalence is supported by an identity. By running the demonstration backwards, starting from void-identity, we can construct a void-equivalent form that matches the desired structure under the specific restriction that Lh = *void*, leaving

substitute	$d(x)_\# = (x \qquad\qquad void \qquad\qquad)$

The prior demonstration that permitted the substitution of e also established a void-equivalence:

$$[(Lh)<o>] <[Lh]> = void = [[Ln \ o]] <[Ln]>$$

We could make a void-substitution and apply enfold to reconstruct the base-e form:[7]

void substitute	$d(x)_\# = (x < \qquad [[Ln \ o]] <[Ln]> \qquad >)$
enfold	$(x <[[((\ [[Ln \ o]] <[Ln]>))]]>)$
substitute	$(x <[[\qquad\qquad e \qquad\qquad]]>)$

What has become apparent is that *the concept of a base itself* has been borrowed from the interpretation. The arbitrary base-# converts to base-e directly by inserting e = (( )) within the additive conversion factor <[[e]]> above. We'll first look deeper to find a justification for *any* base, and then follow that with a void-based construction of the constant e.

Round Unit Transparency

We'll begin with identity, in order to show the essential nature of the limit variable within the derivative.

Let Ln = *void*
$$( ) = ( )$$
$$Ln\ ( ) = (Ln)$$

void substitute

This is a *special boundary structure*: **round unit transparency**. What kind of form, call it A, maintains equivalence when it is both inside and outside a round-bracket?

$$(A) \quad = A\ ( ) \quad ☞ \quad \#^A = A + 1$$

unit transparency

This equivalence leads to two different reentrant equations:

$$A \quad = [A\ ( )] \quad ☞ \quad A = \log_\# (A + 1)$$ cover

and

$$(A)<( )> = A \quad ☞ \quad A = \#^A - 1$$ move

Each of these equations is valid when A = *void*.

$$A = [A\ ( )] = (A)<( )> \quad when \quad A = void$$

round unit transparency

The round-bracket is *transparent* to the presence of A. The putative round distinction does not distinguish inside from outside. We could simply eliminate the non-distinction from the original equation (A) = A ( ), to leave A = A. Equivalently we could render A void-equivalent, constructing the unit identity ( ) = ( ).[8] What stands out is that these two equations match the structural components of the forms of d(x) and e.

$$[(Lh)<o>]\ <[Lh]> = void = [[Ln\ o]]\ <[Ln]>$$
$$[\quad A_{Lh}\quad]\ <[Lh]> = void = [\quad A_{Ln}\quad]\ <[Ln]>$$

The *structural association* between the round-bracket derivative and base-e is due to round-bracket transparency. Each is a different side of the same void-equivalence. As well, the exponential function $\#^x$ is independent of this association, only the power and the log of the limit variable are relevant.

Construction of e

To establish e as the base for the exponential function, it is sufficient to *define* it as the James base.

With $$[[Ln\ o]]<[Ln]> = void, \qquad e =def= ((\ void \ ))$$

What makes e special is that its void-equivalent interior has been defined as a conventional limit equation. The void-equivalent form itself can be independently derived directly from *round unit transparency* for a labeled *void*. Using the embedded Ln notation, and rearranging a bit we can show that for unit transparency in base-e, A = Ln.

$$e = (1 + Ln)^{1/Ln}$$

$$e^{Ln} = (1 + Ln) \qquad ☞ \qquad (Ln)_e = (\ ) Ln$$

The James derivation is

	( )	= ( )
unit transparency	Ln ( )	= (Ln)
cover	[Ln o]	= Ln
compose	[[Ln o]]	= [Ln]
move	<[Ln]> [[Ln o]]	= *void*
compose	((<[Ln]> [[Ln o]])) = (( )) = e	

Although the logarithmic form of the boundary equality leads to multiplication by 0, the exponential form provides an equation to be solved for the base #. Returning to standard notation

$$A = (A)<(\ )> \qquad ☞ \qquad n = \#^n - 1$$
$$\#^n = n + 1$$
$$\# = {}^n\sqrt{(n + 1)} = (n+1)^{1/n}$$

What is unusual here is calling the complex expression, $(n+1)^{1/n}$, a *base*. Broadening the concept of a base is facilitated by the use of base-free exponentials. The boundary form of the equation $n = \#^n - 1$ can be coaxed into exposing the base by using the *explicit base form* of (n). With Ln = *void*,

implicit base #	Ln = (Ln)_# <o>
explicit base b	Ln = (([[b]][Ln]))_b <o>

We can now solve for the base b.

	(([[b]][Ln])) <o> =	Ln
move	(([[b]][Ln])) =	Ln o
cover	[[b]][Ln] =	[[Ln o]]
move	[[b]] =	[[Ln o]]<[Ln]>
cover	b	= (([[Ln o]]<[Ln]>))

The demonstrated base $(([[Ln\ o]]<[Ln]>))$ is in the form of an exponential, which should not come as a surprise.[9]

$$b = (([[Ln\ o]]<[Ln]>)) \quad \text{☞} \quad b = (n+1)^{1/n} \ \textit{with}\ n \to 0$$

We can safely reintroduce Lh using the void-equivalent substitution Ln = $([Lh]<[x]>)$ to return to the definition of a derivative. Both sides of this substitution are independently void-equivalent, Ln by construction and the form to be substituted by taking Lh = *void*.

```
<[    Ln      ]>[[    Ln          o   ]] =  void
<[([Lh]<[x]>)]>[[([Lh]<[x]>)(       )]] =  void    substitute
  <[Lh]>[x]     [[([Lh]<[x]>)(       )]] =  void    clarify/react
  <[Lh]>        [[([Lh]<[x]>)(       )]] = <[x]>    move
  <[Lh]>        [[([Lh]<[x]>)([x]<[x]>)]] = <[x]>   create
  <[Lh]>        [  [Lh x]<[x]>          ] = <[x]>   collect/clarify
```

Now covering each side with a round-bracket, we arrive concurrently at both the *definition* and the *value* of the square derivative.

$$d[x]_\# = (<[Lh]> [[Lh\ x]<[x]>]) = (<[x]>)$$

We have of course simply run the reduction of the square derivative backwards, generating its form from *void*. But where is the base-e? It is both introduced into and removed from the derivative by the limit process Lh. We have essentially removed the *metric* from the derivative concept, a metric introduced by Euler almost three centuries ago.

This derivation was conducted from a purely iconic structural viewpoint. The critical step to avoid limit theory was to safely substitute a void-equivalent label n early by calling upon round-unit transparency. The critical strategy to avoid introducing base-e was to maintain the generic base throughout. We thus arrive at a form that meets the definition of a derivative without appeal to the geometry of tangent slopes at a point. Also slipping into the background is the time-honored e, a creature that apparently evolved from the geometry of exponential curves rather than from the structure of differentiation.

$(void) = void\ (\ )$
when n = *void*
$(n) = n\ (\ )$

37.4 Chain Rule

The Chain Rule allows differentiation to be applied to composite functions, conventionally written as $F(G(x))$. James forms express function composition naturally as nesting of arbitrary brackets, $\{\{x\}_G\}_F$. A **derivative** is the ratio between changes in two things: the function ΔF when its variable changes by a small amount Δx and the size of the change itself Δx.

$$dF(x) = \Delta F_{\Delta x} / \Delta x$$

(Here the subscript is an indicator to make dependencies explicit.) The issue with composite functions is that the "variable" of the outer function is the inner function, while the increment itself is a change of the inner function rather than a change in the variable labeled x. That is

$$dF(G(x)) = \Delta F_{\Delta G} / \Delta G_{\Delta x}$$

Substituting a compound function directly into the form of the derivative results in an error

chain rule ignored

$$dF(G(x)) \neq \Delta F_{\Delta G} / \Delta x$$

The correction is straightforward, the Δx variable needs to be transformed first by the function G.

$$dG(x) = \Delta G_{\Delta x} / \Delta x$$

$$\Delta F_{\Delta G} / \Delta x = (\Delta F_{\Delta G} / \Delta G_{\Delta x}) * (\Delta G_{\Delta x} / \Delta x)$$

This result shows that *the derivative of nested forms is the product of the derivative of each level of nesting.* In Leibniz' lovely notation

$$df(g(x))/dx = df/dx = df/dg * dg/dx$$

Since the evolution of calculus has focused on issues of the continuity and smoothness (differentiability) of functions, the conventional proof of the Chain Rule emphasizes the conversion of the limit variable for the outer function *through* the inner function. So long as the functions are well behaved, small changes eventually propagate down to the bare variable x as small changes. Embedding brackets within James **differentiation frames** achieves the propagation of function application, and thus the chain rule, naturally and transparently by *substitution into nested subforms.*

Differentiation Templates

We have thus far developed the form of the boundary derivatives by following standard techniques closely. The James **differentiation frame template** steps away from convention by using the *nested chain rule* to generate a *single template* that applies to all functions that can be expressed in James notation. We begin with the generic frame for non-nested derivatives

$$\text{d}\{\textit{contents}\} = (\quad \textit{frame-type} \quad [\text{d } \textit{contents}])$$

Only round and square frame types need be considered.

round-bracket frame type:	*contents*	$\text{d}(x) = (\quad x \quad [\text{d}x])$
square-bracket frame type:	<[*contents*]>	$\text{d}[x] = (<[x]>[\text{d}x])$

Angle-brackets are transparent to differentiation because they can be converted into the *constant* J. Forms within a container can be differentiated separately because they are *independent*. Neither needs labeling within the template. For nested containers the differentiation template leaves a trail of results as frame-types. *Each* clarify *step is the structural implementation of chaining.* Here each nested bracket is labeled with a natural number.

$$
\begin{aligned}
\text{d}\{\{\{x\}_3\}_2\}_1 = &(\textit{type}_1 \; [\text{d}\{\{x\}_3\}_2 \qquad\qquad]) \\
&(\textit{type}_1 \; [(\textit{type}_2 \; [\text{d}\{x\}_3 \qquad])]) \qquad\text{substitute} \\
&(\textit{type}_1 \quad \textit{type}_2 \; [\text{d}\{x\}_3 \qquad\quad]) \qquad\text{clarify} \\
&(\textit{type}_1 \quad \textit{type}_2 \; [(\textit{type}_3 [\text{d}x])]) \qquad\text{substitute} \\
&(\textit{type}_1 \quad \textit{type}_2 \quad \textit{type}_3 [\text{d}x] \quad) \qquad\text{clarify} \\
&(\textit{type}_1 \quad \textit{type}_2 \quad \textit{type}_3 \qquad\quad) \qquad\text{substitute/clarify}
\end{aligned}
$$

These *type-trails* may gain additional structure from existing angle-brackets and from containers with multiple contents. Angle-brackets maintain their relative nesting position while multiple contents are bundled as dispersible forms. As an example

$$
\begin{aligned}
\text{d}\{<\{\{x\}_3\{x\}_4\}_2>\}_1 = & \\
(\textit{type}_1 \; [<\text{d}\{\{x\}_3\{x\}_4\}_2 &\qquad\qquad\qquad >]) \quad\text{substitute} \\
(\textit{type}_1 \; [<(\textit{type}_2 \; [\text{d}\{x\}_3 \; \text{d}\{x\}_4 &\qquad\qquad])>]) \quad\text{substitute} \\
(\textit{type}_1 \; [<(\textit{type}_2 \; [(\textit{type}_3 \; [\text{d}x])(\textit{type}_4 \; [\text{d}x])])>]) \quad\text{substitute} \\
(\textit{type}_1 \; [<(\textit{type}_2 \; [(\textit{type}_3 [\;\; o])(\textit{type}_4 [\;\; o])])>]) \quad\text{substitute} \\
(\textit{type}_1 \; [<(\textit{type}_2 \; [(\textit{type}_3 \qquad)(\textit{type}_4 \qquad)])>]) \quad\text{clarify}
\end{aligned}
$$

The structure of a compound nested form *is maintained* by the differentiation process, with all generic brackets { } converted in place into frames of the appropriate type. In the example,

$$d\{ \qquad <\{ \qquad \{ \ x \ \}_3 \{ \ x \ \}_4 \}_2 > \}_1$$

substitute pattern $\qquad \Rightarrow \qquad (type_1 \ [<(type_2 \ [(type_3) \ (type_4)]) \ >])$

We'll further abbreviate the template for readability. Each numeric label now stands in place of the *contents* of the labeled bracket.

$$d\{ \quad <\{ \quad \{x\}_3 \{x\}_4 \}_2 > \}_1$$

substitute pattern $\qquad \Rightarrow \qquad (1 \ [<(2 \ [(3) \ (4)]) \ >])$

disperse $\qquad\qquad (1 \ [< \ (2 \ 3) \quad (2 \ 4) >])$

	contents
1	<(2 [(3)(4)])>
2	(3)(4)
3	x
4	x

Given the James form of a compound function, it is possible to set up a template for a function and simply substitute the frame contents of the relevant labeled bracket to generate the derivative. We'll look first at the simplest non-trivial cases, doubly nested round- and square-brackets, and later at more complex examples.

Double-Round

It's tempting to call the double round form a *power tower*, but that would mix form with interpretation.

round $\qquad d(u)_e = (u \ [du])_e \qquad \text{☞} \ de^u = e^u \ du$

double-round

$$d((u))_e = (\quad (u) \quad [\quad d(u) \quad])$$

d(.) $\qquad\qquad (\quad (u) \quad [(u \quad [du])])$

clarify $\qquad\qquad (\quad (u) \quad u \ [du] \quad)$

enfold $\qquad\qquad ([[((u))][(u)][du] \quad) \ \text{☞} \ de^{e^u} = e^{e^u} e^u \ du$

The double-round template is

	contents
1	(2)
2	u

$$d((u)_2)_1 = (content_1 \ content_2 \ [du])$$

The template pattern for nested round-brackets is apparent.

$$d(...(u)_n...)_1 = (content_1 \ ... \ content_n \ [d \, content_n])$$

For example,

$$d(((u)))_e = (((u)) \ (u) \ u \ [du])_e$$

Double-Square

square $d[u]_e = (<[u]>[du])_e$ ☞ $d \ln u = du/u$

double-square

$d[[u]]_e = (<[[u]]> [\quad d[u] \quad])$

$\qquad\qquad (<[[u]]> [(<[u]>[du])])$ $d[.]$

$\qquad\qquad (<[[u]]> \quad <[u]>[du] \quad)$ clarify

$\qquad\qquad (<[[u]] \qquad [u]>[du] \quad)$ join

$\qquad\qquad\qquad$ ☞ $d \ln\ln u = du/(u \ln u)$

The double-square template is

contents

$\qquad$ 1   [2]

$\qquad$ 2   u

$d[[u]_2]_1 = (<[content_1][content_2]> [du])$

The template pattern:

$d[...[u]_{n...}]_1 = (<[content_1]...[content_n]> [d\,content_n])$

For example,

$d[[[u]]]_e = (<[[[u]]] \; [[u]] \; [u]> \; [du])_e$

37.5 Generalization

Now we'll generate some other functional derivatives as a demonstration of the sufficiency of the differentiation template for well-behaved functions in general.

Product Rule

There are no specific operators in James algebra for product and quotient, instead they are compositions of nested brackets. First the raw computational demonstration of the product rule as a pattern of nested brackets rather than the product of two expressions.

$\qquad\qquad u * v \quad$ ☞ $\quad ([u][v])$

$d([u][v]) =$

$([u][v][\qquad d[u] \qquad\qquad\qquad d[v] \;])$ $d(.)$

$([u][v][(<[u]>[du])] \qquad\qquad (<[v]>[dv])])$ $d[.]$

$([u][v][(<[u]>[du])]) \; ([u][v][(<[v]>[dv])])$ disperse

$([u][v] \quad <[u]>[du] \quad) \; ([u][v] \quad <[v]>[dv] \quad)$ clarify

$(\quad [v] \qquad [du] \quad) \; ([u] \qquad\qquad [dv] \quad)$ cancel

$\qquad\qquad$ ☞ $\quad (u\,dv) + (v\,du)$

Alternatively we could develop a pattern template. For that I'll label each component bracket.

$$([u][v]) \quad \Rightarrow \quad ([u]_2[v]_3)_1$$

contents

1   [2][3]
2   u
3   v

The extruded form below shows the *frame structure* of the derivative without substituting the frame-types for the numeric labels.

$$(type_1 \ [\qquad\qquad\qquad\qquad])$$
$$(type_2 \ [\ ]) \ (type_3 \ [\ ])$$
$$du \qquad\qquad dv$$

Each label is next augmented by its frame-type. Only the square-bracket labels change. The numeric labels now stand in place of the bracket contents.

$$(\ 1 \quad [\qquad\qquad\qquad\qquad])$$
$$(<[2]>[\ ]) \ (<[3]>[\ ])$$
$$du \qquad\qquad dv$$

Finally each numeric label is replaced by the corresponding contents. Here's a listing of what those contents are, although they are easily retrieved by inspection from the original form.

label in context	*contents*
(1 ...)	[2][3]
(<[2]> ...)	u
(<[3]> ...)	v

Assembling:

d(.)
d[.]
dvar

$$([u][v][\qquad\qquad\qquad])$$
$$(<[u]>[\ ])(<[v]>[\ ])$$
$$du \qquad\qquad dv$$

Collapsing the extruded form and simplifying:

d([u][v]) =

substitute
disperse/clarify
cancel

$$([u][v][(<[u]>[du])(<[v]>[dv])])$$
$$([u][v]<[u]>[du])([u][v]<[v]>[dv])$$
$$(\ [v] \qquad [du])([u] \qquad\qquad [dv])$$

☞   (v du) + (u dv)

The labels u, v are generic forms. Were these labels standing in place of variables x, y, their derivatives would convert to o and then clarify to *void*. For example

$$([x][y]) \Rightarrow ([x]_2[y]_3)_1$$

d([x][y]) = ([x][y][(<[x]>[o])(<[y]>[o])])	template
([x][y][(<[x]>)(<[y]>)])	clarify
☞ x y (1/x + 1/y)	

Dispersing the result simplifies the interpretation.

([x][y][(<[x]>)(<[y]>)])	template
([x][y] <[x]>)([x][y] <[y]>)	disperse/clarify
([y])([x])	cancel
y x	clarify
☞ x + y	

Quotient Rule

All the steps for the product rule above were shown explicitly. Now we will abbreviate the generation of the quotient and power rules that follow. Here is the labeled bracket form of division:

$$u / v \quad ☞ \quad ([u]<[v]>) \Rightarrow ([u]_2<[v]_3>)_1$$

< > *does not need to be labeled*

The raw computation of this derivative from bracket primitives is included as a footnote.[10] Here we will continue to leverage the differential pattern template. The only difference from the product template is one transparent angle-bracket.

contents

1	[2]<[3]>
2	u
3	v

$$(type_1 \, [(type_2 \, [du])<(type_3 \, [dv])>])$$

Substituting the frame-types

(1   [(<[2]>[du])<(<[3]>[dv])>])   template

Substituting the content of each bracket and reducing:

([u]<[v]>[(<[u]>[du]) <(<[v]>[dv])>])	substitute
([u]<[v]><[u]>[du]) ([u]<[v]>[<(<[v]>[dv])>])	disperse
([u]<[v]><[u]>[du])<([u]<[v]> <[v]>[dv])>	promote/clarify
(<[v]> [du])<([u]<[v]> <[v]>[dv])>	cancel
(<[v]> [du])([<u>]<[v] [v]>[dv])	demote/join
☞ du/v + (–u dv)/(v v)	

To convert this form into the more common string format, we'll need to create some *extra* boundary structure.[11]

```
         (<  [v]>          [du]) ([<u>]<[v][v]>[dv])
create   (<  [v]><[v]  >[v][du]) ([<u>]<[v][v]>[dv])
  join   (<  [v]  [v]  >[v][du]) ([<u>]<[v][v]>[dv])
collect  (<  [v]  [v]  >[([v][du])([<u>][dv])]])
enfold   (<[([v]  [v])]>[([v][du])([<u>][dv])]])
```

☞ $(v\,du + -u\,dv)/v^2$

Power Rule

The derivative of a power is often introduced within the context of polynomial functions and their binomial expansions, since these algebraic concepts co-evolved with the development of the calculus during the 18th century. Taking the variable x as the implicit variable of differentiation,

$$dx^n = nx^{n-1}$$

modern proofs call upon logarithmic differentiation in order to generalize the power n to any real number. Here we will contrast the derivatives of exponential and polynomial expressions within the context of an expanded concept of a *base*.

$$n^x \quad ☞ \quad (([[n]][x]))_\# = (x)_n$$
$$x^n \quad ☞ \quad (([[x]][n]))_\# = (n)_x$$

The essential difference between these forms comes from the asymmetric relation between power and base, which shows as a transposition of the location of the labels of each. The *structure* of the form itself remains unchanged.

$$dn^x \quad ☞ \quad d(([[n]][x]))_\# = d(x)_n$$
$$dx^n \quad ☞ \quad d(([[x]][n]))_\# = d(n)_x$$

We could develop the form of the derivative of a power directly from its compound James form via differentiation of round- and square-brackets. We could read the form of a power as a multiplication in exponential space and apply the product rule for derivatives. The objective here, however, is not proof but rather the exploration and comparison of each of these techniques within the James algebra. For that we'll build a generic differentiation template for the structure of an arbitrary exponential expression.

Generic Exponential Template

The *differentiation pattern template* for $(([[u]][v]))$ suffices both for polynomial and for exponential expressions in an arbitrary base. Here are some labels to support memory.

u is the base $\Rightarrow$ B
v is the power $\Rightarrow$ P
M is the original form $\Rightarrow$ $(([[B]][P]))$ ☞ B^P
[M] is the content of M $\Rightarrow$ $([[B]][P])$

First we'll label the brackets and build the pattern-template without considering the type of bracket. Both single- and double-bracket templates are enlisted.

$M = (([[B]][P])) \Rightarrow (([[B]_5]_3[P]_4)_2)_1$
$M = (type_1\ type_2\ [(type_3\ type_5\ [dB])(type_4\ [dP])])$

	contents	
1	(2	)
2	[3][4]	
3	[5]	
4	P	
5	B	

Next add the frame-types for the specific bracket types. Only the square-bracket types change.

(1   2 [(<[3]><[5]>[dB])(<[4]>[dP])])

For readability I'll prepare in advance for upcoming reductions by substituting the label [M] for the content represented by 1, and disperse the content 2.

([M][(2 [(<[3]><[5]>[dB]) (<[4]>[dP])])])   enfold
([M][(2 <[3]><[5]>[dB]) (2 <[4]>[dP])])])   disperse/clarify

Next we'll separately substitute into and simplify the two subforms with numeric labels. Expanding each subform:

(2   <[3]><[5]>[dB])
([[B]][P]<[[B]]><[B]>[dB])   substitute
([P]   <[B]>[dB])   cancel

(2   <[4]>[dP])
([[B]][P]<[P]>[dP])   substitute
([[B]]   [dP])   cancel

Recombining the simplified subforms, we have constructed the *generic boundary exponential rule* that applies to differentiation of any expression with the structure B^P:

generic exponential derivative

$$dM = dB^P \quad ☞$$

$$([M] [([P]<[B]>[dB]) ([[B]][dP])])$$

$$☞ \quad B^P ((P/B) dB + (\ln B) dP)$$

We now have the form of several types of derivatives combined into one. The form of this template also identifies the structural contributions of the base and the exponent to the computed derivative.

Constant Base

In the case that the base is constant (e by default), we have $B = (( ))$ and $dB = void$:

$$de^x \quad ☞$$

substitute	$([M] [([P]<[B]>[ ])([[B]][dP])])$
absorb	$([M] [\qquad ([[B]][dP])])$
substitute	$([M] \qquad [[(( ))]][dP])$
clarify	$([M] \qquad [dP])$

$$([M][dP]) \quad ☞ \quad B^P dP \quad \textit{that is} \quad e^x dx$$

Constant Exponent

In the case that the exponent is a constant and the base is variable, we have $dP = void$:

$$dx^n \quad ☞$$

substitute	$([M] [([P]<[B]>[dB])([[B]][ ])])$
absorb	$([M] [([P]<[B]>[dB]) \qquad])$
clarify	$([M] \quad [P]<[B]>[dB] \qquad)$

$$([M] [P]<[B]>[dB]) \quad ☞ \quad B^P (P/B) dB$$

We could continue to simplify this within the James form, however it is sufficient to rearrange the expression to see that

$$dx^n \quad ☞ \quad P B^P/B \ dB = P B^{P-1} dB \quad \textit{that is} \quad nx^{n-1} dx$$

Unit Fraction

Here's the derivative of a generic unit fraction. We'll first simplify M based on the specific form $B^P = B^{-1}$.

With $P = <o>$ *and* $dP = void$

$M = (([[B]][P]))$	
$(([[u]][<o>]))$	substitute
$(<([[u]] \quad)>)$	promote/clarify
$(< \quad [u] \quad >) \quad ☞ \quad 1/u$	clarify

Substituting into the generic template for the derivative of a power. With $M = (<[u]>)$,

du^{-1} ☞

$([\quad M \quad][([P]<[B]>[dB])([[B]][dP])])$	template
$([(<[u]>)][([<o>]<[u]>[du])([[u]][\quad])])$	substitute
$([(<[u]>)][([<o>]<[u]>[du]) \qquad])$	absorb
$(\quad <[u]> \quad [<o>]<[u]>[du] \qquad)$	clarify
$<(\quad <[u] \qquad [u]>[du] \qquad)>$	promote/clarify
$<(\quad <[([u] \qquad [u])]>[du] \qquad)>$	enfold
$☞ \quad -du/u^2$	

Arbitrary Constant Base

In the case of constant base-# other than base-e, we can clearly see the scaling effect of any specific base. In conventional notation

$$d B^P \quad ☞ \quad B^P (P/B \, dB + (\ln B) \, dP)$$

$$d \#^u \quad = \quad \#^u ((u/\#) \, 0 + (\ln \#) \, du)$$

$$= \quad \#^u (\ln \#) \, du$$

Referring to Figure 37-3 for example, changing the base of e^u to $\#^u$ multiplies the derivative by $\ln \#$. The additive conversion factor $[[\#]]_e$ corresponds to multiplying by $\ln \#$.

One strength of boundary differentiation is that the structure of the specific derivatives can be clearly explained and distinguished by the explicit reduction steps from the generic exponential template.

Variable Base and Exponent

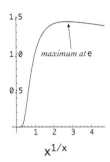

$x^{1/x}$

Finally let's apply the boundary differentiation template to a more complex function commonly found in textbooks. Here both base and exponent are variable.

$$x^{1/x} \quad ☞ \quad ((\lceil[x]\rceil<[x]>))$$

Since this expression is in the form B^P, we'll simply substitute the easily derived components into the generic exponential differentiation template.

$$d\,M = d\,B^P \quad ☞$$

$$([M]\ [([P]<[B]>[dB])\ ([[B]][dP])])$$

with
$$
\begin{aligned}
M &= ((\lceil[x]\rceil<[x]>)) &&☞&& x^{1/x} \\
[M] &= ([[x]]<[x]>) &&☞&& (1/x)\ \ln x \\
B &= x \\
dB &= dx = 0 \\
P &= (<[x]>) &&☞&& 1/x \\
dP &= <(<[x][x]>[dx])> \\
&\ <(<[x][x]>)> &&☞&& -1/x^2
\end{aligned}
$$

Substituting,

substitute $d\,M = ([M]\ [([(<[x]>)]<[x]>[o])\ ([[x]][dP])])$

clarify $([M]\ [(\ \ <[x]>\ \ <[x]>\ \ )\ ([[x]][dP])])$

substitute $([M]\ [<\ \ \ \ \ \ \ \ dP\ \ \ \ \ \ \ >\ ([[x]][dP])])$

At this point an instance of dP has emerged, simplifying the visual complexity of the form. To prepare for collecting the replicas of dP we'll remove the angle-bracket with J-convert and construct the form of collect.

J-convert $([M]\ [(\ \ J\ \ \ \ [dP]\ \ \ \ \ \ )\ ([[x]][dP])])$

enfold $([M]\ [([(J)]\ [dP]\ \ \ \ )\ ([[x]][dP])])$

collect $([M]\ [([(J)[x]][dP])])$

clarify/substitute $([M]\ \ \ \ [<o>[x]][dP]\ \ )$

$$☞ \quad (x^{1/x})\ (-1 + (\ln x))\ (-1/x^2)$$
$$= (x^{1/x})\ (x^{-2})\ ((\ln x) - 1)$$

The process of simplifying the derivative form provides a trace of the evolution of the components of the complex function. The first factor in the above expression is the original function. The second factor is dP, the derivative of the expression that is the exponent. The third component is the *interaction* between the form of B and the form of P as identified by the collect operation. Arrangement converts between sum-of-products and product-of-sums. The two additive components of that interaction are

— −1 contributed by the shared x in B and P and

— ln x contributed by the base B.

The presence of ln is an adjustment between the linear space of the base and the exponential space of the power. Incidentally, should the variable x have itself been a compound form, we would simply not have reduced dx to 1. The structure of the form of B^P does not change and the reduction takes the same steps, resulting in

$$du^{1/u} = (u^{1/u})\,(1/u^2)\,(1 - \ln u)\,du$$

Identifying Inflection Points

$x^{1/x}$ is known to have a global maximum at e. The derivative is equal to 0 at the inflection points.

$$([M]\,[dP]\,[o<[x]>]) = \textit{void}$$

For this form to be void-equivalent the contents of at least one of the three square-bracketed forms must be void-equivalent in order to trigger Dominion. Therefore the three potential inflection points are

$$
\begin{aligned}
M &= (([[x]]<[x]>)) = \textit{void} \\
dP &= <(<[x][x]>)> \ = \textit{void} \\
o<[x]> &= \textit{void}
\end{aligned}
$$

We'll solve each for x. In reverse order,

$$
\begin{array}{lll}
o <[x]> = \textit{void} & & \\
\quad <[x]> = <o> & & \text{move} \\
\quad\quad [x] = o & & \text{cover} \\
\quad\quad\quad x = (o) = (( ))_e & & \text{cover}
\end{array}
$$

(( )) is the generic form of the base. There is an inflection point at x = e. We are in base-e because the frame-types that were used are defined as having base-e. It's fairly easy to see that the other two solutions are infinities. We'll take the first step of solving for x and observe that each runs into a form of infinity.

$$(<[x][x]>) = \quad void$$

cover
$$[x][x] \quad = <[\ ]>$$

and

$$(([[x]]<[x]>)) = void$$

cover
$$([[x]]<[x]>) \quad = [\ ]$$

The net result is that there is only one real inflection point at x = e.

37.6 Remarks

In Section 37.2 we tacitly assumed J is a constant so its derivative is *void*. It's instructive to compute dJ directly.

$$dJ = d[<(\ )>] = d[<(\ )_2>]_1$$

template
$$(<[<(\ )>]>[<d(\qquad)>])$$

template
$$(<[<(\ )>]>[<(void\ [void])>])$$

clarify/void cancel
$$(<[<(\ )>]>[\qquad\qquad])$$

absorb
$$void$$

This example contains an embedded d( ), treating ( ) as a numeric constant. Here's the derivative of the non-numeric constant [ ] with *void* contents. This result is defined in Chapter 42.

$$d[\ ] = (<[void]> [void]) \Rightarrow \textit{indeterminate}$$

The examples in this chapter provide a rough map for exploring the differentiation of well behaved algebraic and transcendental functions. Trigonometric derivatives are included in Chapter 40.5.

The other techniques developed during the evolution of the calculus can probably be transcribed into boundary form, including those of integration. This rich area for the application of boundary techniques has yet to be explored.

Endnotes

1. **opening quote:** A. Artaud (1947) Van Gogh, the man suicided by society. In S. Sontag (ed.) (1988) *Antonin Artaud: Selected writings* p.497.

2. **not to compare the *efficiency* of boundary and algebraic techniques:** The *efficiency* of computation is extremely difficult to assess. No algorithmic technique expressed in software can compete with a customized silicon hardware implementation. Even within a specific domain most algorithms are efficient for some problems and not efficient for others. And herein we're comparing yet another complexity vector, the difference between symbolic and iconic representations.

3. **the form of that specific base is *defined* to be (( )):** In effect the generic base sets aside the numeric conversion factor between two specific bases, to be later supplied when (( )) is bound to a specific value. It is easy to see why the base of a numeric system cannot be 1, since this would be asserting that (( )) = ( ). We'll examine exotic bases more fully in Chapter 43.4.

4. **a single substitution template for differentiation of any well-behaved function:** I've avoided the simpler methods of implicit differentiation in order to demonstrate the derivation from first principles.

5. **the structure of the derivative of each fundamental bracket type:** The evolution of calculus has been focused on the existence and the continuity of functions. The goals here are more modest, so we can accept that *functions of interest* are free of sticky problems. We will assume that the functions already addressed by iconic methods are valid candidates for the methods that follow. These include combinations of common functions {+, x, ^, −, ÷, √, log}, algebraic polynomials, functions that can be cleanly partitioned into component objects, transcendental functions (exponential/logarithmic, trigonometric), and others than can be described by analytic language.

6. **the form would then be indeterminate:** The James form of indeterminacy is the content of Chapter 42. Here is the *form of indeterminacy* that will later also organize the several conventional indeterminate expressions.

$$[\ ]<[\ ]> \ ☞ \ indeterminate$$

7. **apply enfold to reconstruct the base-e form:** The change in polarity occurs during the change of limit variables from Lh to Ln in the round derivative.

8. **constructing the unit identity ( ) = ( ):** When A = *void*, this special boundary equation is a restatement of two of the arithmetic axioms of James calculus,

$$A = [A ( )] \quad and \quad (A)<( )> = A$$
$$= [( )] \quad\quad\quad\quad ( )<( )> =$$

9. **form of an exponential, which should not come as a surprise:** Examining the equation b = ((([n o]]<[n]>)) for various values of n shows that the base continues to increase as n decreases to 0 at which time the equation turns non-numeric, b = ((([ ]<[ ]>)), which is the reason why n must be treated as a limit variable. Here's a chart that explores the range of values for the James form that defines e:

n	*b*
→∞	1
10	1.27
1	2
.0001	2.7169
→0	2.71828... = e
− .1	2.87
− .9	12.92
− .99	104.76
→ −1	∞

10. **from bracket primitives is included as a footnote:** Here is the generation of the quotient rule directly from the derivatives of the three James bracket types.

```
d([u]<[v]>) =

([u]<[v]>[        d [u]<[v]>          ])                              d(.)
([u]<[v]>[        d[u]          <d[v]>])                              du dv
([u]<[v]>[(<[u]> [du])<(<[v]>[dv])>])                                d[.]
([u]<[v]>[(<[u]>     [du])]) ([u]<[v]>      [<(<[v]> [dv])>])         disperse
([u]<[v]> <[u]>     [du] ) ([u]<[v]>      [<(<[v]> [dv])>])           cancel
(  <[v]>             [du] )<([u]<[v]>     [ (<[v]> [dv]) ])>          promote
(  <[v]>             [du] )<([u]<[v]>          <[v]> [dv]    )>       cancel
(  <[v]><[v]> [v][du] )<(   <[v]><[v]> [ u ] [dv]    )>              create
(  <[v]><[v]> [v][du] ) (   <[v]><[v]> [<u>] [dv]    )              demote
(  <[v]><[v]>[([v][du])]) (   <[v]><[v]>[([<u>] [dv])] )             enfold
(  <[v]><[v]>[([v][du]) ([<u>][dv]) ])                               collect
(  <[v]><[v]>[([v][du])<([ u ][dv])>])                              promote
```

11. **create some *extra* boundary structure:** From the James perspective, this extra structure is superfluous. It needs to be added in order to support interpretation into a more familiar but structurally redundant string notation.

Chapter 38

Mapping

Words and pictures belong together.[1]
— *Edward Tufte (1983)*

We have explored J as an imaginary numeric concept. Euler defined J to be a conventional imaginary number with an infinity of values $\pm(2k + 1)i\pi$ for the exponent of the function e^z. The appearance of $i\pi$ indicates a *rotation* in the complex plane and designates the exponent z to be a complex number. We will explore complex rotation and Euler's formula in the next chapter. Here we'll consider J to be a logarithmic *reflection* rather than an imaginary rotation and attempt to avoid both complex numbers and infinities of values. The form of J rather than $i\pi$ provides the power.

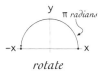

rotate

$$\#^J = -1 \qquad\qquad J = \log_\# -1$$

reflect

Euler considered $\log -1$ to be rotation through 180° thus necessitating the complex plane as an alternative dimension through which to rotate. When we consider J to be a reflection the "imaginary" J lands on the real number line. -1 is the reflection of $+1$, but where does J itself fall? J appears when we apply the logarithmic transformation to negative real numbers, very similar to the appearance

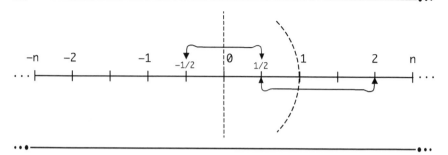

Figure 38-1: *Reflection through line and circle*

of i when we apply the square root transformation to negative numbers. Thus the form of J, [<o>], can be read within our interpretation literally as the logarithm (square-bracket) of the reflection (angle-bracket) of a unit (empty round-bracket).

38.1 Inversion

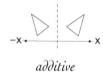

additive

In two dimensions reflection through a *straight line* is **additive inversion**. Negative expressions reflect positive expressions. An expression and its reflection mutually cancel by addition, taking both to the origin 0.

$$A \longmapsto -A \qquad ☞ \qquad A \longmapsto <A>$$
$$A + -A = 0 \qquad ☞ \qquad A <A> = \textit{void}$$

infinite plane

The geometric concept of reflection through a line is usually presented within the context of a **plane** that consists of an infinite number of points, each indexed by a *pair* of real numbers. This permits any plane geometric figure to be reflected in its entirety by attaching a negative sign to each x value. Here we will explore the simpler case of individual real numbers reflected through a *point* on the number line. For familiarity we'll call that point 0, although the James reflection point zero does not exist.

James number line

Reflection through a *unit circle* results in **multiplicative inversion**. The reciprocal of an expression reflects that expression. The two multiplied together mutually cancel to yield the radius of the circle, the unit 1. The James form below reduces via unit cancel, the same transformation mechanism that reduces an additive reflection.

$$A \longmapsto 1/A \qquad ☞ \qquad A \longmapsto (<[A]>)$$
$$A \times 1/A = 1 \qquad ☞ \qquad ([A][(<[A]>)])$$
$$([A] \quad <[A]> \quad) = (\ )$$

The less familiar reflection through a circle provides a visualization of the relation between numbers and their reciprocals. Figure 38-1 provides an illustration. The study of the structural relations between points inside a circle and those outside a circle is called **inversive geometry**. Additive reflections are linear and support Euclidean geometry. Multiplicative reflections are non-linear and lead to non-Euclidean geometry (hyperbolic geometry).

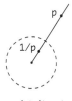

multiplicative

Inversive geometry defines the length of a unit to be the radius of the unit circle. Let P stand for the distance from the origin of a circle of radius r to an arbitrary point outside the circle. The associated point 1/P inside the circle is defined by multiplication of distances such that

$$P \times 1/P = r^2$$

Any point at infinity (P = ∞) reflects to the origin of the circle (1/P = 0). This suggests that there is a circle of points at infinity together forming the circumference of a circle with infinite radius.

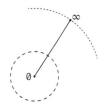

point (s) at infinity

On the circumference of the reflective circle, P = 1/P, which is to say

$$r \times 1/r = r^2 \qquad \textit{only when} \qquad r = 1$$

Reflection through a straight line is a special case of reflection through a circle for which the radius of the reflective circle is infinite and every point on the circumference is zero.[2] Thus additive reflection places the reflective line at zero while multiplicative reflection places the reflective circumference at one. The multiplicative inverse is **anti-conformal**, it maintains the angles of any figure reflected though a circle but reverses the orientation.

infinite radius circle

Within our interpretation we also have two inverse types of **exponential mapping,**

exponential

$$A \longmapsto \#^A \qquad \text{☞} \qquad A \longmapsto (A)$$
$$\#^{\log_\# A} = A \qquad \text{☞} \qquad ([A]) = A$$

logarithmic

$$A \longmapsto \log_\# A \qquad \text{☞} \qquad A \longmapsto [A]$$
$$\log_\# \#^A = A \qquad \text{☞} \qquad [(A)] = A$$

where an exponential expression and its logarithm combine to have no effect on their argument. We might call

inversion

([A]) = A

this **bracket inversion,** reflection through a pair of inversion brackets.

The three types of reflection, or inversion, are fundamentally different.[3]

— **additive/subtractive:** linear reflection, flat geometry, *objects cancel* each other

— **multiplicative/reciprocal:** circular reflection, hyperbolic geometry, *square-bracketed objects cancel*

— **exponential/logarithmic:** functional reflection, iconic geometry, inverse *brackets cancel*

Here we'll take a closer look at how these *bracket reflections* interact with the structure of the conventional number line.

38.2 Plane Thinking

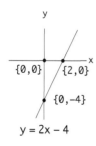

y = 2x – 4

Descartes (along with many others of his time, as is always the case) saw how to convert algebraic equations, such as y = 2x – 4, into pictures drawn out on a flat plane with orthogonal x- and y-axes. The picture of an equation is a line drawn through all the coordinate points that are valid substitutions into the equation. This section introduces the Cartesian and polar perspectives for locating a point on a plane rather than on a line. These concepts will carry into the next chapter as we explore rotation and trigonometry, which will in turn allow us to explore the complex numbers that Euler found to be essential to understanding log –1.

Extrinsic and Intrinsic Perspective

There are many ways to identify the location of a point on a plane. Two of the most common are polar and Cartesian. The polar world-view is one of *orientation and distance* whereas the Cartesian world-view is of *absolute origin and orthogonal decomposition*. Both polar and Cartesian systems standardize distance to an arbitrary unit, defined as the distance between Cartesian unit grid marks and by the radius of a polar unit circle.

orthogonal

We can identify any point on the Cartesian plane by naming its location with a pair of numbers, {x,y}, called *coordinates*. James notation uses round- and square-brackets, so to avoid confusion I'll use **curly braces** to represent a pair of coordinates.[4] The **origin** at the intersection of the two orthogonal axes has the coordinates {0,0}. The rectilinear, externalized infinite set of Cartesian coordinates make more sense as a way of thinking when we know where the origin is. To find the origin we must stand away from the coordinate plane by placing ourselves in a higher dimension. The **extrinsic perspective** pretends that we have god-like abilities — which we do have since we are viewing the coordinate plane from a third dimension — abilities that allow us to interact with the plane and its coordinate system externally and "objectively".[5]

polar

An alternative is the **intrinsic perspective**, the one that is natural for humans within a natural world. The intrinsic perspective makes us the origin. When we move, the origin moves with us, because the origin is anchored to the location of our direct perception. The use of direct distance and angle for coordinates is called the **polar coordinate system**. In place of the orthogonal {x,y} coordinates, we have the {r, θ} coordinates in which **theta**, θ, is the angle we turn through from our initial orientation and r is the direct distance from our location to the point in question. When we move toward the selected point our distance from it changes. In contrast

orthogonal

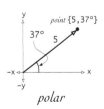

polar

the location of a Cartesian point does not change as we move, rather it is anchored by the origin. Here is the algebraic relationship between orthogonal $\{x,y\}$ and polar coordinates $\{r, \theta\}$.

orthogonal to polar	polar to orthogonal
$\sqrt{(x^2 + y^2)} \Rightarrow r$	$r \cos \theta \Rightarrow x$
$\arctan (y/x) \Rightarrow \theta$	$r \sin \theta \Rightarrow y$

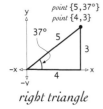

right triangle

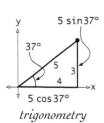

trigonometry

The first orthogonal-to-polar transformation is the Pythagorean theorem, $x^2 + y^2 = r^2$. It is common practice to discard the negative result of the square root function, under an assertion that distance is positive. This bias is a direct result of the extrinsic perspective, for which our location in the picture is taken external to the origin. From the intrinsic perspective our viewing location is mutable. The point $\{5, 37°\}$ is 5 units away from where we putatively stand. But it is –5 units away if we switch perspectives and consider distance *from* the point to our location, and 0 units away should we locate ourselves at that point. In general *semantic interpretation* is not objective. Whatever makes meaning to us is subjective. Objectivity presumes an externalized origin that in turn creates an illusion of detachment from meaning.

The second orthogonal-to-polar transformation is where trigonometry comes in. The trigonometric right triangle combines both Cartesian and polar perspectives. This is most apparent for the polar-to-orthogonal transformations. The sides of a unit right triangle are labeled sin and cos. Both depend upon the same angle θ. The trigonometric *functions* sine and cosine relate the (intrinsic) angle of rotation to the (extrinsic) x and y distances.[6]

Radians

We need one other piece of mechanism. There are two common but different ways to measure angles. Most familiar is the **degree system**, which defines 360 degrees as one complete revolution. This system is ancient, at

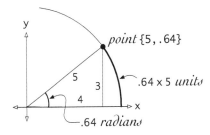

least 4000 years old. The alternative is to measure not the angle, but the distance traveled *along the circumference* of a unit circle. The **unit circle** is just a circle that has been scaled to have a radius the same size as the units 1 and i and J. The total distance of one circumnavigation is 2π, the circumference of the unit circle. Radian measurement does not depend upon the radius of the circle, it measures only a proportion of the 2π circumference of the unit circle.

The idea of traveling along the circumference of a circle is due to the ancient Greeks. Greek mathematics did not include our modern concept of measurement, it focused instead on relationships between geometric components. The degree system is *extrinsic*, we impose it upon a circle for our convenience. The radian system is *intrinsic*, it is inherently part of the nature of a circle. Our 90° rotation is to the ancient Greeks a journey 1/4 of the way around a circle, an *angular distance* of π/2.

38.3 Rotation as Reflection

Rotation itself has an inherent ambiguity. We can count the *number* of complete revolutions around a circle using memory, or we can begin again after each full revolution, never counting "how many". Rotation is taken to be strongly temporal, we usually do not imagine making many full rotations all at the same time. Rotation also encourages the idea that turning can be disassembled into angles with relatively infinite precision. This perspective comes from the association of angular measurement with a fraction of the circumference subtended by the **radian** measure of angle. Linear distance has been presumed to be continuously subdividable since Aristotle, as has the 360 angular **degrees** that we have inherited from the Babylonians. In contrast, *a reflection is discrete.*

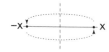

If we limit "rotation" to only π radians, to only turning around or reflecting, then the idea of an angle vanishes entirely as would the process of rotating. The 180° reflection from +1 to −1 is characterized by a different type of transformation, binary rather than continuous.

Geometrically we think of reflection as *across* a line, as if the line were a mirror. This line is sometimes even called the *mirror line*. To reflect values on one side of the x-axis to the other side, the mirror line is the vertical y-axis that defines the location x = 0. The x-axis extends from the origin in opposite directions to include both positive and negative values. This in turn confounds reflection with the concept of negation. Reflection is a change in *polarity*.

A reflection of an object from one side to the other followed by a reflection of the image from the other side back returns to the original starting point of the object. To maintain this symmetry, we establish that negative times negative is positive. This decision confounds addition of radians (rotation) with multiplication of signs (state change). Rotation in a plane also supports heading in one of two directions, clockwise and counterclockwise. The two are analogous to the negative/positive directions of the number line. Thus the concept of **orientation**, how we traverse a circle's circumference, is inextricably linked to the meaning of negation. It's necessary to make the relationship between rotation and negation explicit. Although consistent the relationship is not necessary. In the next sections we will indeed dissolve the association between rotation, reflection and negation.

J Reflection

In the James form numeric reflection across the x-axis
(what is called negation) is replaced by the constant J.
Algebraic negation and geometric reflection are formally
both **involutions**, each is its own inverse. J however is an
object as well as an operator. *Presence of J is not the inverse
of its absence.* We are in conceptually different territory.
As we shall see J identifies an imaginary extension of the
logarithmic x-axis, "on the other side" of negative infinity.

James calculus has no zero, so there is a hole at conventional 0 on the James number line. Due to J-void, any
even number of replicas of J can be found in that hole,
as well as all other void-equivalent forms.[7]

Geometrically any rotation can be constructed from two
reflections. Translation too is composed of two reflections.
Reflection is the single primitive underlying geometric
transformation in space. As a reflection without memory,
J embodies no concept of orientation. J-transparency
allows the real number line to be independent of the act
of reflection.

J-transparency

[<(A)>] = A [<( )>]

Algebraically we can reflect a form by placing it in
angle-brackets. Angle-brackets themselves are shorthand
for a **J-frame**.

$$A <A> = A (J [A]) = \textit{void}$$

J-conversion

We now need to abandon the idea of rotation until the
next chapter and look instead at a one-dimensional line
with a hole of nonexistence at the origin.

38.4 Drawing the Line

Geometry teachers make a point. Arithmetic teachers draw
the line. They usually draw it on the walls, around the edge
of the classroom above the windows where it can domi-
nate both vision and thought. It is called the **number line**.
Kids learn to chant the sequence: *"1, 2, 3, ..."* to infinity.

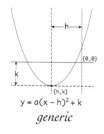

$y = a(x - h)^2 + k$

generic

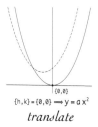

$\{h,k\} = \{0,0\} \implies y = a\,x^2$

translate

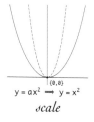

$y = a x^2 \implies y = x^2$

scale

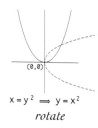

$x = y^2 \implies y = x^2$

rotate

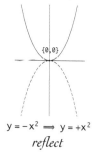

$y = -x^2 \implies y = +x^2$

reflect

Students are then introduced to negative numbers as a reflection of the positives and to fractions stuffed inconveniently between the integers. Later we might learn that there are an infinity of unit fractions between 0 and 1, reflecting the natural numbers as unit reciprocals.[8] In the process a learner might rediscover the ancient Greek idea that there is an outward infinity and an inward infinity, both on the same line and both without limit.[9]

Perspective

We can non-destructively translate, rotate, reflect and scale functions by *changing viewing perspective*. From the Cartesian perspective the origin and the coordinate axes are frozen as part of the symbolic representation of a function. The function itself then appears as a static line drawn within the Cartesian plane.

> *Symbolic expressions represent a rigid coordinate framework. Iconic forms represent generic intention.*

The common transformations of a two-dimensional figure are illustrated in the sidebar for an arbitrary parabola. These transformations can convert a generic quadratic function F into the simpler squaring function f.[10]

$$F(x) = (\pm a)(x - h)^2 + k \quad \longmapsto \quad f(x) = x^2$$

Self-multiplication and its inverse, the **square root**, are particularly important since they generate both sign-blind and imaginary numbers.

Quadratic Space

A single variable function f maps a relationship between values $f(x)$ expressed along the y-axis to a line of values x along the x-axis. The function f usually curves through the two dimensions of an x/y coordinate plane, however the function itself is just another line in the plane, a one dimensional structure within a two dimensional space.

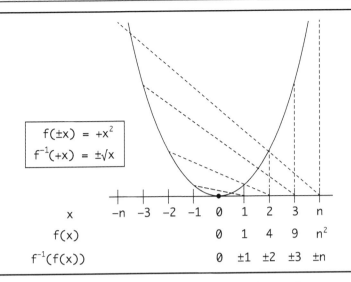

x		−n	−3	−2	−1	0	1	2	3	n
f(x)						0	1	4	9	n^2
$f^{-1}(f(x))$						0	±1	±2	±3	±n

$$f(\pm x) = +x^2$$
$$f^{-1}(+x) = \pm\sqrt{x}$$

Figure 38-2: *Self-multiplication projected onto the* x-axis

We can map f(x) onto the linear scale of the horizontal number line by pairing the values on the vertical y-axis with the associated values on the x-axis. Figure 38-2 shows a graphic representation of self-multiplication, abbreviated as $f(x) = x^2$, over the entire range of positive and negative values of x. The spatial display of the y-axis in Figure 38-2 is *projected* downward onto the linear scale of the x-axis, in effect overlaying two sets of values on one line, one set structured as x and the other set structured as f(x). The f(x) scale is then a *recalibration* of the x-axis. In the figure of self-multiplication the size of the steps between unit x-axis values (i.e. the unit distance between the whole numbers) is now variable, each step is two units more than the prior step. For the projection of f(x) onto the horizontal axis, the distance from 0 to 1 is 1 unit; the distance between 1 and 2 is 3 units; 2 and 3 are 5 units apart, etc.

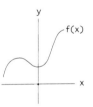

But what is particularly interesting about this function is that the original *negative* x values are all converted into positive values. The mapping $\pm x \longmapsto x^2$ also assigns all −x to their corresponding squared positive values on the

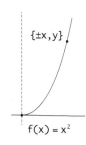

{±x,y}

f(x) = x²

number line. As we have previously observed, self-multiplication is sign-blind. This mapping is **two-to-one**, two x values are converted into one f(x) value. When the inverse square root function is applied to f(x), the mapping becomes one-to-two, both the positive and the negative values of x are resurrected, but now they are bound together as indistinguishably equivalent (*identical*) values of the square root function. One way to visualize this is to imagine that the left-side of the parabola does not exist, it is overlaid on top of the right-side while the x-axis is composed of bipolar numbers, ±x.

Birth of i

What then has happened on the left-side of 0, where the negative x values were? The well known answer is that they have retreated into our imagination. Figure 38-3 shows this finesse.

We create left-of-zero as the *imaginary numbers* by allowing self-multiplication to return in a negative numeric result.

$$x^2 = -n \qquad therefore \qquad x = \sqrt{-n}$$

The imaginary domain is very much like Alice's *Through the Looking Glass* wonderland. If we consider the y-axis to be a mirror, we could say that the right side of the parabola is "real" while the left side is an image, an *imaginary reflection* of the real side. Although f(x) does not generate negative y values, we imagine them into existence by creating a *different kind* of "negative" x named xi. We give up numeric homogeneity along the x-axis by associating each point with two types of unit. The right side contains the real numbers and the left side contains the imaginary numbers. The left side inhabitants are designated by ni; they live in the imaginary *i-land*.

What we have done (indeed what Euler did nearly three centuries ago) is not that strange. After all, the left side is already a different type of unit, "–" x 1. Only the label has been changed, to "i" x 1. Self-multiplication collapses +n

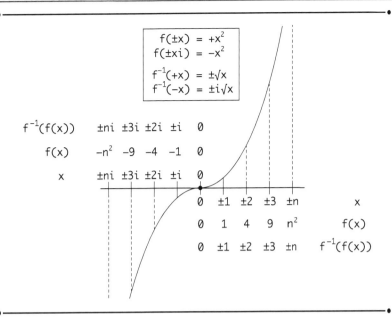

Figure 38-3: *Imaginary self-multiplication projected onto the* x-axis

and −n into ±n. The inverse square root function retrieves exactly that, ±n, from the values of the x^2. These bundled bipolar numbers describe how x^2 and $\sqrt{x}$ behave.

$+n \longmapsto \pm n \times 1$ ☞ $n \longmapsto ([n][o])$

$-n \longmapsto \pm n \times i$ ☞ $<n> \longmapsto ([n][i])$

Seeing the ± numbers as bipolar composites is precisely what Euler proposed:

> The square root of a given number always has a double value, thus negative as well as positive can be taken.[11]

$\sqrt{(x^2)} = \pm x$

In the intervening years this perspective has lost respect. Instead of composing the x-axis as an i to ± continuum, the newly minted +ni and −ni were assigned their own orthogonal *dimension*, creating the complex plane.

This may be asking for a significant stretch of the imagination but in a sign algebra i is a **half-reflection**

operator
multiplication

i x i = −
− x − = +

half-negation

i(i) = −
−(−) = +

operator. Although multiplication treats i as an object, functionally it is an operator. i applied to i yields the negation operation. Similarly negation applied to negation yields a positive. In this operator calculus −i is a one-and-a-half negation operator. As well, ±1 can be taken as a natural way that numbers are. From the perspective of self-multiplication the negative unit, −1, is a secondary distinction, not deserving to share the x-axis with the bipolar numbers. This tension is due directly to the design decision to have − x − = +.

To offer a quick connection to James algebra, the angle-bracket — that container that is an amalgam of all conventional inverse operations — is an epiphenomenon. It can be treated as an abbreviation for something more fundamental, the **J-frame**.

J-conversion

$$<A> =\partial ef= (J [A])$$

When n = 1,

$$<o> =\partial ef= (J [o]) \qquad ☞ \qquad -1 = \#^{J+0}$$

$$[<o>] =\partial ef= J \qquad ☞ \qquad J = \log\# -1$$

Since self-multiplication leads to bipolarity, defining x^2, $\sqrt{x}$ and i in terms of multiplication is problematic. The James forms include no concept of multiplication. Frames then permit disassociation of ±1 and ±i from their imposed definition as *products*. For example, although x^2 indicates the self-multiplication of x, the James form $((([x]][2]))$ does not.

Exponential Space

The exponential function uses the real numbers to indicate the extent to which a specific base is self-multiplied. Figure 38-4 shows the projection of an exponential curve $f(x) = b^x$ onto the linear x-axis. Although x ranges over the entire number line, from negative to positive infinity, the exponential transformation converts all x values to *positive* $f(x)$ values. Yes this situation is analogous to the obliteration of negative numbers by self-multiplication.

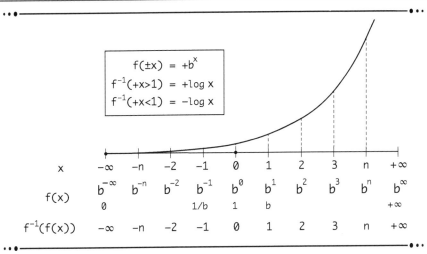

Figure 38-4: *The exponential function projected onto the* x-axis

Their resurrection will take the same path: positing a new imaginary unit indicated by a special symbol.

$$b^x = -1 \quad \textit{therefore} \quad x = \log_b -1 \overset{def}{=} J$$

The exponential function hijacks the linear x-axis values by converting them from additive entities to multiplicative entities. What was plus-1 becomes times-b, where b is an arbitrary number greater than 1, the **base**.[12] We cannot of course use times-1 cause that changes nothing. To convert additive numbers into their multiplicative counterparts, the exponential function must convert the additive identity, 0, into the multiplicative identity, 1. This conversion in effect leaves no room for an exponential value to be negative. For $f(x) = b^x$ there is literally no other side of zero. The distinction between positive and negative becomes a distinction between greater-than-1 or less-than-1 (again lending credence to the suspicion that −1 is not fundamental).

In the case of $n \longmapsto n^2$, the existent −n values on the x-axis are melded with the +n values to yield the new bipolar creature ±n. Loosely, − ⇒ ±. In the case of $x \longmapsto b^x$, the negative signs attached to x are converted into the division operation. Loosely, − ⇒ ÷. The exponential function

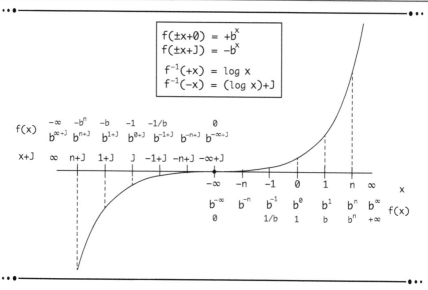

Figure 38-5: *The imaginary exponential function projected onto the x-axis*

applies to all x values, including irrationals. The explicit base form of the exponential assures compatibility by passing x through logarithmic (i.e. irrational) space.

$$(x)_\# = ((([x][[\#]]))_\# \qquad ☞ \qquad \#^x = \#^{\#\log_\# x + \log\log_\# \#}$$

What then happens on the other side of b^x? What does a negative result of the exponential function mean? As you might expect, it's imaginary and can be constructed, like self-multiplication, by creating new imaginary x values and labeling them with a new symbol.

Birth of J

Figure 38-5 shows the imaginary reclamation of negative values for the exponential function. The new imaginary domain is additive rather than multiplicative, with the x-axis calibrated as logarithms of real numbers. The negative numbers on the left side of the figure are designated by +J; they live in the imaginary *J-land*. The inhabitants are labeled as ±n + J.

$$+n = \pm n + 0 \qquad ☞ \qquad n = (\ [n])$$
$$-n = \pm n + J \qquad ☞ \qquad <n> = (J\ [n])$$

J-land differs significantly from i-land primarily because the negative numbers on the number line have not been obliterated by sign-blindness. Instead they are co-opted for use as designators of unit fractions. We then have the following relationship between the common operators of arithmetic, both direct and inverse. The diversity of arithmetic operators are indeed the same operation at different levels of nesting.

$b^{-n} = 1/b^n$

$\log_\# A$ ☞	[A]	$\log_\# -A$ ☞	J [A]
+A	([A])	-A	(J [A])
1 x A	(([[A]]))	1/A	((J [[A]]))
#^{A}	((([[A]])))	#$^{1/A}$	(((J [[A]])))

Logarithmic Space

The logarithmic transformation maps exponents onto the number line. Evenly spaced ticks on the number line are labeled by orders of magnitude, not by evenly spaced counting intervals. This mapping is common enough to support a special type of graph paper, **log paper**, that displays base-10 exponents as integers on the y-axis. The scaling between units is times 10, not plus 1. Log paper is used when we need to graph an exponentially large range of numbers, say from 1 to 100,000.

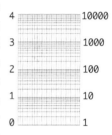

The logarithmic mapping transforms multiplication into addition by taking additive linearity as order of magnitude and forcing the linear scale to take multiplicative steps. With log paper we can add distances between coordinate values to achieve multiplication. That's also how a slide rule works. And we can see this amazing transformation directly in James forms:

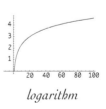

logarithm

a x b	☞	([a][b])	
log (a x b)	☞	[([a][b])]	cover
		[a][b]	clarify
	☞	log a + log b	

38.5 Conic Sections

Plane slices through a solid cone generate the conic sections: the circle, ellipse, parabola and hyperbola. These geometric curves have been studied throughout the history of mathematics, particularly by the ancient Greeks. We have explored the parabola as the self-multiplication function. The circle will be a central topic for trigonometry in Chapter 40. The conic circle, the trigonometric functions, the imaginary i and the logarithm are deeply connected. The conic hyperbola, the natural base-e and the logarithm are also all deeply connected.

Here we'll briefly explore the connection between addition, multiplication, conic sections and logarithms. These relationships are so intertwined that we will take logarithms to be more fundamental to arithmetic than is multiplication itself.

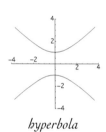

hyperbola

The form of multiplication is ([A][B]). A **unit hyperbola** has the algebraic form

$$A \times B = 1 \quad \text{☞} \quad ([A][B]) = (\ )$$

The hyperbola models inverse relations in which one parameter increases as the other decreases. As A increases along the x-axis, the height B along the y-axis decreases proportionally. It's precisely the same relation as between points inside a unit circle and points outside as defined by inversive geometry.

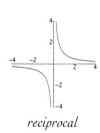

reciprocal

The reciprocal exhibits scaling invariance. Since the two variables are related by multiplication, this is best visualized as invariance of area.

$$f(x) = 1/x \qquad f^{-1}(x) = x$$

The void-based version of the hyperbola is

$$[A][B] = void$$

This in turn is the sum of the logarithms of the A and B coordinates of each point along the hyperbola. The logarithms of the coordinates add up to 0, turning multiplication into addition.

$$[A][B] = void \quad ☞ \quad \log A + \log B = 0$$

With $A = n$ *and* $B = 1/n$

$$\log n + \log 1/n = \log n - \log n = 0$$

The form that serves as the multiplication unit is ( ), while the unit for addition is ([ ]). This relationship is similar to the structure of the unit circle, for which

$$A^2 + B^2 = 1 \quad ☞ \quad ([A][A])([B][B]) = ( )$$

In void-based terms

$$[([A][A])([B][B])] = void \qquad \text{cover}$$

The coordinates of the unit circle specify the values of the trigonometric functions, while the logarithm of the sum of their self-multiplications is 0. The coordinates of a unit hyperbola specify the values of the reciprocal function, while their logarithms add to 0.

To emphasize the family resemblance between circles and hyperbolas, we can rotate the orientation of the x-y coordinate system of the hyperbolic reciprocal function by 45°.

$$A = x + y \qquad B = x - y \qquad A = 1/B$$
$$(x + y) = 1/(x - y)$$
$$(x + y)(x - y) = 1$$
$$x^2 - y^2 = 1$$

Alternatively a hyperbola is a circle on the complex plane.

$$x^2 + (iy)^2 = 1$$

38.6 Composite Number Lines

The number line in Figure 38-6 shows our interpretation of the three *operator spaces* of James algebra,

— **exponential:** inside round-brackets   (A B)

— **additive:** the contents of any brackets   {A B}

— **logarithmic:** inside square-brackets   [A B]

exponents	$10^{-\infty}$	10^{-3}	10^{-2}	10^{-1}	10^{0}	10^{1}	10^{2}	10^{3}	10^{∞}
numerals	0	.001	.01	.1	1	10	100	1000	∞
logarithms	$-\infty$	-3	-2	-1	0	1	2	3	∞

Figure 38-6: *The positive composite number line*

This composite number line shows the usually additive number line in the middle row compressed exponentially. The linear scale takes "unit" steps that multiply by base-10. The exponential scale on the top row shows these steps in exponential notation, so that $1 = 10^{0}$, $100 = 10^{2}$, etc. The logarithmic scale on the bottom row shows the logarithms of the unit steps. The logarithmic scale now resembles a conventional number line with steps of one unit each. The entire figure thus shows the logarithmic transformation as it applies to an additive number line. The exponential and the logarithmic scales accommodate the entire range of real numbers, from negative to positive infinity, leaving the center numeric scale without negative numbers. This circumstance is a consequence of the definition $10^{-N} = 1/10^{N}$.

The top composite number line in Figure 38-7 reinserts the negative real numbers, creating an initial problem for the exponential and logarithmic scales. The *labeling* solution is simply to add +J to the logarithmic values (and to the exponents) on the left side of zero. The logarithms of negative numbers are then their numeric magnitude *plus* J. This labeling is analogous to attaching the imaginary marker i, except that the J marker is *added* to an expression while the i marker multiplies an expression.

The lower blowup extension in Figure 38-7 shows the number line spanning from −1 to +1, completing the gap directly above it. Here we see negative values as exponents that identify smaller and smaller numbers. Rather than obliterating the negative numbers like the

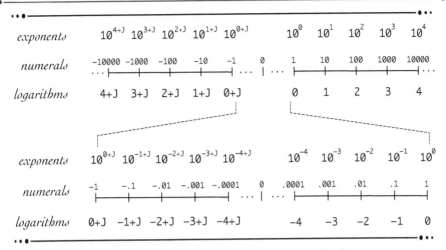

Figure 38-7: *The entire composite number line*

x^2 mapping does, here all of the negative logarithms fall between 0 and 1. As negative exponents approach negative infinity, their associated numeric magnitudes approach 0. On the left side of 0 the negative logarithms are all supplemented by +J.

Figure 38-8 serves as a summary. The reflected exponentials and logarithms on the left of 0 are *imaginary*, populating a new imaginary territory, **J-land**. But the presence of J is more than a label, it is how these numbers work. Notice that the exponential $10^{0+J} = -1$. The *magnitude* is 1; the added J indicates only that the original value is negative rather than positive. Numbers like -10000 have a magnitude of 10^4 and a polarity of J.

$$-1 \quad \text{☞} \quad 10^{0+J} = 10^0 \times 10^J \quad \text{☞} \quad 1 \times -1$$
$$-10000 \quad \text{☞} \quad 10^{4+J} = 10^4 \times 10^J \quad \text{☞} \quad 10000 \times -1$$

Consistent with J-transparency, J does not impact magnitude. The form of J is independent of its contents. J is also independent of the exponential and logarithmic base so that

$$J = \log_{\#} -1 \quad \text{and} \quad \#^J = -1$$

J-transparency
$$[<(A)>] = J \ A$$

It should be clear that the exponential use of J *incorporates no new computational results*. Only the perspective differs.

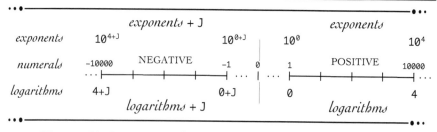

Figure 38-8: *Numeric domains on the composite number line*

Here is the general case of a negative number with an explicit base.

explicit base   – Bⁿ   ☞   <((([[B]][n]))>

We'll immediately substitute the generic base B = (( )).

substitute   <((([[(( ))]][n]))>ᵦ
clarify   <(n)>ᵦ
J-convert   (J   n)ᵦ   ☞   Bⁿ⁺ᴶ

Adding J to the exponent of a negative number transfers its polarity to its exponent. Two simple examples:

-1   ☞   <( )>_# = (J)_#   ☞   #⁰⁺ᴶ
J-convert   -2¹   ☞   <(o)>₂ = (J o)₂   ☞   2¹⁺ᴶ

J provides a new notational method for handling mappings that themselves eliminate the negative numbers, such as $f(x) = x^2$ and $f(x) = \log x$. Within James algebra negative numbers do not need to exist on the *linear* number line, a perspective consistent with treating the angle-bracket as an abbreviation rather than a fundamental numeric

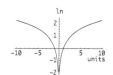

logarithms of positive and negative numbers

form. The J notation is a *new representational paradigm* in which numbers as numeric bases are sign-free while their exponents carry both order of magnitude and polarity.

James Number Line

The next composite number line in Figure 38-9 shows the James forms for exponential, linear and logarithmic numbers. Every quadrant is informative. For orientation the middle row shows decimal numbers with steps marked in powers of ten. Above them are the boundary forms that correspond to these numbers. In the lower

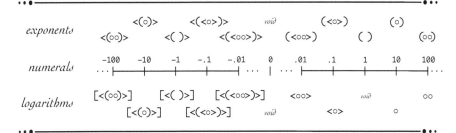

Figure 38-9: *James forms on the composite number line*

right logarithmic quadrant James digits are simply collections of units, the same as in ensemble arithmetic.[13] In the upper right quadrant the outermost container is a round-bracket which tells us that the forms can be interpreted as exponential. Below these round-bracket forms, the outermost brackets have been removed in the conversion of exponential forms to logarithmic forms.

The negative quadrant on the top left reflects the positive quadrant across *void* by enclosing each form in an angle-bracket, or alternatively by appending J. For example:

$$-10 \quad \text{☞} \quad <(\ o\ )> = (J\ \ o\ ) \qquad \text{J-convert}$$
$$-.1 \quad \text{☞} \quad <(<o>)> = (J\ <o>) = (J\ (J)) \qquad \text{J-convert}$$

And finally the lower left quadrant shows the James forms of the imaginary logarithms of negative numbers. For example,

$$\log_{10} -10 \quad \text{☞} \quad [<(\ o\ )>] = J\ \ o \quad \text{☞} \quad 1 + J \qquad \text{J-transparent}$$
$$\log_{10} -.1 \quad \text{☞} \quad [<(<o>)>] = J\ (J) \quad \text{☞} \quad -1 + J \qquad \text{J-transparent}$$

The composite number line is not a simple place.[14] We have not addressed the many types of infinity that bound these lines, nor the real numbers tucked between all possible rational numbers. Egregiously missing from the numeric number line is the James *void*, the hole filled by numeric zero. Understanding these generic forms of James numbers is a convenience but not a necessity. What is important is that once we change to expressing rational numbers as exponents and logarithms, surprises do occur. Here we found polarity in exponential space.

38.7 Equivalence of Systems

The assertion that iconic formal systems do *not* map onto symbolic systems is essential for James algebra to be of mathematical interest. If James arithmetic is equivalent to, say, Peano's arithmetic then the distinction between symbolic and iconic is inconsequential. We have just changed the appearance of things without changing any of the things themselves and without changing their behavior.

There is some trickiness even to specifying what the criterion for equivalence is. Simply put, there is a many-to-one mapping between symbolic and iconic systems. An icon is worth a thousand symbols. Just as importantly, the native concepts of a symbolic system (such as ordering, grouping, specified arity, explicit bases, negation and multiplication) do not correspond to the native concepts of an iconic system (such as void, containment, unspecified arity, arbitrary bases and nesting). We could connect the two types of representational systems via the idea of a binary contains relation between container and contents, however the difficulty there is that this single relation is mapped onto all the standard functions of arithmetic, with variety provided only by the varieties of boundaries. There is a severe mismatch of object types.

Homomorphism

Homomorphism is a technical term to describe two mathematical systems that are structurally the same except for changing the representation of things. Figure 38-10 shows the mechanism used to prove structural equality across different string-based mathematical systems. The algebraic definition is

$$h(a * b) = h(a) \text{ ¤ } h(b)$$

Please excuse the ugliness. $*$ and ¤ are generic symbols for two different operations in two different worlds, *World 1* and *World 2*. The **morphism**, or *mapping function,* h is the roadway between these worlds.[15]

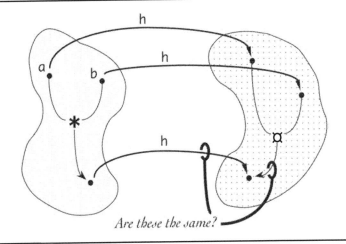

Figure 38-10: *Structure preserving maps*

The entire approach of establishing symbolic homomorphism is built upon the assumption of comparing two *symbolic* systems. The mechanism of comparison itself requires conformance to the rules of symbolic algebra. As well the mathematical concept of morphism applies only between systems with the same type of objects. Relations, for example, do not map to functions; matrices do not map to geometric curves. How then does ☞ manage to work?

The interpretation indicator, the *mapping* finger ☞, is the highway h that joins symbolic and iconic conceptualizations. The finger however does not go in two directions (which would define an isomorphism) because it *deletes* rather than maps when we shift from symbolic expression to iconic form. We can shift back from iconic form to symbolic expression by providing the missing symbolic components. In so doing we can freely create a diversity of interpretative *readings*, all of which preserve a single meaning but do not preserve the conceptual necessities of symbolic structure.

The mathematical language of mappings presumes the constraints of mathematical groups which in turn embody strictly symbolic concepts. The homomorphism picture in Figure 38-10 presumes, for example, that two objects (more generally, a fixed number of objects) will be combined by the * and ¤ operators. Containers, in contrast, contain any cardinality of forms while pattern transformations can be composed of zero, one or many concurrent but separate pattern matches.

Leave Void Out of It

The trouble begins when h goes off looking for 0 in the iconic world. h(0) and h(0+0) *do not exist*. And what is ¤ in the iconic world? The only potential operation we have is the relation of containment. Certainly *void* does not contain *void*. Neither does ¤ exist because there is no iconic operation capable of acting upon *void*, much less finding something that is not there. Although we can safely say from the symbolic perspective that *void void = void* this construction violates both structural and interpretative intentions of void-based systems. The only available operation is that one container contains another, given that both exist. *Representational existence* is never a question in a void-based calculus since void-equivalent forms can be brought into existence at any time. *Semantic existence*, on the other hand, is not supported within a pattern-matching system. It is also illegitimate in a mathematical system to convert a meta-token in the metalanguage such as *void* into an actual object within the mathematical system. A deeper problem is that all void-equivalent forms pervade all depths of any manifest form and can be arbitrary brought into representational existence within any container and with any number of replicas.

Pattern Matching

The complexities of maintaining a mapping can be redefined by a variety of implementation strategies, something mathematicians do not usually consider. Pattern-matching, for example, does not include the concept of a function. What would pass for a function with regard to output could include pattern algorithms and constraints that violate the assumptions of functional algebra. Differences at the foundational level are not so easily set aside as mere implementation details. It is the transitions inside each domain that do not match up, even though the final results do correspond. The mechanisms on the symbolic side must take into account commutativity and associativity of operators, while the iconic side lacks these concepts. The iconic side can proceed with arbitrary bases (using #) while the symbolic side cannot. The *implementation details* within each system are vastly different, so much so that the internal diagrams in Figure 38-10 cannot be aligned. The inability to be able to map the *theory of functions* onto an iconic pattern-matching regime can be severe. James algebra for instance has no concept of either multiplication or division, although specific compound patterns can be interpreted as multiplication and division. Dominion takes an excursion through an infinite form, as another example, in the process of "multiplying by zero". The pattern-matching mechanism, although assumed by *both* systems, is vastly different in each. **Functional pattern-matching** proceeds step-at-a-time while respecting the definitions of each specific function. **Iconic pattern-matching** is in parallel with no functional or relational boundaries. Patterns are determined solely by matching boundary *structure* without specific functional signatures.[16]

Figure 26-1 in Volume II lists how the essential concepts of symbolic algebra are deconstructed by an iconic system. In this section we have yet to consider subtraction or division or logarithms but we know that the symbolic side gets quite messy while the iconic side requires one additional constant, J.

The Finger

To make the finger work across symbolic and iconic domains, we have ignored the details of formal mappings, making only side comments about

— the hole associated with the concept of 0

— the replacement of value by form

— the unlimited void-equivalent forms in the abyss that themselves have no meaning

— the vast differences between symbolic functions (and relations and sets) and iconic structural pattern-matching, and

— the many-to-one mappings that permit multiple readings and multiple valued forms.

Going from James iconic form to symbolic expression, the finger works because it is coming from a tiny world that includes only configurations of two types of symbolic structure (exponential and logarithmic interpretations of ( ) and [ ] respectively) and one constant, J. Although this mapping generates quite exotic symbolic expressions, the conceptual structure of well-behaved symbolic arithmetic is highly redundant and is, underneath, precisely that small.

Going from symbolic expression to iconic form, the finger works because the iconic form is tolerant of the symbolic redundancies, needing only three pattern transformations to remove the illusory diversity. The vast majority of the clean up is the application of clarify to strip away layered complexity hidden in the symbolic distinction of most functions. Functions are excellent *macros* for algebraic simplification and transformation but are at best only that, tools for conceptual organization rather than stand-alone unique concepts. Put another way, the finger does not work in purely symbolic terms, it works because the iconic approach lets us avoid the complexity of symbolic morphisms.[17]

38.8 Remarks

There are several important aspects of the mappings in this chapter.

— The interpretation of forms consisting of round- and square-brackets ranges simultaneously across conventional exponential, linear and logarithmic scales.

— Translation and rotation can each be expressed as a composition of two reflections, providing a natural geometric interpretation of the angle-bracket, which in turn is the constant J.

— Logarithms and exponents re-purpose negative numbers, providing room on the composite number line for the new domain of J.

The ideas of mapping and morphism are themselves not well-suited for void-based pattern transformation systems. What we have is *faux amigos*, false friends expressed in clashing languages. What is surprising is that we can cross the finger of interpretation at all. The exposition in these volumes is deeply biased toward current technique with only occasional partial excursions into the vastly different realm of iconic thinking. We will return to the formal iconic image languages of Volume I in Chapter 44.

In constructing a map between conventional and boundary forms we have been picking low fruit by assuming that the boundary forms that correspond to natural operations of conventional arithmetic are somehow special. We have concentrated on the form of multiplication ([.][.]) while treating forms such as ((.)[.]) and ((.)(.)) and [(.)(.)] lightly. We have also introduced a fairly radical shift in notation: the polarity property has been moved into exponential space, leaving magnitudes as pure signless forms. Euler's equation moves the polar coordinate system of the complex plane into exponential space in order to explain the behavior of J. In the next chapter we'll unite the J-frame with Euler's concept of J to simplify both his explanation of rotation in the complex plane and his resultant logarithms with an infinity of values.

Endnotes

1. **opening quote:** E. Tufte (1983) *The Visual Display of Quantitative Information* p.180.

2. **every point on the circumference is zero:** And in three dimensions, Tristan Needham observes

> The close connection between inversion in a circle and reflection in a line also persists: reflection in a plane is a limiting case of inversion in a sphere.

T. Needham (1997) *Visual Complex Analysis* p.135.

3. **three types of reflection, or inversion, are fundamentally different:** Reflection is a more general concept than reflection across a line or across a circle. Given some restrictions imposed by the concept of continuity, reflection through an arbitrary function is well-defined. James Reflection is an inversion through J, as specified by the J-occlusion theorem.

$$A \ (J \ [A]) \ = \ void$$

4. **curly braces to represent a pair of coordinates:** Curly braces are also used for sets, but not here. These coordinate curly braces also should not be confused with the use of the *generic James boundary* in the prior chapter.

5. **interact with the plane and its coordinate system externally and "objectively":** Viewing a surface from the third dimension allows us to identify the *curvature* of the surface.

6. **angle of rotation to the (extrinsic) x and y distances:** The tangent is the ratio of sine to cosine. Arctan is the inverse of the tangent. Whereas the tangent gives us the ratio if we know the angle, arctan gives the angle if we know the ratio between the x and y distances.

$$arctan \ (3/4) \ \Rightarrow \ 37°$$

7. **as well as all other void-equivalent forms:** Symbolic 0 continues to be a problem for iconic systems, while *void* is a problem for symbolic systems.

8. **reflecting the natural numbers as unit reciprocals:** Seeing a fraction as a circular reflection is diligently ignored in contemporary math education, possibly because of the relatively new and emotionally turbulent discovery of non-Euclidean geometries.

9. **both on the same line and both without limit:** Well after the number line has made its impression, we might learn that there is a *larger* infinity of real numbers stuffed between the fractions. Later still we may be told that the uncountably dense number line is insufficient to hold *all* the numbers, we will need another dimension no less to explore the structure of complex numbers on the complex plane.

10. **convert a generic quadratic function f into the simpler squaring function F:** The generic form of the quadratic in the example is the **vertex** form, in contrast to the more familiar **standard** form, $F(x) = ax^2 + bx + c$. The illustrated transformations are the **similarity** group (*translate, rotate, scale*).

11. **thus negative as well as positive can be taken:** L. Euler (1771) *Complete Guide to Algebra* §150.

A reason we condense rules that provide *options*, a reason we use exclusive or, XOR, rather than inclusive or, OR, is that our mathematical and cognitive histories have had a great difficulty with the logical concept of disjunction. Having a number with *both* polarities is not convenient for functional thinking. When traveling a path of transformation, an OR branch offers a *choice* of the next transformation. Using XOR logic to choose one path is *sequential processing*. Computationally we can go back to try the other path if we have made a poor choice. Making a wrong guess is expensive, guaranteeing that the computation becomes intractable since the number of choices can increase exponentially with no assurance of the concrete termination that is enforced within physical reality. The *parallel processing* option is OR logic; take all available paths at the same time. Technically, we are exchanging SPACE in the form of multiple concurrent processors for TIME in the form of sequential steps and backtracking. The XOR logic of one-or-the-other, in both concept and process, reduces or at least delays complexity. The OR logic of one-and-both maintains *ambiguity*, which has been inappropriately interpreted as failure to make a decision.

12. **where b is an arbitrary number greater than 1, the base:** A unit fraction base reflects the exponential function through the vertical line $x = 1$ since

$$b^{-x} = (1/b)^x$$

13. **collections of units, the same as in ensemble arithmetic:** Ensemble arithmetic is described in Chapter 2.2 of Volume I.

14. The composite number line is not a simple place: I've attempted to condense a great amount of structural information into small diagrams and hope that the diagrams are not impenetrable.

15. *mapping function,* h is the roadway between these worlds: For example consider two sandwich shops, SandOne and SandTwo. You go to SandOne and buy a ham sandwich with extra mustard. Now you go to SandTwo, find their ham sandwich and ask for their extra mustard. If you end up with the same ham sandwich from both shops, then there is a morphism between the ham sandwiches. The concept is much broader, the sameness might include all sandwiches and all extra condiments. And, of course, typical of math, we forget all the actual details. The sameness of sandwiches does not include the other factors that make life interesting (type of bread, quality of mustard, cost of sandwich, pleasantness of service,…).

16. boundary structure without specific functional signatures: In computer science a *signature* specifies the symbols used to identify a specific function, the arity and ordering of the function arguments, the types of each input, output and variable, and often incidental information such as polymorphisms that identify symbols that may be used across different types. Boundary structure is usually insensitive to arity, ordering, variable types and other non-boundary structural constraints.

17. the iconic approach lets us avoid the complexity of symbolic morphisms: I am certain that professional mathematicians look *through* the symbolic haze into the heart of mathematical beauty. In coming from a different field (silicon programming and design) that insists upon extreme minute rigor while also being responsible for the education of novices, the narrative in these volumes addresses more the pragmatism of symbolic math than the beauty of mathematical abstraction.

Chapter 39

Complex

The shortest and best way between two truths of the real domain often passes through the imaginary one.[1]
— Jacques Hadamard (1945)

Complex numbers were forced upon the mathematical community in the sixteenth century as Cardano, Bombelli and others sought to solve polynomial equations. Their dilemma is illustrated by Figures 38-2 and 38-3 in the previous chapter. Euler's phenomenal equation, discussed in this chapter, connects complex numbers to trigonometry and to the complex plane, initiating acceptance and exploration of this new domain of mathematics, a domain that lead to the vast field of complex analysis and installed complex numbers as fundamental denizens of analytic theory.

Gerolamo Cardano
1501-1576

Rafael Bombelli
1526-1572

A complex number is an amalgam of two incommensurable types of units, *real* and *imaginary*. I'm going to present complex numbers in an unusual format, in order to emphasize that each component of this amalgam is simply a real number attached to a unit indicator by multiplication. The **unit indicator** tells us which of the two incommensurable worlds a real number occupies, either the 1-*land* ruled by the unit 1 or the i-*land* ruled by the unit i. For simplicity, units are all scaled to be the same size. We have also encountered the third type of unit that rules the J-*land*, which like i encapsulates the much maligned fourth type of unit, −1. We will take a closer look at *rotation*, the mode of travel between these worlds initiated by Euler's equation. The imaginary J simplifies circular rotation to linear *reflection* while collapsing the complex plane that supports rotation into discrete fractional reflection through a real number line. **Polarity** operates in linear space as positive/negative while i operates in exponential space as rotation and J operates in logarithmic space as reflection.

$$1 \times 1 = 1$$
$$-1 \times -1 = 1$$
$$i \times i = -1$$
$$-i \times -i = -1$$
$$J + J = 0$$
$$-J + -J = 0$$
$$(J) \times (J) = 1$$
$$(\ J \ J\ ) = 1$$
$$(\ J/2\ ) = i$$

Self-multiplication allows i creatures to morph into negative polarity creatures in the 1-world. Self-multiplication again allows the negative real creatures to change their polarity (their affiliation, their attitude) to positive. Thus these worlds are not completely incommensurable. As a biological metaphor, multiplication provides procreation of the species, while self-multiplication provides genetic diversity. The additive J-creatures on the other hand are substantively different.

39.1 J-frames

The magnitude frame was introduced in Chapter 8.4 as a type of scientific notation in which the frame-type is the order of magnitude expressed in an arbitrary base and the frame-content is the numeric form being multiplied by the order of magnitude.

frame
(type [contents])

$$(power\ [value])_{base} \quad ☞ \quad value \times base^{power}$$

The J-frame is similar but instead of magnitude it manages polarity.

$$(J\ [value])_{base} \quad ☞ \quad value \times base^{J} = value \times -1$$

Within the James abstraction, there are of course no values, bases or powers. Frames are not a fundamental new concept, they are simply a recurrent structural notation that highlights a different perspective on numeric form.

J-frame Reflection

The angle-bracket reflects its content. The J-conversion theorem expresses angle-brackets as a **J-frame**.

$$<A> = (J [A]) \quad \text{☞} \quad -A = \#^{J+\log_\# A} = -1 \times A$$

J itself is a square-bracket form. Its domain is logarithmic (within the interpretation). The J-frame also represents a *multiplication*, in this case by enlisting −1 as the unit indicator. This is consistent with the model of negation as a multiplication by −1. The interpretation of (J) is both an imaginary exponential expression and a constant on the real number line, thus allowing us to avoid reference to the complex plane.

$$(J) \times (J) = 0$$

Setting the J-frame content to 0 standardizes the unit magnitude of the imaginary expression "−1".

$$<0> = (J [0]) = (J) \quad \text{☞} \quad -1 = \#^{J+\log_\# 1} = \#^J$$

The J-frame transfers the **negation operation** from a polarizing multiplier of an expression to a *reflection constant* J added to the power of a sign-free expression.

$$<A> = (J [A]) \quad \text{☞} \quad -1 \times A = \#^{J+\log A}$$

This shift in representational strategy integrates the sign algebra with the rules of exponents, effectively eliminating the need to confound polarity (+ and −) with multiplication.

In contrast to our conventional absolute polarity signs, J can be modified by a numeric value to achieve **partial polarity**, within the strict condition that J does not support tallies that generate integer cardinality. For an integer N the form is degenerate, leaving the content polarized as either positive or negative.

J-void tally

J *even*

$$([J][N]) = void$$

J *odd*

$$([J][N]) = J$$

$$(([J][N]) [content])_{base} \quad \text{☞} \quad content \times base^{J \times N}$$

The form of **fractional reflection** is

unit fraction J $\quad$ $(([J]<[N]>)\ [content])_{base}$ ☞ $content \times base^{J/N}$

Fractional reflection and *partial polarity* are new ways to conceptualize Euler's idea of rotation through the complex plane.

The J/2 Frame

The J/2-frame is a special case of a J-frame with a fractional frame type of J/2.

J/2 frame $\quad$ $(J/2\ [content])_{base}$ ☞ $content \times base^{J/2}$

This frame specifies the relation between the unit 1 and the unit i. The form of i is direct:

$$i =label= (-1)^{1/2}$$ ☞ $((\,[\,[<o>]\,]<[2]>))$

substitute $\quad\quad\quad\quad\quad\quad\quad\quad$ $((\,[\quad J\quad]<[2]>))$

substitute $\quad\quad\quad\quad\quad\quad\quad\quad$ $(\quad J/2\quad\quad\quad)$

enfold $\quad\quad\quad\quad\quad\quad\quad\quad\quad$ $(\quad J/2\quad [o]\quad)$

$$☞\ 1 \times base^{J/2}$$

The J/2-frame standardizes the unit i to the unit o without associating i with the concept of a complex plane. We could at this time abbreviate (J/2) by the symbol i but that would prematurely dispose us to abandon real numbers and refocus in the realm of complex numbers. We will do that a bit later while exploring Euler's equation.

39.2 i and J

The square root of negative one, i, is considered to be the quintessential imaginary. We so much overemphasize the natural counting units that other types of unit such as i must be imaginary. What is natural and what is imaginary is simply an *historical artifact* and not embedded in the types of numbers themselves.[2] As a type of unity i is as important as –1 and almost as important as +1. As a type of unity J is also as important as –1.

In Chapter 32.1 the form of i is deduced by solving a simple quadratic equation. The variable x turns out to be i.

$$x^2 + 1 = 0 \quad \text{☞}$$

$((([x]][2])) \, o =$		*void*
x	$= ((([<o>]] <[2]>))$	solve
i	$= (([\quad J \quad] <[2]>))$	substitute
i	$= (\qquad J/2 \qquad)$	substitute

The imaginariness of i comes from the composition of two inverse operations, negation and square root. It is the child of the negative creature and the fractional exponent creature, but only if we consider −1 to be more fundamental than i itself. Alternatively we could apply direct operations to i and to J to *define* what is meant by negative one.

$$i \ = \sqrt{(-1)} \qquad\qquad J \ = \log_{\#}(-1)$$
$$i^2 = \ -1 \qquad\qquad \#^J = \qquad -1$$

Negative one is defined here by exponential expressions, with the fundamental unit i as the *base* in one case and the fundamental unit J as the *exponent* in the other. The three imaginaries, −1, i and J, are thus deeply related.

$$i^2 = -1 = \#^J \qquad\qquad\qquad \textit{structure of } -1$$

In James form,

$$([i][i]) = <o> = (J)$$

There is a problem, since it is also the case that

$$(-i)^2 = -1$$

$$(\pm i)^2 = -1$$
$$\#^{\pm J} = -1$$

Basically i is sign-blind, so that i = ±i. J too is sign-blind, J = ±J .

Reentrant Definitions

Let's temporarily imagine disconnecting −1 from its definition as the reflection of +1 and *define* −1 as i^2.

$-1 =_{def}= i^2 \quad \text{☞}$	$(([[i]][2])) =$	$<o>$	
	$([[i]][2]) \ =$	$[<o>] = J$	cover
	$[[i]][2] \ =$	$[J]$	cover
	$[[i]] \ =$	$[J]<[2]>$	move
	i	$= ((([J]<[2]>))$	cover
	i	$= (J/2)$	substitute

Thus

$$i = (J/2) = (([[<o>]]<[2]>)) \quad ☞ \quad (-1)^{1/2}$$

This makes i a fundamental unit and provides a defini-tion of i that is self-referential:

$$i = -1/i \quad ☞ \quad i = (<<[i]>)> = (<[<i>]>)$$

The reentrant form of i can be described as: *the logarithm of negative i is equal to the negative logarithm of i.*

$$\begin{aligned}
i &= (<[<i>]>) \\
\text{cover} \qquad [i] &= <[<i>]> \\
\text{cover} \qquad <[i]> &= \quad [<i>] \quad ☞ \quad \log -i = -\log i
\end{aligned}$$

This leads to a useful theorem, J/2 **toggle**, a structure that occurs in the definitions of the trigonometric func-tions in the next chapter.

J/2 toggle

$$<(J/2)> = (<J/2>)$$

Demonstration:

$$\begin{aligned}
i &= <(<[\quad i \quad]>)> \\
\text{substitute} \qquad (J/2) &= <(<[(J/2)]>)> \\
\text{clarify} \qquad (J/2) &= <(< \quad J/2 \quad >)> \\
\text{cover} \qquad <(J/2)> &= (<J/2>)
\end{aligned}$$

Here's a void-based construction of the J/2 toggle theorem:

$$\begin{aligned}
&\qquad\qquad\qquad\quad void \\
\text{J-void object} \qquad & J \qquad\qquad J \\
\text{substitute} \qquad & [<(\quad)>] \; J/2 \quad J/2 \\
\text{J-transparent} \qquad & [<(J/2)>] \; J/2 \\
\text{bridge} \qquad & [<(J/2)>] \; J/2 = \quad void \\
\text{move} \qquad & [<(J/2)>] \qquad = <J/2> \\
\text{cover} \qquad & <(J/2)> \qquad = (<J/2>) \quad ☞ \quad -\#^{J/2} = \#^{-J/2}
\end{aligned}$$

The self-referential form of i mimics the self-referential definition of −1:

J self-inverse $\qquad\qquad -1 = 1/-1 \quad ☞ \quad <o> = (<[<o>]>)$

This definition can be transcribed into the self-referential form of J.

$$\begin{aligned}
-1 = 1/-1 \quad ☞ \quad <o> &= (<J>) \\
\text{cover} \qquad [<o>] &= <J> \\
\text{substitute} \qquad J &= <J>
\end{aligned}$$

feature	i *form*	J *form*
definition	$(-1)^{1/2}$ ☞ (J/2)	$\log_\# -1$ ☞ [<o>]
reentrant	i = <(<[i]>)>	J = <J>
−1 form	([i][i]) = <o>	(J) = <o>
relation	i = (J/2)	J = [i][i]
toggle	<[i]> = [<i>]	<(J/2)> = (<J/2>)
Euler π	π = ([2][i][[i]])	π = (J/2 [J])

Figure 39-1: *Structural comparison of* i *and* J

Expressing the unit 1 as the self-multiplication of −1 leads directly to J-self-inverse which itself is equivalent to declaring J to be sign-blind. J is imaginary because it is its own additive inverse. i is imaginary because it is its own negative multiplicative inverse. From this perspective, J is a simpler, more elementary imaginary number than i and indeed simpler than the imaginary −1 given the assumption that addition is more elementary than multiplication.

J-void object

−1 x −1 = 1 ☞

([(J)][(J)]) = o

(J   J) = o

If i is indeed composed of J, then we should be able to derive the behavior of i as theorems that incorporate J. We can begin by demonstrating a fundamental property of i, that $i^2 = -1$, based on the definition that i = (J/2).[3]

i^2 ☞ ([i][i])
([(J/2)][(J/2)])   substitute
(J/2   J/2)   clarify
(J   ) ☞ −1   substitute

Shared Structure

Figure 39-1 presents some of the structural comparisons between i and J. J is equal to two replicas of [i].[4]

J = [i][i]   **[i] replication**

We'll solve for J within the definition of i:

i^2 ☞ ([i][i]) = <o>
[i][i] = [<o>] = J   cover

i *expression* ☞	J *form*
i^0 $\quad = 1$	$\#^0 \quad = \quad$ ( ) = ( )
$i^1 = i^0 \times i = 1 \times i = 1i$	$\#^{J/2} \quad = \quad$ ([i]) = (J/2)
$i^2 = i^1 \times i = i \times i = -1$	$\#^J \quad = \quad$ ([i][i]) = (J)
$i^3 = i^2 \times i = -1 \times i = -1i$	$\#^{3J/2} = \quad$ ([i][i][i]) = (3J/2)
$i^4 = i^3 \times i = -i \times i = 1$	$\#^{J+J} = ($[i][i][i][i]$)$ = (J J)

Figure 39-2: *Cyclic forms of* i

There are many other structural relationships within the forms of i. Here's one of the most notorious.[5]

$$i^{i^i} = -i$$

A power tower of the imaginary unit is the negation of that unit. We'll decompose the task, first i^i.

$$i^i \quad ☞ \quad ((([i]][i]))$$

Now raising i^i to the power of i,

	i^{i^i} ☞	
hybrid		$((([\quad i^i \quad]][i]))$
substitute		$((([((([i]][i]))]][i]))$
clarify		$((\quad [[i]][i] \quad [i]))$
substitute		$((\quad [[i]] \quad J \quad))$
substitute/clarify		$((\quad [J/2] \quad J \quad))$
J-convert		$(< \quad J/2 \quad >)$
J/2 toggle		$<(\quad J/2 \quad)> \quad ☞ \quad -i$

To recapitulate, J carries the conventional concept of negation as a full reflection across the number line. i carries a half-negation which is expressed conventionally in a second imaginary dimension that forms the complex plane.

39.3 Cyclic Forms

Before going full circle we can explore *cyclic forms*, a quantized type of iterated behavior for which values repeat after a whole number of iterations. The structure of both i and J is cyclic. Naturally these cycles are *coupled*.

i has a cycle of four while J has a cycle of two. One way to see the coupling between the two is to examine their equivalent forms displayed in Figure 39-2.

i has a *multiplicative cycle*. The imaginary i oscillates through four phases, each phase is a result of multiplying the prior phase by i itself. J has an *additive cycle*. The corresponding J oscillates by self-addition between *present or absent*, between existent and nonexistent.

The phases of i can be illustrated in many different ways. Each type of model engenders a type of thinking.[6]

Phase of i	0	...	1	...	2	...	3	...	0
Power of i	i^0	...	i^1	...	i^2	...	i^3	...	i^4
Pattern of i	1	...	i	...	-1	...	-i	...	1
Cycle of i	$\Rightarrow$	...	$\uparrow$	...	$\Leftarrow$	...	$\downarrow$	...	$\Rightarrow$
Phase of J/2	*void*	...	J/2	...	J	...	3J/2	...	*void*

The **phases** make four transitions through unique values labeled 0 to 3. The **power** model identifies the process of multiplying by i. We could also view the successive transformations outside of a temporal model, as a repetitive **pattern** spread out in space. The **cycle** is a rotation through four quadrants of a circle. Finally each step of the cyclic behavior can be seen as an addition of J/2.

The pattern of i passes through four different unit types. We can also observe that i consists of two interwoven cycles of two. This becomes apparent when we record the powers of i as complex numbers, keeping track of both the real and the imaginary components independently. The cycles of i are also expressed below as an ordered pair of unitary values.

$$
\begin{aligned}
i^0 &= 1 + 0i &\Rightarrow \{ 1, 0\} &\quad \text{☞} \quad (\quad) \\
i^1 &= 0 + 1i &\Rightarrow \{ 0, 1\} &\quad (\quad J/2) \\
i^2 &= -1 + 0i &\Rightarrow \{-1, 0\} &\quad (J\quad) \\
i^3 &= 0 + -1i &\Rightarrow \{ 0, -1\} &\quad (J\ J/2) \\
i^4 &= 1 + 0i &\Rightarrow \{ 1, 0\} &\quad (\quad)
\end{aligned}
$$

The sequence of complex numbers associated with each of the phases of i shows that the real component cycles through two types of units, 1 and –1, passing through 0 in between. The imaginary component cycles through the same two units, 1 and –1, but *out of phase* with the real component. i is *a composite of two replicas of the same binary oscillation.* As powers of i accumulate, the fourfold oscillation in the real domain never peaks at the same time as the oscillation in the imaginary domain. Geometrically we might say that the two domains are orthogonal. Algebraically we'd say they are coupled by a constant. The quantized oscillation is *reflection* from 1 to –1, the cycle of J. i is thus composed of two out-of-phase replicas of the J cycle, just like the cosine wave is out-of-phase with the sine wave.

Since the presence of J stands in place of the *concept of negation*, the phase shift is literally one-half of a reflection. The label i then stands for a *half-negation*, an imaginary concept only if we see the operation of negation as an indivisible whole. For the multiplicative cycle of i, one-half of a multiplication is the familiar concept of the square root. For the equivalent additive cycle of J, one-half of an addition is the familiar concept of the fraction.[7]

39.4 The Complex Plane

The complex plane is a two-dimensional space in which each point is identified by an ordered pair of coordinates $\{a, b\}$. The first number is taken to index a location on the horizontal axis and is designated as real; the second number indexes a location on the vertical axis which is designated as imaginary. Thus every complex number has a unique location on the complex plane.

0+3i	1+3i	2+3i
0+2i	1+2i	2+2i
0+1i	1+1i	2+1i
0+0i	1+0i	2+0i

lattice points on the complex plane

$$a + bi =def= \{a,b\}$$

The two axes meet at the **origin**, the point 0 + 0i.

As John Stillwell observes:

One of the reasons for the simplifying power of complex numbers is their two-dimensional nature. The extra dimension gives more room for solutions of equations to exist.[8]

The idea of placing an imaginary i-axis perpendicular to the real 1-axis was originally conceived as a geometry problem by Caspar Wessel, a surveyor, at the turn of the nineteenth century. Although Wessel's paper[9] includes the seeds of vector algebra, Gauss named and popularized the complex plane as points in a space rather than as vector-like rays emanating from an origin. Jean-Robert Argand first published the geometric interpretation of the complex plane, so the complex plane is also named the **Argand plane** after him.

Caspar Wessel
1745-1818

Jean-Robert Argand
1768-1822

The real numbers a and b can be modified by attaching yet another indicator, -1, which extends the positive complex plane into four quadrants surrounding the origin. The *polarity* of both 1 and i is deeply embedded into our assumptions about how numbers work. What was once an signless number N grew with the invention of negative numbers into a multivalued number ±N that was then disassembled into the now dominant +N and −N. The −1 world is commensurable with the +1 world by design, the two of them can mix together freely. That's why we tend to forget that they are essentially different worlds.

Complex numbers thus combine four separate types of unit, 1, i, −1 and −i, that are themselves derivative of two bipolar pairs ±1 and ±i. The negative sign specifies a *direction* rather than a magnitude. The relation between +1 and −1 is a rotation of π radians while the relation between +1 and +i is a rotation of π/2 radians.

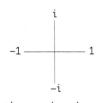

the complex plane

Our exploration of J has thus far been algebraic, looking at iconic patterns of containment as equality relations. With the visual model of containers as delimiting boundaries, the algebra of J has a decidedly geometric (non-arithmetized) flavor since *there is no underlying system of measurement in James forms.* Containers are not coordinate systems. Just like the James forms were anchored to the number line in the prior chapter, we are now in the process of anchoring containment forms to the geometry of complex numbers.

Real and Imaginary Units

Here is a conventional complex number, $a + bi$, laid out with unit labels and polarities recorded explicitly.

$$a + bi =def= (a \times \pm 1) + (b \times \pm i)$$

The imaginary part is brought into existence by multiplying b by i. This is the same mechanism that brings negative numbers into existence.

$$-a = a \times (-1) \quad ☞ \quad ([a][(\text{ J })]) = (\text{ J } [a])$$
$$bi = b \times \sqrt{(-1)} \quad ☞ \quad ([b][(J/2)]) = (J/2 [b])$$

The creatures of the negative world are represented in the reflective world of J by (J [a]). Those of the imaginary world of i take the form (J/2 [b]). The form of a positive complex number is therefore

$$a + bi \quad ☞ \quad a ([\text{ i }][b])$$
substitute $\quad a ([(J/2)][b])$
clarify $\quad a (\text{ J}/2 \text{ } [b])$

The square root operation corresponds to a unit fraction of J. The James form provides the convenient shorthand not only for $(-1)^{1/2}$ but for any *unit fraction power* of –1.

$$(-1)^{1/1} \quad ☞ \quad (J/1)$$
$$(-1)^{1/2} \quad\quad\quad (J/2)$$
$$(-1)^{1/N} \quad\quad\quad (J/N)$$

There are thus **families of imaginary numbers**, (J/N [b]), each family identified by a different fraction 1/N of a reflection. The logarithm of the imaginary component bi exposes the unit fraction as a composition of two additive components, a magnitude $\ln b$ and a partial reflection J/N.

$$\ln bi \quad ☞ \quad [(J/N [b])] = J/N [b] \quad ☞ \quad i\pi/N + \ln b$$

Getting Around

Complex numbers identify points on the complex plane using an extrinsic origin and an orthogonally decomposed coordinate system. A base raised to the power of a complex number, e^{a+bi}, identifies a point on the complex plane in polar coordinates. It consists of a magnitude, e^a, multiplied by a rotation e^{bi}. Viewed in the context of a circle, e^a is the radius with the variable a representing a distance. e^{bi} is the rotation with the variable b representing a radian measure of rotation.[10] If we take the orthogonal form of a complex number to be $\{a,b\}$, then the polar form is

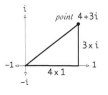

$$\{a,b\} \;\Rightarrow\; \{r\cos\alpha,\; r\sin\alpha\} \qquad \textit{orthogonal}$$
$$\{r,\alpha\} \;\Rightarrow\; \{e^a,\; e^{bi}\} \qquad\qquad \textit{polar}$$

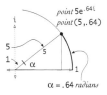

Simply said, the orthogonal coordinates are expressed in linear space while the polar coordinates are expressed in exponential space. We'll look at this conceptualization popularized by Gauss next. In preparation I'll introduce a slight notational change and relabel b within $a + bi$ by a Greek letter α (alpha) to emphasize that the inclusion of i in an exponent designates b to be an *angle*. We have done this before when referring to $i\pi$, with $\alpha = \pi$. Accepting that the James form is restricted to rational angles, we can generalize the Euler model of the complex angle α.

$$i\alpha \quad ☞ \quad (J/2\,[\alpha]) \qquad\qquad J = (J/2\,[\pi])_e$$

39.5 Euler's Equation

Euler's equation shows how to convert $\{a,b\}$ orthogonal coordinates into $\{r,\alpha\}$ polar coordinates on the complex plane. This simplified version applies to a unit circle.

$$e^{i\alpha} = \cos\alpha + i\sin\alpha$$

and

$$e^{-i\alpha} = \cos\alpha - i\sin\alpha$$

Euler equations
for the unit circle

The equation is a cacophony of mathematical concepts and appears at first quite surprising since it relates trigonometric functions to an exponential expression all within the context of complex numbers. The variable α is the

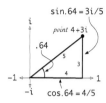

sin.64 = 3i/5

point 4+3i

.64

5

3

4

−1

1

−i   cos.64 = 4/5

polar parameter of angular orientation. Having limited the expression to a unit circle, the polar distance is simply 1 unit. The trigonometric image in the margin shows a rotation of .64 *radians* from the horizontal.

Euler identified, indeed defined, a morphism between trigonometric functions on the complex plane and exponential functions with imaginary powers. Don't let the trigonometric functions fool you. The right-side of Euler's equation is just a complex number, $a + bi$, expressed in orthogonal coordinates with $a = \cos \alpha$ and $b = \sin \alpha$. The $\pi/2$ shift between sin and cos is the same as the domain shift between the 1-axis and the i-axis of the complex plane. Very literally, the sine and cosine functions measure the mixture of real and imaginary components for any complex number. By convention, cosine is real and sine is imaginary. The imaginary i, like the number 1, is an indicator telling us to head in the vertical rather than the horizontal direction.

The left-side exponential expression in Euler's equation, $e^{i\alpha}$, is shorthand for rotation through α *radians*. $e^{i\alpha}$ can no longer be understood to be a magnitude, instead the imaginary i indicates that the exponent should be interpreted as a rotation rather than as a regular power. The exponent of $e^{i\alpha}$ is a complex number expressed in polar coordinates. In contrast, e^{α} is an irrational number with α taken as the *distance measure* of α radians. From this perspective the Euler expression $e^{i\alpha}$ is a very clever *change in notation* that allows a direct conversion between orthogonal and polar coordinates. This then is the key for removing the mystery: Euler changed the *definition* of the exponent of an exponential function. The finesse works due to the convergence of two measurement techniques.

— Angular measurement in radians is *intrinsic* to the polar coordinate system and can be converted to the distance measurements of the orthogonal coordinate system by the trigonometric functions.

— The exponential space of iα converts multiplication into addition so that angles are added together when exponential expressions are multiplied.

The imaginary i is a polarity label, the same as 1 and −1, but it adds a *new type of polarity*, the **half-negation**. The half-negative is then visualized quite nicely as a 90° orthogonal rotation that generates the i-axis of the complex plane. That in turn works because we initially defined a *full negative* to be a 180° rotation from the original positive direction of the 1-axis. Since 180° is also a J reflection, i is also a **half-reflection**.

Euler's Identity

Here is Euler's famous identity that is reputed to unite the important constants of arithmetic, {0, 1, π, e, i}, with the important operations, {+, ×, ^}.

$$e^{i\pi} + 1 = 0$$

Euler identity
for unit circle

Don't get too blown away, e and π and i are all there together because they are *co-defined* by one another in the first place. When Euler's identity is solved for π, we find that Euler has cast π as a nightmare of negativity:

$$\pi = (-1)^{-(2^{-1})} \times \ln{-1}$$

$$e^{i\pi} = -1$$
$$i\pi = \ln{-1}$$
$$\pi = i^{-1} \times \ln{-1}$$
with
$$i = (-1)^{1/2}$$
$$1/2 = 2^{-1}$$

The structure of π is the product (in both the multiplicative and the consequential senses) of two quite different things. We are dividing the imaginary unit J by the imaginary unit i to get a concrete real number larger than unity. Our common metaphors for multiplication will all fail. Neither imaginary unit can be visualized as the side of a rectangle for example. No wonder Benjamin Peirce said about Euler's identity:

Benjamin Peirce
1809-1880

It is absolutely paradoxical; we cannot understand it, and we don't know what it means, but we have proved it, and therefore we know it must be the truth.[11]

Modern scholars are not so appalled, but just as wondrous. From Keith Devlin: "Euler's equation reaches down into the very depths of existence."[12]

Special Cases

The Euler identity is a simplification of Euler's equation with the angle of rotation α equal to π radians.

Euler reflection
$e^{i\pi} = -1$

$\qquad$ *For* $\alpha = \pi,$ $\qquad$ $e^{i\pi} = \cos \pi + i \sin \pi$

$\qquad\qquad\qquad\qquad\qquad\quad e^{i\pi} = \;\;-1 \;\; + \;\;\; 0$

Euler's identity *rotates* through π radians (180°) from 1 to –1. That is, Euler's identity is Euler's equation *when the rotation is a reflection.*

$$when \;\; \alpha = 0 \qquad e^{i0} = 1$$
$$when \;\; \alpha = \pi \qquad e^{i\pi} = -1$$

Similarly J *reflects* 1 through the origin to arrive at –1.

$$(\;) = \qquad o \qquad \text{☞} \qquad \#^0 = 1$$
$$(J) = ([<o>]) \qquad \text{☞} \qquad \#^J = -1$$

Thus the Euler identity directly relates complex rotation to the reflective constant J.

$$(J)_e \qquad \text{☞} \qquad e^J = e^{i\pi} = -1$$

Euler's equation also provides a definition of i. By rotating through $\pi/2$ radians (90°), Euler's equation aligns with the i-axis.

$\qquad$ *For* $\alpha = \pi/2,$

Euler half reflection
$e^{i\pi/2} = i$

$\qquad\qquad\qquad\qquad e^{i\pi/2} = \cos \pi/2 + i \sin \pi/2$

$\qquad\qquad\qquad\qquad e^{i\pi/2} = \;\;\;\; 0 \;\;\; + i$

$\qquad\qquad \text{☞} \qquad\qquad i = (i\pi/2) = (J/2)$

The James analog of Euler's identity is the J-self-occlusion theorem. The primary difference is that the James form eliminates the *rotational* component $i\pi$.

J-self-occlusion
$\qquad$ J ([J] [(J)]) = *void* $\qquad \text{☞} \qquad$ J + (J x $\#^J$) = 0

Euler identity
James analog

$$1 \; x \; e^{i\pi} + 1 = 0$$
$$J \; x \; \#^J \;\; + J = 0$$

39.6 π and J

From the James perspective, $\#^J = -1$ is *independent* of base-e. It is Euler's identity that locks base-e to the circular concept of π. The value $i\pi$ presumes rotation. We can assert

$$J_e = \ln e^J = \ln e^{i\pi} = i\pi$$

but to conform to convention we must also assert

$$J_\# \neq i\pi$$

even though there is no explicit base associated with i or π. This restriction appears to be a *universal assumption* that has found its way into textbooks and computational engines.[13] It indicates an *explicit conceptual difference* between complex rotation of π radians and Cartesian reflection.

We can bring $J_\#$ and J_e into computational alignment by compensating $J_\#$ for the hidden base-e of $i\pi$.

With $e^J = -1$

$$J_e = \ln e^J = \log_\# e^J \times \ln \# = J_\# \times \ln \#$$

☞ $\quad J_e = [(J)]_e = ([[(J)]] \; <[[e]]>)_\#$
$\qquad\qquad\qquad ([\quad J\quad] \; <[[e]]>)_\#$ $\qquad$ clarify

Here's the relationship between the two base systems.

$J_e \qquad\quad = ([J] \; <[[e]]>)_\#$ $\qquad$ hybrid
$[J_e]_\# \qquad = [J] \; <[[e]]>_\#$ $\qquad$ cover
$[J_e][[e]]_\# = [J]_\#$ $\qquad$ move
$([J_e][[e]])_\# = \quad J_\#$ $\qquad$ ☞ $J_\# = J_e \times \log_\# e$ $\quad$ cover

Another substantive difference is that *reflection does not invoke imaginary numbers*. To maintain consistency Euler's identity is completely dependent upon the model of rotation in the complex plane established by Euler's equation. We arrive at several fascinating consequences:

— J shows up quite naturally in Euler's identity.
— J is base-free, but to associate it with $i\pi$ requires a constant of proportionality.
— The coupling of i and π is a symbolic definition that extends the *meaning* of i and π.
— J has different conventional meanings in Cartesian and complex space.

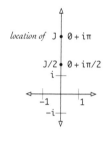

location of J

J/2 is a Cartesian mirror

As a complex number the real component of J is 0, while its imaginary component is π, placing J on the complex i-axis.

$$J = 0 + πi = \{0, iπ\}$$

As an imaginary number bi, J is a rotation of iπ/2 times a *scaling factor* b of 2. J/2 is a rotation of iπ/2 with a scaling factor of 1. This interpretation is forced because the real component of J and of J/N is 0. However when J is taken as an exponent (J), it becomes the *real number* −1 on the Cartesian x-axis.

The relationship that Euler established between i, π and J requires us to think in specific ways. The imaginary J is a distance along the i-axis. The real J is a location on the logarithmically scaled x-axis. Euler's famous identity then connects six concepts of unity, $\{1, −1, e, i, π, J\}$.

Imaginary Pi

If we adopt Euler's model of imaginary exponents, $e^{iα}$, as rotations then i and π become deeply connected. The most concise statement of their relationship is J:

$$J_e = iπ$$

DeMorgan, forever a foe of negative numbers, knew this relation, which he satirized as

$$π = J/i \quad and \quad π = circumference/diameter$$
$$therefore \quad J:i \;::\; 2πr:2r$$

Imagine a person with a gift of ridicule, [he might say] First that a negative quantity has no logarithm; second that a negative quantity has no square root; thirdly that the first nonexistent is to the second as the circumference of a circle is to the diameter.[14]

Here is a demonstration of the relation between J and π.

hybrid $J = iπ$ ☞ $J = ([\; i \;][π])$

substitute $J = ([(J/2)][π])$

clarify $J = (\; J/2 \; [π])_e$

conventional	☞	J *form*
$-1 = e^{i\pi} = e^J$		$<o> = ((([i][\pi])) = (J)$
$J_e = i \times \pi$		$J = (J/2\ [\pi])_e$
$J_\# = i \times \pi \times \log_\# e$		$J = (J/2\ [\pi][[e]])_\#$
$\pi = J \times e^{-J/2}$		$\pi = (<J/2>\ [J])_e$
$\pi = J/i = J \times -i$		$\pi = ([J]<[i]>) = ([J][<i>])_e$
$\pi = -2 \times i \times \ln i$		$\pi = <([2][i][[i]])>_e$

Figure 39-3: *Structural comparison of* π, i *and* J

The James form for π radians is

$(J/2\ [\pi])_e =$	J	
$J/2\ [\pi]\ =$	$[J]$	cover
$\pi\ = (\ \ <J/2>\ \ [J])_e$		move/cover

$$\pi \quad ☞ \quad (<J/2>\ [J])_e \quad ☞ \quad Je^{-J/2} \qquad \textbf{form of } \pi$$

To eliminate the angle-brackets within the form of π, we can call upon J/2-toggle and J-conversion.

$$(<J/2>) = <(J/2)> = (J\ \ J/2) \qquad \text{J/2 toggle/J-convert}$$

Taking care to remember that the form of J does not accumulate, we can risk a further abbreviation for J J/2,

$$\pi = (3J/2\ [J])$$

From the perspective of a reflection $J/2 = <J/2>$, so that 3J/2 reduces via J-self-inverse. We might also note in advance that

$\pi/2 = J/(2i)$	☞	$\pi/2 = (3J/2\ [J/2])$
$\pi/N = J/(Ni)$	☞	$\pi/N = (3J/2\ [J/N])$

Figure 39-3 shows the relationships between i and J that implicate π, in both conventional and James notation. We can now interpret expressions and forms as comparisons between rotation and reflection. Specifically, the structural relationships are J/2-frame variants of one another.

$i = e^{J/2}$	☞	$i = (\ \ J/2\ [o])$
$J = i \times \pi$		$J = (\ \ J/2\ [\pi])$
$\pi = J / i$		$\pi = (J\ J/2\ [J])$

39.7 Reflection

Rotating from +1 through π radians to −1 lands back on the conventional number line. A "rotation" of J does not necessarily need to pass through the i coordinate, it does not need to implicate i and it does not need to leave the real number line. Here the change in perspective is to see a 180° reorientation *not as a rotation* but as *a single reflection*. J acts more like a change of sign than like a rotation through an angle. Figure 39-4 provides a brief comparison of the models of i and J.

Fractional Reflection

An analogous J complex number is formed by adding the J-fraction J/N to a real number:

complex form $a + i\alpha$ ☞ a J/N

In contrast to i complex numbers, the imaginary part of a J-complex number is quite limited. J will exist or it will not. Although J is imaginary, it is imaginary at the same level as −1. To the extent that the imaginary component represents an angle, it is a **J-fraction**.

The image of traveling around a circle permits a conceptualization of *fractions of* J as partial reflections. We could take the perspective of inversive geometry as fractional reflection *through* a circle, coupling unit fractions inside with natural numbers outside. Or we could take an intrinsic viewpoint *along* the circumference of a circle, orienting the current direction as 0. A fractional part of J then becomes a *phase shift*. Thus J/2 can be envisioned as:

— a relocation
— a half-reflection
— a half-negation
— a phase shift
— a conversion to unit fractions
— a trigonometric function
— a specific constrained rotation.

perspective	i *form*	J *form*
angular (radians)	π/2	π
complex number	0 + 1i	−1 + 0i
exponential	e^{iπ/2}	e^{J}
James	[i][i]	(J/2)
Euler	cos π/2 + i sin π/2	cos π + i sin π
polar	iα	(J [α])
orthogonal coordinates	{0,1}	{−1,0}

Figure 39-4: *Models of the relationship between* i *and* J

Alternatively the J/2-frame identifies the types of units.

```
        void      =    (J/2 [   ])    ☞    0
         ( )           ((J/2 [   ]))        1
        (J/2)          (J/2 [ o ])          i
( J     J/2)           (J/2 [<o>])         −i
( J/2   J/2)           (J/2 [ i ])         −1
(       J/2 [J])       (J/2 [ J ])         −π
( J     J/2 [J])       (J/2 [ J ])          π
(<J/2>  J/2 [J])       (J/2 [ π ])          J
```

Should these forms be expressed in base-#, the resultant values of the units 1, −1, i and −i would not change. *Units are indeed base-free.*[15]

From the structural perspective,

J/2 = i × (π/2)   ☞   ([J][1/2]) = ([i][π][1/2])

and

J/N = i × (π/N)   ☞   ([J][1/N]) = ([i][π][1/N])

N itself is defined to be an integer. In effect, the J/2 frame has taken the place of Euler's i marker to indicate the rotational/angular perspective. J-fractions replace the concept of *radian*. To conform to the fractional reflection model, we'll limit observations to discrete values, units and rotations, in particular to rational fractions of both π and J.

Alignment

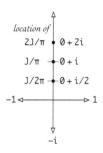

location of
2J/π • 0 + 2i
J/π • 0 + i
J/2π • 0 + i/2
−1 ← → 1
−i

In the complex plane all (J/2 [α]) points fall along the i-axis. This is of course equivalent to the location of points 0 + iα in the complex plane. The reflection J/2 becomes the angular measurement π/2 while α is the *distance* measurement on the i-axis.

reflection	*complex point*	*location on i-axis*
(J/2 [ ])	0 + 0i	0
(J/2 [o])	0 + 1i	1
(J/2 [π])	0 + πi	π
(J/2 [iπ])	$0 + πi^2$	−π
(J/2 [α])	0 + αi	α

This relation does not regard i or J as numeric forms, they are instead both markers that indicate we have *changed interpretation dynamically* from magnitude to rotation in the case of i and to fractional reflection in the case of J. (J/N) results in J playing the same role as Euler's power function $e^{iα}$.

$$(J/N) \quad ☞ \quad \#^{J/N} \quad ☞ \quad e^{iπ/N}$$

J defines a conceptual *unit*, while i is parameterized by the constant π to define a conceptual unit *circle*.

$$J \quad ☞ \quad iπ$$
$$J/N \quad | \quad iπ/N$$
$$(J/N)_e \quad | \quad e^{iπ/N}$$

When interpreted as $\log_\# -1$ the form of J thus contains within it

— the conversion factor from units to radians
— the form of i without invoking an imaginary value
— the form of base-e without specifying a base.

The N Roots of −1

The form of (J/N) holds within it another interpretation as the N roots of −1.

$$(\quad J/N \quad)$$

substitute $\quad ((\lbrack \quad J \quad \rbrack <\lbrack N\rbrack>))$

substitute $\quad ((\lbrack\lbrack<o>\rbrack\rbrack<\lbrack N\rbrack>)) \quad ☞ \quad (-1)^{1/N}$

Not only is i a marker that converts π/N into a rotation, it is also implicated in the roots of –1 as *fractional powers* of i^2.

$$\#^{i\pi/N} = (-1)^{1/N} = (i^2)^{(1/N)} = i^{2/N}$$

For partial reflection (i.e. rotation)

$$e^{a+J/N} \quad \text{☞} \quad (a \;\; J/N)$$
$$\text{☞} \quad e^a \times e^{J/N} = e^a \times (e^J)^{1/N} = e^a \times (-1)^{1/N}$$

J-fractions generalize to *any rational fraction* (Chapter 35.6), permitting arbitrary rational angles as arguments to cosine and sine. In moving from complex numbers to J fractions the second imaginary dimension of the complex plane is no longer fundamental. J *sums* such as N + J can be seen to lie on the real logarithmic number line.

Figure 38-3 projects $f(n) = n^2$ onto the x-axis, replacing negative n values with their imaginary counterparts ni. Relabeling n = α for our current context,

$$i\alpha = \alpha(-1)^{1/2} \quad \text{☞} \quad ([i][\alpha]) = (J/2 \, [\alpha])$$

Similarly

$$\alpha(-1)^{1/3} \quad \text{☞} \quad (J/3 \, [\alpha])$$

For simplicity, let α = 1. The point (J/3) has magnitude 1 and direction of π/3. J/3 is 1/3 of a reflection, which is at an angle of π/3 from the 1-axis. The point (J/3) is indeed at an angle of 60° rather than 90°. However J/3 is a discrete rational unit fraction. Just like J/2 defines the i-axis, J/3 defines a different axis that is conceptually independent of both J/1 and J/2. The difficulty is in converting between these axes. In general,

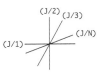

$$\alpha(-1)^{1/N} \quad \text{☞} \quad (J/N \, [\alpha])$$

Within the multiplicative formulation of iπ/N, conversion is standardized by two orthogonal coordinates, a + bi. Each J/N opens up a *relatively orthogonal domain* that transforms into other domains by *addition of fractions*. These fractions correspond to Euler's addition of angles.

Sign-blind Reflection

The sign-blindness of J extends to the concept of reflection. The rotational properties of clockwise and counterclockwise are not distinguished. For a reflection the direction of approach (i.e. from above or from below) is not a relevant concept. Positive and negative angles and rotations are not distinguished.

sign-blind J-fraction
$$J/N = <J/N>$$

Reflected J-fractions such as $<J/2>$ can be toggled to remove the angle-bracket.

J/2 toggle
$$<J/2> = <[(J/2)]> = [<(J/2)>] = J \quad J/2 =label= 3J/2$$

An angle of $5\pi/4$ has the reflective form $((\,[J]\,[5/4]\,))$. Due to J-parity this form reduces

hybrid	$((\,[J]\,[5/4]\,))$
substitute	$((\,[J]\,[4/4\ 1/4]\,))$
disperse	$((\,[J]\,[4/4]\,))\ (\,[J]\,[1/4]\,))$
substitute	$((\,[J]\,[\ o\ ]\,)\ (\,[J]\,[1/4]\,))$
clarify/substitute	$(\quad J \qquad\qquad J/4 \qquad)$
enfold/J-convert	$<(J/4)>$

Sign-blind Rotation

The Euler identity as well is sign-blind. Here the conventional demonstration of $e^{\pm i\pi} + 1 = 0$ asserts that a full rotation of 2π is the same as no rotation at all.

$$e^{i\pi} + 1 \quad =?= \ e^{-i\pi} + 1$$
$$e^{i\pi} \qquad =?= \ 1/e^{i\pi}$$
$$e^{i\pi} \times e^{i\pi} \ =?= \ 1$$
$$e^{i2\pi} = e^{i0} = e^{0} = 1$$

In effect

$$e^{i\pi} = -1 \qquad and \qquad e^{-i\pi} = -1$$
$$\ln e^{i\pi} = \ln -1 \qquad\qquad \ln e^{-i\pi} = \ln -1$$
$$i\pi = J_e \qquad\qquad\qquad -i\pi = J_e$$

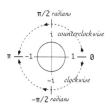

$\pi/2$ *radians*
i counterclockwise
$\pi \ -1 \qquad 1 \ 0$
-i clockwise
$-\pi/2$ *radians*

When $i\pi$ is interpreted as a rotation, rotating clockwise by π is indeed the same as rotating counterclockwise by π. This is also just a re-framing of the sign-blindness of J. For completeness, here is the boundary demonstration of the above equivalence between $e^{i\pi}$ and its conjugate $e^{-i\pi}$. We'll again assign the base-e to the boundary forms.

$e^{i\pi} =?= e^{-i\pi}$ ☞

(iπ)$_e$	=	(< iπ >)$_e$	hybrid
([<o>])	=	(<[<o>]>)	substitute
<([o])>	=	<(<[o]>)>	promote
<( )>	=	<(< >)>	clarify
<( )>	=	<( )>	void cancel

The rules that regulate taking the logarithm of an exponential expression are constrained by exceptions.

$$\ln e^{-i\pi} \neq -i\pi \ln e$$

This constraint is quite different than dividing by zero and quite different from the two values generated by taking a square root. Logarithms are suspect in a different way: direction of approach matters. This suspicion does not occur within the James form since J-fractions do not preserve direction of rotation. The conventional interpretation of $\ln e^{i\pi}$ also includes an infinite number of rotations, which we will see next.

39.8 Euler Rotation

Earlier we saw the simplified version of the Euler equation for a unit circle. Here is Euler's formula for a generic circle:

$$e^{a+i\alpha} = e^a \times e^{i\alpha} = e^a \times (\cos \alpha + i \sin \alpha)$$

Euler equation
principle value

Polar distance is incorporated by separating the real part of the complex power as a multiplier, e^a. This scaling factor multiplies the radius of the unit circle. When there is no extent along the 1-axis, $a = 0$, which makes the radius $e^a = 1$.

There is another complexity (of the infinite variety) that was defined by Euler to explain the meaning of J. The expression $e^{a+i\alpha}$ maps many-to-one onto its complex value since α can include any number of rotations around the polar circle.[16]

$$e^{i\alpha} = e^{i(\alpha+2\pi)} = e^{i(\alpha+4\pi)} = e^{i(\alpha+2k\pi)} \quad \text{with } k \text{ in } \mathbb{Z}$$

The **logarithm** of a complex number then must have infinitely many values for each complex number.

$$\ln e^{i(\alpha+2k\pi)} = i(\alpha + 2k\pi) \qquad \textit{with } k \textit{ in } \mathbb{Z}$$

To cover all possible rotations Euler's equation is modified by adding $2\pi k$ radians for each of k additional full rotations. k is an integer so both positive counterclockwise and negative clockwise rotations are included. Bluntly, k is the *memory* function. Dynamically k is *time*. This infinite extension provides a cyclic, phase-oriented interpretation of imaginary numbers, as well as providing a definition of what it means to raise a constant to the power of a complex number. Here's what Euler's equation looks like with a repeating imaginary (angular) component.

$$e^{i(\alpha+2k\pi)} = \cos(\alpha + 2\pi k) + i\sin(\alpha + 2\pi k)$$

And here's a non-zero real component, showing Euler's equation in full generality. Base-e is raised to the power of an infinite number of complex numbers.

Euler equation
generic

$$e^{a+i(\alpha+2k\pi)} = e^a \times e^{i(\alpha+2k\pi)}$$
$$= e^a \times (\cos(\alpha + 2k\pi) + i\sin(\alpha + 2k\pi))$$

Reintroducing the cyclic component of Euler's identity results in a formula that rejects J-void tally and therefore incorporates all the possible tallies of J.

$$J = i(\pi + 2k\pi) = i\pi(2k + 1)$$

This result allows J to have an infinite set of values generated cyclically:

☞   J = ([i][π][([k][2]) o])

substitute/clarify   (J/2 J/2 [J] [([k][2]) o])

substitute   (J [J] [([k][2]) o])

disperse/clarify   (J [J] [k][2]) (J [J])

J-convert/clarify   ([<J>] [k][2]) <J>

promote/join   <([J] [k][2]) J>

The label J now refers to an *infinity of forms*.

$$J =\partial ef= <J \ ([J][k][2])> \qquad \textit{with } k \textit{ in } \mathbb{Z}$$
☞   ..., −3J, −J, J, 3J, 5J, ...

Euler's definition of J has some undesirable consequences. The non-mathematical elements of time and memory are simply graceful ways to avoid defining J as a completed infinity. J-parity expediently reduces the cyclic structure to a single form.

$$([J][k][2]) = void$$

Complex Logarithms

In general, the logarithm of a complex number is defined as

$$\ln (a + ib) = \ln |z| + i \text{ angle } z$$

where

$$|z| = |(a^2 + b^2)^{1/2}| \quad and \quad \text{angle } z = \arctan b/a$$

This definition is derived directly from the polar representation of complex numbers pioneered by Euler. The exponential/logarithmic inverse has a multiplicity of values, cycling by 2π any number of times (k can be any integer).

$$e^{\ln (a + bi)} = (a + bi) + 2k\pi i$$

The complex logarithm expressed as an exponent returns the argument of the exponent for all complex numbers z, except 0.

$$\#^{\log\# z} = z \quad \text{☞} \quad ([z]) = z \quad with \quad z \neq void$$

However, the other face of Inversion, $[(z)] = z$, no longer holds. The logarithm of an exponential does not conveniently reduce. Because the logarithm now has an unlimited number of imaginary values, we do not know which one is intended.

$$\log_\# \#^z \neq z \quad \text{☞} \quad [(z)] \neq z$$

The convenient fix to limit ambiguity is to limit the angles accepted by the trigonometric functions to one full rotation. This is the **principal value of the complex logarithm**. The angles subtended go from $-\pi$ to $+\pi$, with the exact value of $-\pi$ excluded to avoid overlap at -1. The overlap at π radians is usually associated with the design decision that

$$\ln i = +i\pi/2 \quad while \quad \ln -i = -i\pi/2$$

So long as we stay within the principal values, the logarithm does not become ambiguous. Rotating two $\pi/2$ radians in two different directions lands on either $+i\pi$ or $-i\pi$. But these refer to the *same* location. James algebra invokes a design restriction to accept sign-blindness as a natural consequence of the axioms. The alternative solution is to not keep track of the *direction of approach*. The source of the concepts *approach-from-above* and *approach-from-below* are the dual values, $\pm i$, generated by the square root operation. Figure 38-3 shows a model that emphasizes singular objects such as $\pm n$ and $\pm ni$ that are multivalued and not bifurcated.

In terms of equality, for complex values w and z equality is no longer maintained when applying the logarithm to both sides of an equation.

$$e^w = e^z \quad \text{\textit{does not imply}} \quad w = z$$
$$\text{☞} \quad (w) = (z) \quad \text{\textit{but}} \quad [(w)] \neq [(z)]$$

Although the angle of rotation passes through 0 degrees, $\log 0$ cannot be defined, since there is no complex value that satisfies $e^z = 0$. And, oh, the main purpose of logarithms, to convert multiplication into addition, might also fail if we stray outside of the principal values.

$$\log_{\#} (z_1 \times z_2) \neq \log_{\#} z_1 + \log_{\#} z_2$$
$$\text{☞} \quad [([z_1][z_2])] \neq [z_1][z_2]$$

39.9 Powers of J

We have seen that multiplying by i converts an exponent into a rotation. What does it mean to multiply by J? Here is a list of the interpretations of the first few powers of J from the perspective of the Euler identity.

$$
\begin{aligned}
J^0 &= 1 \times \pi^0 = 1 \\
J^1 &= i \times \pi^1 = i\pi \\
J^2 &= -1 \times \pi^2 = -\pi^2 \\
J^3 &= -i \times \pi^3 = -i\pi^3 \\
J^4 &= 1 \times \pi^4 = \pi^4 \\
J^N &= (i\pi)^N = i^N \times \pi^N
\end{aligned}
$$

model	implementation	expression	form
negative	multiply by −1	$a \Rightarrow -a$	$a \Rightarrow (J [a])$
circular	rotate by $i\pi$	$0 \Rightarrow \pi$	*void* $\Rightarrow (<J/2>[J])$
exponential	power as $i\pi$	$e^{i0} \Rightarrow e^{i\pi}$	$(\ ) \Rightarrow (J)$
James	reflect J	$0 \Rightarrow J$	*void* $\Rightarrow J$
trigonometric	sine π	$\sin 0 \Rightarrow \sin \pi$	*Chapter 40*

Figure 39-5: *Turning around*

These powers are in cycles of 4, just like i except that the exponent of π increases. Thus the powers of J mix both cyclic and multiplicative behavior. Like the powers of i,

$$J^4 = \pi^4 \quad but \quad J \neq \pi$$

Self-multiplying real numbers changes magnitude while self-multiplying imaginary numbers changes direction. J however is additive. Self-adding J changes direction while self-multiplying J changes both magnitude and direction. J then stands somewhere between real and imaginary numbers.

39.10 Remarks

The relation between i and J, between multiplicative and additive indicators, between rotation and reflection, can be phrased simply as ways to *turn around*. Several of these are listed in Figure 39-5. In the figure, ⇒ signifies one-half of a full rotation.

Complex analysis and the utility, beauty and power of the multiplicative imaginary i has dominated mathematics for over two centuries. This is of course appropriate for such a fascinating construction. Are there more amazing types of number out there waiting to expand our conceptual horizons? Are there amazing types of numbers that simplify our conceptual understanding of arithmetic? The next chapter is a purely exploratory journey into the implications of J on a field as old as civilization itself, trigonometry.

Endnotes

1. **opening quote:** J. Hadamard (1945) *An Essay on the Psychology of Invention in the Mathematical Field* p.123. This oft repeated quote begins, in Hadamard's text, with "It has been written that...", suggesting that the original is not due to Hadamard. A.I. Shtern did find the quote written in Paul Painlevé *Analyse des travaux scientifiques* (1900) p.1-2. "It came to appear that, between two truths of the real domain, the easiest and shortest path quite often passes through the complex domain."

2. **not embedded in the types of numbers themselves:** Imagine a world in which self-multiplication was taken to be fundamental rather than Peano's self-addition.

$$1 + 1 = 2 \quad =fantasy\Rightarrow \quad 1 \times 1 = 1^2 = \pm1$$

The discovery of the multiple roots of 1^2 might then motivate a unified attitude toward +1 and −1, possibly finding that addition and subtraction are equally important.

3. **based on the definition that** i = (J/2): I've taken advantage of the hybrid notation in this demonstration asserting directly that J/2 J/2 = J. As was demonstrated in Chapter 35.6 adding J-fractions is the same as adding regular fractions but with a very different type of numerator that cannot be tallied.

4. **J is equal to two replicas of** [i]: We can now see where the 2 in J/2 comes from.

5. **Here's one of the most notorious:** Self-multiplication of the power tower of i is returns −1 via J.

$$\left(i^{i^i}\right)^2 \quad ☞ \quad ([<(J/2)>][<(J/2)>]) \qquad \text{substitute}$$
$$<<([(J/2)][(J/2)])>> \qquad \text{promote}$$
$$(\quad J/2 \qquad J/2 \quad) \qquad \text{unwrap/clarify}$$
$$(\qquad J \qquad) ☞ -1 \qquad \text{substitute}$$

6. **type of model engenders a type of thinking:** Different visualizations of the underlying phase transitions energize different areas of the brain, different physiological changes in the brain and different cognitive functions. Here we are expanding mathematics into humanistic realms under the banner that math is a human activity.

7. **is the familiar concept of the fraction:** We could have identified the negative reflection –N to be one-half of the positive object N, so that two negative halves add together to give the original positive. It might look like this:

1	one whole		
–	one half	*such that*	$- + - = +$
i	one quarter	*such that*	$i + i = -$

When this scheme takes place in exponential space then indeed the + operations convert to x operations and we are back to the conventional number system.

8. **more room for solutions of equations to exist:** J. Stillwell (2010) *Mathematics and its History* p.275.

9. **Although Wessel's paper:** C. Wessel (1797) On the analytic representation of direction: An attempt. *Philosophical Transactions*, Royal Danish Academy of Sciences (1799).

10. **with the variable b representing a radian measure of rotation:** There appears to be no standard for writing a complex number as either $a + bi$ or $a + ib$. Florian Cajori's *History of Mathematical Notations* (1928) has no entry. Thomas' most influential *Calculus* textbook (1951) uses ib, as does Roger Penrose (2004) in *The Road to Reality*. Many other authors write bi, as do Courant & Robbins (1941) in their *What is Mathematics?*. Wikipedia uses both within the same article. The same ambiguity exists with regard to writing either $e^{i\alpha}$ or $e^{\alpha i}$. A clear majority use $e^{i\alpha}$ except for Penrose and Wikipedia who use both. It gets rather silly when the choice includes $e^{ni\alpha}$ or $e^{in\alpha}$ or $e^{i(\alpha+2k\pi)}$ etc. In this text I write bi and $e^{i\alpha}$, except when I don't.

11. **know it must be the truth:** Benjamin Peirce, Charles Peirce's father, is quoted in E. Kasner & J. Newman (1940) *Mathematics and the Imagination* p.103.

12. **down into the very depths of existence:** Keith Devlin is quoted in P. Nahin (2011) *Dr. Euler's Fabulous Formula* p.1. Like many famous quotes, this one is widely credited to Devlin, citing his qualifications but without offering a source.

13. **found its way into textbooks and computational engines:** Changing the dependence on base-e would percolate changes throughout the calculus. It is thus preferable to establish a separate line of thought based upon reflection and not derived from Euler's identity. However, without extending

into established mathematical results that conform to Euler's definition, it
is also the case that

$$\text{with} \quad \# \neq e \qquad \#^{i\pi} + 1 = 0$$

14. **as the circumference of a circle is to the diameter:** A. DeMorgan (1915)
A Budget of Paradoxes Vol1. p.319-320. Online 10/19 at http://www-history.
mcs.st-andrews.ac.uk/Quotations/De_Morgan.html and at books.google.com

15. ***Units are indeed base-free:*** A long-standing mathematical aesthetic is
that the theorems of arithmetic should be base-free. As a measurement,
however, the value of π depends upon it's ubiquitous **unit circle**. The choice
of base interacts with the radius of a unit circle due to Euler's definition
that $e^{i\pi} = -1$. As a dimensionless ratio, π does not require the radius to be
unitary. Instead circularity is defined intrinsically as a constant curvature.
James forms are intentionally base-free, however here we find π and e
explicitly tangled together. A question we are exploring is whether or not
either is essential/fundamental/unitary.

It is possible to define the magnitude of 2π to be what we
now call 1, a design decision that would convert the magnitude of our conventional 1 to the value $1/(2\pi)$. Scaling
circumference to radius converts π to 1 and converts J to
i. Culturally we have chosen 1 as our unit, making π not
a unit but rather a comparison to 1. The linear unit 1 is

so deeply ingrained into our concept of arithmetic that to suggest that it is
a design decision with consequences might sound bizarre. Our notation
explicitly hides the influence of 1. We write a instead of $1a$ for real numbers,
$a + bi$ instead of $a1 + bi$ for complex numbers, a instead of $a/1$ for ratios,
etc. The circumference of a circle however provides an overt option as the
fundamental circular unit, as do e and J.

16. **can include any number of rotations around the polar circle:** With
rotation we can go two and three times around. Aside from phenomenal
rotations, such as 7200 rotations each minute for a mechanical hard-drive
storage device, we hear about multiple rotations a lot from Olympic sports.
Gymnasts and divers and extreme skiers rotate their bodies multiple times.
Not only do we need to identify a 360° rotation, we must also be able to
identify 720° and 1080° rotations. Measured in radians these rotations are
2π and 4π and 6π. The compact disc player rotates through 240π radians
every second.

Chapter 40

Trigonometry

Without knowledge of triangles there is no trigonometry;
... without trigonometry we put back the clock millennia
to Standard Darkness Time and antedate the Greeks.[1]
— George Pólya (1963)

Trigonometry has evolved over thousands of years, from describing right triangles to describing circular motion to describing physical and electromagnetic waves to providing conceptual structure for complex analysis. Four millennia ago the Babylonian and Egyptian civilizations found that when the angles of a right triangle are held constant, the ratios of any two sides remain constant regardless of the size of the triangle. These ratios developed into the familiar functions sine, cosine and tangent.

Here we will develop trigonometry without regard to triangles, rotations, waves, geometry or analytic algebra. The central concept is the **reflection** J; the only tools are the James axioms implemented by pattern substitution. We will call upon the idea of a unit fraction of J and Euler's mapping of trigonometric and exponential functions. Of course, we will also need to refer to more familiar concepts involving triangular and circular relations within the metalanguage in order to anchor the James imaginary structure of *fractional reflection* to familiar concepts.

The intent is to try to stay as close as possible to simple arithmetic while still accommodating the form of J. Since Euler provided the currently accepted definition of our interpretation of J as ln −1, an objective is to deconstruct and simplify his work. The motivation continues to be a desire to explore alternative ways of thinking about elementary arithmetic and geometry. And of course Chapter 39.6 establishes an intimate relation between J, i and π.

The trigonometric functions map dimensionless ratios of lengths to angles. Since a right triangle is extremely simple, with three sides and one variable angle, understanding one trigonometric function leads quickly to understanding the others. We'll first focus on a restricted version of the cosine function.

The goal is to replace the imaginary concept i with the boundary form J, and thus to eliminate the dependency of the Euler equation on the complex plane. The primary modification is the conversion of the concept of rotation through two-dimensional complex space into the imaginary concept of a **partial reflection** on a one-dimensional number line. Sinusoidal oscillation in one-dimension illustrates that trigonometry does not require a two-dimensional spatial geometry. In fact the common display of sine waves takes a one-dimensional oscillation between −1 and +1 and adds a linear time dimension, in effect condensing dynamic temporal behavior into a static spatial display. Alternatively we can define π to be the time it takes a sine oscillation to travel from 1 to −1. One-dimensional examples include

— the movement of water molecules in a wave

— the path of a pendulum (without procession)

— the up and down bobbing of a spring

— the standing wave in a vibrating string

— the back-and-forth oscillation of air molecules that propagates sound.

40.1 The Form of Reflection

Chapter 39.5 introduces Euler's unit circle equations that convert between orthogonal and polar coordinate systems. For an arbitrary angle α measured in radians,

$$e^{i\alpha} = \cos\alpha + i\sin\alpha$$
$$e^{-i\alpha} = \cos\alpha - i\sin\alpha$$

Euler equations

The association of trigonometric ratios with exponential expressions allows a quite natural transition between geometry and James forms interpreted as exponential and logarithmic functions. Solving the two equations above for the sin and cos yields

$$\cos\alpha = (1/2)(e^{i\alpha} + e^{-i\alpha})$$
$$\sin\alpha = (1/(2i))(e^{i\alpha} - e^{-i\alpha})$$

exponential trigonometry

S_α Notation

We'll introduce a convenience abbreviation S_α within the James form to bundle the concept of **rotation as reflection** into a single label. The Greek letter alpha, α, indicates an arbitrary angle of rotation with the explicit constraint that α is quantized by π/N. The J/2 frame provides the equivalent of Euler's rotation indicator i.

$i\alpha$ ☞ S_α =*label*= (J/2 [α])   *with* α = π/N *and* N *in* $\mathbb{Z}$

S_α stands in place of a J-fraction.

S_α = (J/2 [	α	])		hybrid
(J/2 [	π/N	])		substitute
(J/2 [	π	][1/N])		substitute
(J/2 [(<J/2> [J])][1/N])				substitute
(J/2	<J/2> [J]	[1/N])		clarify
(		[J]	[1/N])	cancel
		J/N		substitute

Here is the exponential component of Euler's equation expressed as a James form.

$e^{i\alpha}$ ☞ (S_α) = (J/N)   *with* α = π/N

Euler rotation to James reflection

Later we'll demonstrate that the quantized unit fraction generalizes to multiples and to sums of reflections, just

angle ☞	J/2 frame	exponential expression ☞	reflective form
0	(<J/2> [ ]) = *void*	e^0	( )
π/6	(<J/2> [J][1/6])	$e^{i\pi/6}$	(J/6)
π/2	(<J/2> [J][1/2])	$e^{i\pi/2}$	(J/2)
5π/6	(<J/2> [J][5/6])	$e^{i5\pi/6}$	(5J/6)
π/1	(<J/2> [J])	$e^{i\pi}$	(J) = <o>
2π	(<J/2> [J J]) = *void*	$e^{i2\pi}$	(J J) = o
π/N	(<J/2> [J][1/N])	$e^{i\pi/N}$	(J/N)
kπ/N	(<J/2> [J][k/N])	$e^{ik\pi/N}$	(kJ/N)
π/3 + π/4	(<J/2> [J/3 J/4])	$e^{i(\pi/3 + \pi/4)}$	(J/3 J/4)

Figure 40-1: *Angles, reflections and their exponential form*

like the Euler exponential generalizes to multiples and sums of angles. Specifically, in hybrid notation

$$e^{i(k\alpha+\beta)} \quad ☞ \quad (S_{k\alpha+\beta}) = (J/2 \, [k\alpha \, \beta])$$

We'll assume that α and ß have a common fractional decomposition N and that no angles multiply or sum to more than 2π. That is, full rotations do not accumulate. We could say that α is modulo 2π. Figure 40-1 shows various conventional angles, their exponential expressions and their James forms.

The S_α notation is subscripted with the *interpretation* of the angle of rotation α as a unit fraction of π. This is a potentially controversial notational choice since it confounds a labeled James form S with a parameter α from the interpretation. Maintaining a reminder within the James form of the conventional *angle of rotation* may help to bridge the gap between the spatial thinking of the complex plane and the linear thinking of the number line. Should the context of α be unambiguous, we'll drop the subscript and write S.

The S label helps to visually highlight symmetries in the form of J-fraction trigonometric functions.

With α = π/N *and* S = J/N *and* N *in* ℤ

> cos α = ([(S) (<S>)]<[2]>)
> sin α = ([(S)<(<S>)>]<[2i]>)

form of cosine and sine

These forms are expressed more conveniently as

2 cos α	☞	(S) (<S>)
2i sin α		(S)<(<S>)>
2 sin α		(<J/2> [(S)<(<S>)>])

At this point the James forms are literal transcriptions of Euler's equations.

40.2 Cosine

Unit reflection takes place along the 1-axis, getting us from +1 to −1 (and back). The cosine function is also situated on the 1-axis, also varying from +1 to −1. The conventional value of the cosine is determined by the projection onto the real 1-axis of the radius as it rotates around the origin of a unit circle. Cos α *is a projection of the unit semicircle onto the* 1-axis. The projection is similar to the projection of both the parabola and the exponential curve onto the 1-axis explored in Chapter 38.4. The measure of the cosine function is linearized by mapping onto the linear number line with the evenly spaced units of the number line defined by fractions of π. The π of course comes from the radian measure of the circumference of a semicircle.

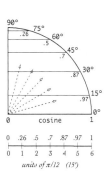

With appropriate notational conventions the cosine function can be represented in Cartesian, polar, exponential or James coordinate systems. Of particular importance, orthogonal coordinates can be expressed in terms of the trigonometric functions.

With r = √(x² + y²) *and* α = arctan y/x

$$\{x,y\} \quad \Rightarrow \quad \{r \cos α, r \sin α\} \qquad \textit{orthogonal coordinates}$$

Polar coordinates can be expressed as exponentials:

$$\{r,α\} \quad \Rightarrow \quad \{e^a, e^{iα}\} \qquad \textit{polar coordinates}$$

James forms express the same coordinate or polar location as a containment structure.

James form

$$\{r, \alpha\} \quad \Rightarrow \quad (r \, (J/2 \, [\alpha]))_\#$$

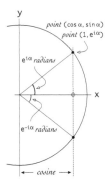

point (cos α, sin α)
point (1, $e^{i\alpha}$)

$e^{i\alpha}$ *radians*

$e^{-i\alpha}$ *radians*

← *cosine* →

In Euler's exponential notation a trigonometric function is the average of a base-e exponential and its conjugate. The exponent is a complex number while its reciprocal is the **conjugate** of the complex number. In the case of a unit circle, the real component of the exponent is zero.

$$2 \cos \alpha = e^{0 + i\alpha} + e^{0 - i\alpha}$$

We'll use this exponential expression to generate the James form, and for easier reading compute 2 cos α. To come to an understanding of the James form of trigonometric functions, we will focus on the S subforms.[2] The S notation is shorthand for the Euler exponent iα, so that (S) ☞ $e^{i\alpha}$.

$$2 \cos \alpha = (e^{i\alpha} + e^{-i\alpha}) \qquad \textit{with} \quad \alpha = \pi/N$$

hybrid

$$\text{☞} \quad (i\alpha)(<i\alpha>)$$

substitute

$$(S)(<S>) \qquad \textit{with} \quad S = J/N$$

The sum of (S) and (<S>) defines the cosine as well as the identities associated with it. The James form of the cosine can be read as a combination of a fractional reflection J/N and its opposite polarity across the x-axis <J/N>. In turn (S) as (J/N) is the form of the Nth root of −1 while (<S>) is the respective complex conjugate.

J-fraction cosine

$$2 \cos \pi/N \quad \text{☞} \quad (J/N)(<J/N>)$$

Trigonometric identities are tightly woven, providing transformations for half-angles, double-angles, sums of angles and multiples of angles. The following section shows that this diversity is redundant, an artifact created by an excess of planar distinctions introduced by the concept of rotation. Later we will explore the *reflective* cosine, a simplification that eliminates the implicit rotational model as well as the factor of 2 in the definition of the cosine.

Cosine Symmetry

The fundamental symmetry of the cosine function is that it is *sign-blind* to its argument. The demonstration is elegant.

$$\cos\ \alpha = \cos(-\alpha)$$

$2 \cos \alpha$ ☞ $\quad$ (<S>)($\quad$ S $\quad$)

$\quad\quad\quad$ (<S>)(<<S>>) $\quad$ ☞ $\quad$ $2 \cos(-\alpha)$ $\qquad$ wrap

Geometrically the magnitude and polarity of the cosine of a rotation π/N in the positive direction (conventionally counterclockwise) is the same as that of a rotation in the negative direction (clockwise). Reflection of the angle α is inert since the geometric reflection is across the x-axis from +y to −y while the James form does not extend into the y-axis (or in the case of complex numbers, the i-axis).

Figure 40-2 verifies the James form with some essential values of the cosine function. These results place the value of cosine on the 1-axis for rotations of 0, π and 2π radians, and on the i-axis for +π/2 and −π/2 radians. The James computation places the angle α within the form of S_α and then places S_α within the form of the cosine, $(S_\alpha)(<S_\alpha>)$. The figure also shows the computation of the roots of −1 from the single form (S_α). This mapping suggests that the cosine can be determined from one instance of S_α rather than two, and that the multiplication of the cosine by 2 might be treated as an artifact of the two-dimensional rotational model. In Euler's conceptualization the factor of 2 arises from averaging the exponential complex number $e^{a+i\alpha}$ and its conjugate $e^{a-i\alpha}$. Averaging is necessary to eliminate the imaginary sine component of the computation from the cosine as a complex number.

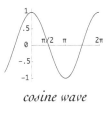

cosine wave

$e^{\pm i\alpha} = \cos \alpha \pm i \sin \alpha$

Cosine Squared

We'll need $\cos^2 \alpha$ for several trigonometric relations, so here is the S form for $\cos^2 \alpha$.

$4 \cos^2 \alpha$ ☞ $\quad$ ([2 cos α][2 cos α]) $\qquad$ hybrid

$\quad\quad\quad$ ([(S)(<S>)][(S)(<S>)]) $\qquad$ substitute

$\quad\quad\quad$ (S S)(S <S>)(<S> S)(<S><S>) $\qquad$ disperse/clarify

$\quad\quad\quad$ (S S)($\quad$)($\quad$)(<S><S>) $\qquad$ cancel

$\quad\quad\quad$ ($\quad$ 2S $\quad$)($\quad$ <2S> $\quad$) oo $\qquad$ join/substitute

$\quad\quad\quad\quad$ ☞ $\quad$ $(e^{i2\alpha} + e^{-i2\alpha}) + 2$

angle ☞ S_α (S)(<S>)	☞ *expression*
$\alpha = 0$ $S_0 = (J/2 \ [\ ]) = void$	
$\Rightarrow$ $(\ )(< >)$	2 cos 0
$(\ )(\ \ )$	$1 + 1 = 2$
cos *void* = o	cos 0 = 1
$(([J][\ ])) = (\ )$	$(-1)^{0/1} = 1$
$\alpha = \pi/2$ $S_{\pi/2} = J/2$	
$\Rightarrow$ $(J/2)\ (<J/2>)$	2 cos $\pi/2$
$(J/2)<(\ J/2\ )>$	0
cos J/2 = *void*	cos $\pi/2 = 0$
$(([J]<[2]>)) = (J/2)$	$(-1)^{1/2} = i$
$\alpha = \pi$ $S_\pi = J$	
$\Rightarrow$ $(J)(<\ J\ >)$	2 cos π
$(J)(<[(J)]>)$	$-1 + (1/-1) = -2$
cos J = <o>	cos $\pi = -1$
$(([J][o])) = (J)$	$(-1)^{1/1} = -1$
$\alpha = -\pi/2$ $S_{-\pi/2} = <J/2>$	
$\Rightarrow$ $(<J/2>)\ (<<J/2>>)$	2 cos $-\pi/2$
$(<J/2>)<(\ <J/2>\ )>$	0
cos <J/2> = *void*	cos $-\pi/2 = 0$
$(([J]<[<2>]>)) = (<J/2>)$	$(-1)^{-1/2} = 1/i$

Figure 40-2: *James cosines for multiples of* $\pi/2$

Squaring the cosine doubles the S forms. That is, the 1/N fractional reflection has been doubled to 2/N.[3] Therefore

$$4 \cos^2 \alpha = 2 \cos 2\alpha + 2$$
$$\cos^2 \alpha = (\cos 2\alpha + 1)/2$$

Here is the form of $\cos^2$ compared to the form of cos.

form of cosine 2 cos α ☞ (S)(< S>)

form of cosine² 4 cos² α ☞ (2S)(<2S>) 2

We must take care that the multiplier 2 in the hybrid form 2S above is not read as the construction of two J forms which would trigger an application of J-void. It is S that is doubling, not J itself; the hybrid 2S form helps to keep this clear. It is better here to consider both i and J as labels rather than operators.

Cosine Identities

We can use the forms of cos and $\cos^2$ to demonstrate other trigonometric identities. Here for example is the **double angle identity for cosine** which is a direct rearrangement of the construction of the $\cos^2 \alpha$ on the prior page.

$$\cos 2\alpha = 2 \cos^2 \alpha - 1$$

Although there are coherent geometrical and algebraic proofs of this identity, we are approaching it without the Pythagorean equation, indeed without the second dimension. Doubling a partial reflection doubles S both by definition and by construction. The demonstration of the $\cos 2\alpha$ relation is identical to the demonstration of the form of $\cos^2 \alpha$ above. Double angles and squared trigonometric functions are the same thing *by construction*.

$$4 \cos^2 \alpha - 2 \quad ☞ \quad (2S)(<2S>) \text{ oo } <oo>$$
$$(2S)(<2S>) \qquad\qquad \text{cancel}$$
$$☞ \ 2 \cos 2\alpha$$

The **multiple-angle formulas** use the exponential form of cosine and sine to provide a succinct representation, making $\cos 2\alpha$ a simple instance. In general

$$2 \cos k\alpha = e^{ik\alpha} + e^{-ik\alpha} \quad ☞ \quad (kS)(<kS>)$$

Again a comparison,

2 cos α	☞	(S)(< S>)
2 cos 2α		(2S)(<2S>)
2 cos kα		(kS)(<kS>)
4 cos^2 α		(2S)(<2S>) 2

The form of the cosine can be parameterized by any rational multiple of π radians, and thus any rational fraction of a single reflection. The general theme that is unfolding:

Operations on the quantized angle α transfer directly to the same operations on S.

We have seen, for example, these mappings.

$$S = (J/2 \ [\ \alpha \ ])$$
$$<S> = (J/2 \ [<\alpha>])$$
$$2S = (J/2 \ [2\alpha \ ])$$
$$kS = (J/2 \ [k\alpha \ ])$$

Next we will see that the sum and difference of angles maintains an analogous $J/2$ frame structure.

$$S_\alpha \ S_\beta = (J/2 \ [\alpha \ \beta])$$

Sum of Angles

The product/sum formulas convert trigonometric functions of the sum of angles to products of functions for single angles. For example,

$$2 \cos \alpha \ \cos \beta = \cos(\alpha + \beta) + \cos(\alpha - \beta)$$

The structural relationships between multiplying functions and adding angles is demonstrated again below. We'll disassemble the above identity into three pieces and for simplicity presume that both α and β are rational fractions. First the sum of angles.

$$S_\alpha \ \ = (J/2 \ [\alpha \ \ \ \ \ \ ])$$
$$S_\beta \ \ = (J/2 \ [\ \ \ \ \beta \ ])$$
$$S_{\alpha+\beta} = (J/2 \ [\alpha \ \ \beta \ ])$$
$$S_{\alpha-\beta} = (J/2 \ [\alpha \ <\beta>])$$

Demonstration:

	S_α	S_β
substitute	$(J/2 \ [\alpha])$	$(J/2 \ [\beta])$
collect	$(J/2 \ [\alpha$	$\beta])$
label		$S_{\alpha+\beta}$

Here are the cosine forms for the sum of angles.

$$2 \cos(\alpha + \beta) \ ☞ \ (S_\alpha \ S_\beta \ )(<S_\alpha \ S_\beta>)$$
$$2 \cos(\alpha - \beta) \ ☞ \ (S_\alpha \ <S_\beta>)(<S_\alpha> \ S_\beta \ )$$

The sum of two double angle cosines has S forms in four different combinations.[4]

$$2 \cos(\alpha + \beta) + 2 \cos(\alpha - \beta) \ ☞$$

disperse/clarify

$$(S_\alpha \ S_\beta)(S_\alpha \ <S_\beta>)(<S_\alpha> \ S_\beta)(<S_\alpha><S_\beta>)$$

There are no interior square-brackets, so these forms do not reduce and are not directly interpretable as multiplication. Since potentially canceling pairs are separated by round-brackets, they do not cancel. To demonstrate the identity, we now need to disperse the product form, precisely as we did for $\cos^2$. In this case the two middle terms do not cancel.

$$(2 \cos \alpha) \times (2 \cos \beta) \;\; ☞$$
$$([(S_\alpha)(<S_\alpha>)][(S_\beta)(<S_\beta>)])$$
$$(S_\alpha \; S_\beta)(S_\alpha \; <S_\beta>)(<S_\alpha> \; S_\beta)(<S_\alpha><S_\beta>) \quad\quad \text{disperse/clarify}$$

This final product form is identical to the sum of angles form. Therefore

$$4 \cos \alpha \; \cos \beta = 2 \left(\cos(\alpha + \beta) + \cos(\alpha - \beta)\right)$$

The primary observation from this exercise is that the notation and conceptualization of cosine hides within it the idea that sums of angles and products (and squares) of the cosine function are different ways to disperse form, quite analogous to distribution of numeric multiplication over addition. At this point we can say,

Any linear transformation of a quantized angle of rotation can be expressed as a fractional reflection.

There are a plethora of other trigonometric identities that we could explore, but what would now be beneficial is to see the James form of the sine function.

40.3 Sine

Euler's exponential rotation functions also define the sine of an angle. There are shorter routes, in particular deriving the form of sine from the form of the cosine.

$$\sin \alpha = \cos(\pi/2 - \alpha) = \cos(\alpha - \pi/2)$$

Subtracting $\pi/2$ from the cosine argument shifts the sine wave backward by 1/4 of a wavelength relative to the cosine wave, aligning the two functions. For example,

$$\sin 0 = \cos(0 - \pi/2) = \cos(-\pi/2) = 0$$

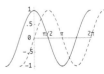

- - *sine wave*
—— *cosine wave*

Having abandoned the vertical direction (both common and complex), it is tempting to believe that the sine is everywhere zero. This does not take into account its direct connection to the cosine. It is the same oscillation but shifted in time, or in linear space, changing just like the offset cosine. The significant difference in the flattened perspective is that the sine must be sign-blind in the (nonexistent) vertical direction. Just like the cosine, a negative angle is not different from a positive angle since negative rotation cannot be distinguished from positive rotation.

Sine as Cosine

We'll derive the form of the sine directly from the offset (phase shifted) cosine.

$$\sin \alpha = \cos(\alpha - \pi/2)$$

This direct relationship does not require the i-axis; the J/2 frame occurs naturally, embedded in the π/2 offset.

$$S_\alpha = J/N \quad \textit{with} \quad \alpha = \pi/N$$

The conversion is essentially completed at the second step (indicated by an asterisk). The rest of the demonstration is rearranging and collecting the J/2 forms.

$$2\ \cos(\alpha - \pi/2) \quad ☞$$

	(S_α $<S_{\pi/2}>$)($<S_\alpha$ $<S_{\pi/2}>>$)
*react/substitute	(S_α $<J/2>$)($<S_\alpha>$ J/2)
create	(S_α $<J/2>$)($<S_\alpha>$ J/2 J/2 $<J/2>$)
substitute	(S_α $<J/2>$)($<S_\alpha>$ J $<J/2>$)
enfold	([(S_α)] $<J/2>$)([$(<S_\alpha>$ J)] $<J/2>$)
collect	([$(S_\alpha$)($<S_\alpha>$ J)] $<J/2>$)
enfold/J-convert	([$(S_\alpha$)< $(<S_\alpha>)$ >] $<J/2>$)

I'll use the hybrid notation to expose the form of i.

hybrid	$(<J/2>$ [$(S_\alpha)<(<S_\alpha>)>$]) = 2 sin α
cover	$<J/2>$ [$(S_\alpha)<(<S_\alpha>)>$] = [2 sin α]
move/cover	$(S_\alpha)<(<S_\alpha>)>$ = ([2 sin α] J/2)
enfold	$(S_\alpha)<(<S_\alpha>)>$ = ([2 sin α] [(J/2)])
	☞ 2i sin α

Exponential Sine

Now we'll construct the sine directly from its exponential definition. Since the constructions are very reminiscent of cosine, we can be terse.

$$2i \sin \alpha = (e^{i\alpha} - e^{-i\alpha}) \quad \text{☞} \quad (S_\alpha) < (<S_\alpha>) >$$

The structure of the sine is similar to that of cosine, in particular the presence of the S subforms. The scaling factor of 2i acknowledges the imaginary i-axis. Comparing the structure of sine and cosine,

2i sin α	☞	(S)<(<S>)>
2 cos α	☞	(S) (<S>)

form of i sine
form of cosine

The multiplication of sine by i in the scaling factor seems strange. I'll convert it into a form with the same multiplier as the cosine. The reflection that sine acquires in this conversion will come in handy when comparing to cosine.[5]

$$2 \sin \alpha \quad \text{☞} \quad ([1/i][(S)<(<S>)>]) \qquad \text{hybrid}$$
$$(<J/2> [(S)<(<S>)>]) \qquad \text{substitute,clarify}$$

The imaginary i-axis of sine is a J/2 frame. Here's the new comparison.

$$2 \cos \alpha \quad \text{☞} \quad (\qquad [(S) (<S>)]) \qquad \textbf{form of cosine}$$
$$2 \sin \alpha \quad \text{☞} \quad (<J/2> [(S)<(<S>)>]) \qquad \textbf{form of sine}$$

Sine Symmetry

Let's confirm the essential symmetries of sine. For the sine a negative rotation changes the polarity of the entire function. This means only that the polarity of each S form changes. And this adjustment is exactly what is needed to compensate for the change from α to −α in the symmetry of the sine.

$$\sin \alpha = - \sin -\alpha$$

As we saw with cosine, the form of α and the form of S are tightly coupled. Recall that a negative angle converts directly into <S>.

angle ☞ S_α	(S)<(<S>)>	☞	*expression*

$\alpha = 0$ $S_0 = (J/2\ [\ ]) = void$

$\Rightarrow$ ( )<( )>   2i sin 0

void   0

sin *void* = *void*   sin 0 = 0

$\alpha = \pi/2$ $S_{\pi/2} = J/2$

$\Rightarrow$ (J/2)<(<J/2>)>   2i sin π/2

(J/2) (J/2)

([[(J/2)][2])

(J/2 [2])   2i

sin J/2 = (J/2 [2])/2i   sin π/2 = 1

$\alpha = \pi$ $S_\pi = J$

$\Rightarrow$ (J)<(< J >)>   2i sin π

(J)<(<[<o>]>)>

(J) (<[o]>)

(J) ( )   −1 + 1 = 0

sin J = <o> o /2i = *void*   sin π = 0

$\alpha = -\pi/2$ $S_{-\pi/2} = <J/2>$

$\Rightarrow$ (<J/2>)<(<<J/2>>)>   2i sin −π/2

<(J/2) (J/2)>

<(J/2 [2])>   −2i

sin <J/2> = <(J/2 [2])>/2i   sin −π/2 = −1

Figure 40-3: *James sines for multiples of π/2*

---

2 sin α ☞ (<J/2> [(S)<(<S>)>])

react   (<J/2> [<<(S)>>(<S>)>])

promote   <(<J/2> [<(S)>>(<S>)]>

wrap   <(<J/2> [<(<<S>>)>>(<S>)]>

☞ −2 sin −α

Figure 40-3 checks the James sine for critical values. The values of α are the same as those for cosine in Figure 40-1 however the S forms need to be multiplied by 1/2i to express the value of the sine. Here is the origin of the sine's scaling factor.

$$1/2i \quad ☞ \quad (<[([\quad i \quad] \quad [2])]>)$$
$$(<[([(J/2)] \quad [2])]>) \qquad \text{substitute}$$
$$(< \quad J/2 \quad ><[2] \quad >) \qquad \text{clarify/split}$$

In Figure 40-3 this scaling is necessary only for $\alpha = \pm\pi/2$.

$$(S_{\pi/2})<(<S_{\pi/2}>)> = (J/2 \; [2]) \quad ☞ \quad 2i$$

$$\sin J/2 = ([\quad 1/2i \quad][\quad 2i \quad])$$
$$([(<J/2><[2]>)][(J/2 \; [2])]) \qquad \text{substitute}$$
$$(\; <J/2><[2]> \quad J/2 \; [2] \;) \qquad \text{clarify}$$
$$(\qquad\qquad\qquad\qquad) \quad ☞ \quad 1 \qquad \text{cancel}$$

The figure also illustrates the symmetry of $\sin -\pi/2$:

$$\sin <J/2> = <\sin <<J/2>>> = <\sin J/2> \qquad \text{unwrap}$$

The generic form of the *fractional reflection* sine has been demonstrated to be

$$2i \; \sin(\pi/N) \quad ☞ \quad (J/N)<(<J/N>)> \qquad \textbf{J-fraction sine}$$

Like the cosine this form generalizes to sums and multiples of π/N.

Sine Squared

Here's the form of $\sin^2$ to be used next in the Pythagorean theorem. For simplicity the scaling factor is multiplied out.

$$(2i \; \sin\alpha)^2 = -4 \; \sin^2\alpha$$

$4 \; \sin^2\alpha \quad ☞$

$$<(\; [(S)<(<S>)>] \; [(S)<(<S>)>] \;)>$$
$$<(S \; S)<(<S> \; S)><(S \; <S>)><<(<S><S>)>>> \qquad \text{disperse/clarify}$$
$$<(S \; S)<(<S> \; S) \quad (S \; <S>)> \quad (<S \quad S>) \quad > \qquad \text{unwrap/join}$$
$$<(S \; S)<(\qquad) \; (\quad)> \; (<S \quad S>)> \qquad \text{cancel}$$
$$<(2S)(<2S>)> \; oo \qquad \text{substitute/react}$$

Here is the surprising comparison of $\cos^2$ and $\sin^2$.

$$4 \cos^2\alpha \quad ☞ \quad (2S)(<2S>) \quad 2 \qquad \textbf{form of cosine}^2$$
$$4 \sin^2\alpha \quad ☞ \quad <(2S)(<2S>)> \; 2 \qquad \textbf{form of sine}^2$$

40.4 Pythagorean Theorem

Combining $\cos^2 \alpha$ with $\sin^2 \alpha$ yields the Pythagorean identity. From here it is obvious that

$$4 \sin^2 \alpha + 4 \cos^2 \alpha = 4$$

since

$$4 \sin^2 \alpha + 4 \cos^2 \alpha \quad \text{☞}$$

hybrid   <(2S)(<2S>)>   2   (2S)(<2S>) 2

cancel   2   2   ☞   4

Comparing the form of cosine with the form of sine, we can see that the scaling factor i is just a way to express *one-half of a negative*. Well, technically one-half in exponential space and the square root in linear space. Conventionally we have a difficult time applying operators to operators, as in $\sqrt{-}$, but with the boundary forms nesting operators is natural since each form is both object and operator.

Both $\sin^2$ and $\cos^2$ contribute one-half of the final numeric result. Squaring doubles the S forms in each of sin and cos, that is why the squares are divided by four rather than by two. Sine includes the $1/(2i)$ scaling factor solely to provide a form that when self-multiplied generates a negative. The negative is necessary in order to cancel the positive contribution of cosine. And fundamentally, the doubled S forms are identical so that they can cancel. (<J/2> [...]) creates the phase offset of $\pi/2$, and is thus the primary differentiation between the two functions. This offset must be compensated, and that's what <(S)> does, reflecting (S) in this metaphor, through π radians.

Tangent

The tangent is defined as the ratio of sine to cosine. We'll convert this expression to the James form directly by substituting the forms of sin and cos after canceling the mutual factor of 2.

$$\tan \alpha = \sin \alpha / \cos \alpha$$

tan α = (<J/2>[(S)<(<S>)>]) / (S)(<S>)   hybrid

      (<J/2>[(S)<(<S>)>]<[(S)(<S>)]>)   clarify

We'll continue to work with S forms after separating the scaling factor $1/i$.

tan α = (S-form-of-sin α/S-form-of-cos α) x $1/i$

   ☞ ([(S)<(<S>)>]<[(S)(<S>)]>) x $1/i$ substitute/hybrid

The objective is to combine the S forms as much as possible.

   i tan α ☞

([(S)<(<S>)>] <[(S   )(<S>)]>)

([(S)<(<S>)>] <[(S S <S>)([o] <S>)]>)   create/enfold

([(S)<(<S>)>] <[([(S S)   o] <S>)]>)   enfold/collect

([(S)<(<S>)>] < [(2S)   o] <S> >)   substitute/clarify

([(S)<(<S>)>] < [(2S)   o]> S)   react

(S <[(2S) o]> S) ([<(<S>)>]<[(2S) o]> S)   disperse/clarify

(S <[(2S) o]> S)<(<S> <[(2S) o]> S)>   promote/clarify

(2S <[(2S) o]>)<(<[(2S) o]>)>   substitute/cancel

([(2S)]<[(2S) o]>) ([<o>] <[(2S) o]>)   enfold/demote

([(2S) <o>] <[(2S) o]>)   collect

Returning to the form of the tangent.

tan α ☞ ([(2S) <o>] <[(2S) o]>) x $1/i$ hybrid

     (<J/2> [(2S) <o>]<[(2S) o]>)   J/2 frame/clarify

  ☞ $-i\,(e^{i2\alpha} - 1)/(e^{i2\alpha} + 1)$

Euler Form

We have sufficient structural information about sin and cos to revisit to the Euler equation. Currently we have

$e^{i\alpha}$ ☞ ((J/2 [α])) = (S) ☞ cos α + i sin α

   with   2 cos α ☞ (S) (<S>)

           2i sin α ☞ (S)<(<S>)>

Now we can demonstrate that the general Euler equation is valid using James forms, without calling upon the concepts of exponentiation or rotation into a complex plane.

We'll need to show that

$$\cos \alpha + i \sin \alpha \ =?= \ e^{i\alpha}$$

or more conveniently

$$2 \cos \alpha + 2i \sin \alpha \ =?= \ 2e^{i\alpha}$$

☞   (S)(<S>) (S)<(<S>)> =?= (S)(S)

cancel   (S)   (S)   = (S)(S)

The James axioms have provided a substantively different way to understand Euler's equation. From the James perspective the appearance of i is not so much an introduction of the complex plane as it is an attempt to record *one-half* of a reflection. We have replaced the concept of exponentiation as rotation by the James concept of a J/2 frame, S = (J/2 [α]). And we have replaced the concept of trigonometric functions with the idea of splitting (S) into two parts. Although Euler's excursion into the complex plane makes seminal contributions to the discipline of complex analysis, neither i nor the complex plane appear to be strictly necessary for trigonometric functions.

DeMoivre's Theorem

Abraham DeMoivre
1667-1754

DeMoivre's theorem relates an exponential power to multiplication of angles. It was a precursor to Euler's theorem.

$$e^{i\alpha} = \cos \alpha + i \sin \alpha$$

In standard notation, DeMoivre's theorem looks impressive.

$$(\cos \alpha + i \sin \alpha)^n = \cos n\alpha + i \sin n\alpha$$

The theorem seems to require proof by induction, since the arbitrary power on the left-side is computationally onerous. We'll use the left-side of Euler's equation for which $e^{i\alpha} = (S)$:

$(\cos \alpha + i \sin \alpha)^n$ ☞   (([[(S)]][n]))

clarify   (([S][n]))

substitute   (nS   )

An earlier multiple-angle insight applies to the right-side,

$$2 \ \ \cos k\alpha = (kS) \ (<kS>)$$
$$2i \ \sin k\alpha = (kS)<(<kS>)>$$

The demonstration of Euler's equation in the prior section applies directly.

```
2 (cos nα + i sin nα)   ☞
          (nS)(<nS>)(nS)<(<nS>)>
          (nS)        (nS)                        cancel
              ☞ 2 (cos α + i sin α)ⁿ
```

40.5 Derivatives

Let's apply boundary differentiation to find the structural derivatives of sin and cos. We'll verify well-known results while calling upon only boundary forms:

$$dcos\ \alpha = -sin\ \alpha$$
$$dsin\ \alpha =\ \ cos\ \alpha$$

I'll show each step in the derivation since this is a refrain of Chapter 37. We'll first note that dS = (J/2).

```
dS = d(J/2 [α]                    )
        (J/2 [α][dJ/2 d[     α    ]])        d(.)
        (J/2 [α][     (<[α]> [dα])])        dc/d[.]
        (J/2 [α][     (<[α]> [ o])])        dvar
        (J/2 [α]        <[α]>      )        clarify
        (J/2                       )  ☞  i   cancel
```

S replaces the Euler technique with an equivalent structure based on J reflection, S = J/N, with N representing a fractional reflection. The derivative of S is (J/2). The steps in the differentiation above eliminate the *concept* of an angle α. This supports the idea that S is a *half-reflection*, a simple fraction of polarity rather than a denizen of the unit circle.

dCosine

Our concept of cosine lies completely on the 1-axis. It's derivative is a function only of S. We can read the form of the cosine as the combination of a round-bracketed form S with its round-bracketed reflection <S>. The hybrid factor 2 is there only to compensate for having two S forms.

	2 cos α = (S) (<S>)
du dv	2 dcos α = d(S) d(<S>)
d(.)/d<.>	(S [dS])(<S> [<dS>])
enfold	([(S)][dS])([(<S>)][<dS>])
promote/demote	([(S)][dS])([<(<S>)>][dS])
collect	([dS][(S)<(<S>)>])
substitute/wrap	([<<(J/2)>>][(S)<(<S>)>])
promote	<([<(J/2)>][(S)<(<S>)>]>>
J/2 toggle/clarify	<(<J/2> [(S)<(<S>)>]>>
	☞ 2 −sin α

A conventional derivation of dcos might progress from first principles using the definition of the limit derivative while introducing trigonometric identities that convert the sum of angles cos(x+h) into the *product* of functions, cos(x)cos(h) − sin(x)sin(h). This in turn calls upon either an arduous geometric construction or Euler's equation. The latter case uses the same structural foundations as the James approach. The former case uses an equivalent body of geometric knowledge in the Cartesian rather than the complex plane.

The James derivation above allows us to watch the evolution of the structure of the sin at the collect step. We can also see the origin of the scaling factor i in the form of the sin since dS = i. The *process* of differentiation requires the concept of half-reflection. Toward the end of the demonstration the sin takes on a negative value as a phase adjustment to realign polarity, that is, to shift the sin backwards to match the value of the cos.

dSine

We can see the same type of evolution for the derivative of the sine.

$$2 \ \sin α = \ (<J/2> \ [(S)<(<S>)>])$$
$$2 \ dsin α = d(<J/2> \ [(S)<(<S>)>])$$

This time we will use the *generic differentiation template* from Chapter 37. For simplicity, let K be the constant J/2.

```
(<K> [(S)<(<S>)>])  ⇒  (<K> [(S)₃<(<S>)₄>]₂)₁
```

contents

1	<K>[2]	
2	(3)<(4)>	
3	S	
4	<S>	

```
(1 [                                    ])
    (<[2]> [                        ])
        (3 [  ]) <(4 [    ])>
          dS          <dS>
```

As a constant dK = 0. Collapsing the template and dispersing,

```
(1 [(<[2]> [(3 [dS]) <(4 [<dS>])>])])        template
(1 [(<[2]> [(3 [dS]) (4 [ dS ]) ])])         promote/unwrap
(1   <[2]> [(3 [dS]) (4 [ dS ]) ] )          clarify
(1 <[2]> 3 [dS]) (1 <[2]> 4 [dS])            disperse/clarify
```

We know that dS = (J/2) = (K). Substituting for 1 and dS,

```
(<K>[2]<[2]> 3 [(K)]) (<K>[2]<[2]> 4 [(K)])   substitute
(<K>[2]<[2]> 3   K ) (<K>[2]<[2]> 4   K  )    clarify
(            3   ) (            4       )     cancel
(            S   ) (           <S>      )     substitute
                ☞  2 cos α
```

This sequence is common. We begin by transcribing into the James boundary form and then discover that most of the boundary distinctions are superfluous. The reduction sequence shows in detail the relationship between sine and cosine. The massive cancellation suggests that cos is a more natural basis for trigonometric functions since it does not embed multiple half-reflections.

Now we'll try an experiment to eliminate the factor 2 (i.e. the divisor 1/2) within the definition of sine and cosine.

40.6 Reflective Trigonometry

Thus far we have transcribed trigonometry into James form without intentional innovation. The concept of an *angle* was historically an essential feature of a *triangle*. Later the angle was reconceptualized to be a fraction of a full rotation of 2π radians around a unit circle centered at {0, 0}. The unit circle *redefines* the units on the number line as angular rotation with 1 ☞ 0 and −1 ☞ π. Euler then mapped the idea of rotation into exponential space with a new type of unit that

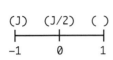

(J) (J/2) ( )

−1   0   1

redefines 0 on the number line as a rotation of π/2 radians so that 0 ☞ i. Now we'll explore the idea that angles can be reconceptualized as fractions of the unit reflection J to arrive at a trigonometry based on 1D reflection rather than 2D rotation, with 1 ☞ ( ), 0 ☞ (J/2) and −1 ☞ (J).[6]

Reflective Cosine

The James form of cosine exposes a redundancy.

$$2 \cos \alpha = (S)(<S>) \quad with \quad S = (J/2 \ [π/N]) = J/N$$

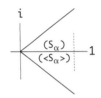

The cosines of positive and negative angles are equal. Both are necessary in order to cancel the imaginary part of S as a conventional complex number. This is also apparent in the symmetry of the cosine function,

$$\cos \alpha = \cos(-\alpha)$$

From the perspective of a cosine J/N is sign-blind.

$$S = J/N = <J/N> = <S>$$

To eliminate redundancy we'll redefine cosine *without a direction of rotation* by asserting +α = −α. The shift in perspective is from i as a complex rotation to J/2 as a half-reflection. Since S = <S> the factor of two in the form of cosine simply recognizes the duplication of (S). We'll name the **reflective cosine** rcos with an argument in terms of S.

reflective cosine

$$2 \ rcos \ S = (S)(S)$$
$$rcos \ S = (S) \quad with \quad S = J/N$$

All values of J/N *fall on the i-axis* as the radians associated with the angle π/N. $e^{iπ/N}$ generates a complex number z with Re(z) = cos J/N and Im(z) = sin J/N by Euler's formula. In building trigonometry on the features of J as a full reflection it's immediate that

rcos	0 = ( )	☞	cos 0	= 1
rcos	J/6 = (J/6)		cos π/6	= Re($e^{iπ/6}$)
rcos	J/2 = (J/2)		cos π/2	= 0
rcos	J/1 = (J)		cos π	= −1
rcos	2J/1 = (J J) = ( )		cos 2π	= 1
rcos	J/N = (J/N)		cos π/N	= Re($e^{iπ/N}$)

Without a vertical i-axis both 0 and i are sign-blind

$$(J/2) = i = 0 \quad and \quad (<J/2>) = -i = 0$$

Although π is still an active participant, it is a convenience label for J. Partial rotations are also partial reflections however the metric is no longer the 2π radians of the unit circle. It is fractions[7] of log −1 with the established mapping that

π/N *radians* ☞ J/N *fraction of a reflection*

Euler's shift in perspective places polar coordinates in an exponential space.

circular π ⇒ *exponential* i *with* $e^{i\pi} = -1$

Here we are moving polar coordinates into logarithmic space. The conversion is direct,

circular π ⇒ *logarithmic* J *with* J = iπ
exponential i ⇒ *logarithmic* J *with* J = [i][i]

The reflective cosine connects to existing mathematical tools that can *calculate* rcos for an arbitrary rational reflection. These tools are conceptualized in terms of rotations and angles so only the cognitive model changes for computation. The values of cos and rcos can be determined by calling upon the stepping stone J = iπ.[8]

$$\text{rcos } J/N = (J/N)_e \quad ☞ \quad \cos \pi/N = e^{i\pi/N}$$

The challenge is to find the x-coordinate of a specific point on a semicircle, or to find the projection of that point onto the x-axis. As an example, $\alpha = 30° = \pi/6$, with $S_{\pi/6} = J/6$

$$\text{rcos } J/6 \Rightarrow (\pi/6)_e$$

The principle value of a rotation in radians was defined by Euler to be a complex number

$$\text{rcos } J/6 \quad ☞ \quad e^{i\pi/6} = \sqrt{3}/2 + 1/2\, i$$

where the real part of the complex result, √3/2, is the value of the cosine and the imaginary part, 1/2, is the value of the sine. The projection of the complex coordinates of the point {√3/2, 1/2} onto the 1-axis is the x-coordinate √3/2. The imaginary part is projected onto the i-axis and is thus 0.

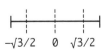

Cyclotomic Alternative

In calculating the value of $e^{(\ln -1)/6}$ a computational engine will transcribe it to $e^{i\pi/6}$ and then use Euler's techniques. This makes it difficult to establish J as a foundational concept. There is another route. Computationally Euler's exponential expression maps to the roots of −1.

$$e^{i\pi/N} = (-1)^{1/N}$$

Taking the logarithm of both sides shifts the equality from the exponential space of e to the logarithmic space of J.

$$\ln e^{i\pi/N} = \ln (-1)^{1/N} = 1/N \times \ln -1$$

$$i\pi/N = J/N$$

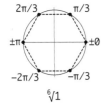

$2\pi/3 \qquad \pi/3$

$\pm\pi \qquad \pm0$

$-2\pi/3 \qquad -\pi/3$

$\sqrt[6]{1}$

The **cyclotomic equation** $x^n = 1$ has n solutions that are the n roots of unity.[9] The values of $1^{1/n}$ construct a regular n-gon in complex space with vertices falling on the complex unit circle. The n roots are spread evenly around a unit circle, each separated by $2\pi/n$ radians. The equation is closely related to DeMoivre's equation which provides its solutions.

deMoivre $\qquad e^{i\pi/n} = (\cos \pi + i \sin \pi)^{1/n} = \cos \pi/n + i \sin \pi/n$

substitute $\qquad e^{i\pi/n} = (\qquad -1 \qquad)^{1/n} = \cos \pi/n + i \sin \pi/n$

Similarly the solutions to $x^N = -1$ are arranged symmetrically on the complex unit circle in a slightly more complicated structure.[10] The x-coordinates of these roots align with the J/N unit fractions. Computing the rcos requires only a conversion from polar coordinates $\{1, \pi/N\}$ to orthogonal coordinates $\{rcos, rsin\}$. In DeMoivre's equation the value of rsin is always 0. The other solutions around the unit circle are the multiples of 1/N such as 3/N and (N−1)/N. Since reflection has no memory there are only N values. Centering the rotation on the positive i-axis, the range of x values covers the circle from −π to π, or more accurately from our perspective from (J) to ( ) in N quantized steps. The magnitude of N can be arbitrarily small.

$i = (-1)^{1/2}$

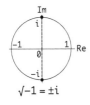

Im

-1 $\qquad$ 1 Re

0

$-i$

$\sqrt{-1} = \pm i$

$$e^{J/N} = rcos\ J/N + i\ rsin\ J/N$$

$$rcos\ J/N = e^{J/N} = (-1)^{1/N}$$

In the example of a one-sixth reflection J/6, the six evenly spaced values of rcos J/6 are for example the *real parts* of

$$e^{J/6},\ e^{3J/6},\ e^{5J/6},\ e^{-5J/6},\ e^{-3J/6},\ e^{-J/6}$$

with the principle value being $e^{J/6}$. In contrast to the circular diagrams that show the complex rotational solutions to Euler's equation, rcos has only one-half of the solutions since positive and negative y-values are collapsed.

$$\text{rcos } J/6 = \{e^{J/6},\ e^{3J/6},\ e^{5J/6}\}$$

As well for rcos, $e^{J/6} = -e^{5J/6}$ by symmetry.

$$\text{rcos } J/6 = \sqrt{3}/2 \qquad \text{rcos } 3J/6 = 0 \qquad \text{rcos } 5J/6 = -\sqrt{3}/2$$

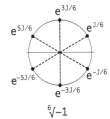

Fractions of Polarity

The imaginary i as $(-1)^{1/2}$ is a special case, an instance of a broader concept of **fractions of polarity**. We have observed that J aligns with a reflection that indicates a *change* in polarity, either $1 \Rightarrow -1$ or $-1 \Rightarrow 1$.[11] Direction of change is irrelevant. Expressing this simplification in radians, $+\pi = -\pi$. Using J we have removed π from trigonometry and with it the concept of circular rotation.

$$\text{rcos } J/N = (J/N) \quad \text{☞} \quad e^{\pi/N} = (-1)^{1/N} = i^{2/N}$$

The Nth root of -1 divides the concept of reflection into N unit fractions. These in turn provide new non-orthogonal axes, generally called **basis vectors**, that permit a richer non-orthogonal perspective on trigonometry.[12]

Reflective Sine

Analogous to cosine, we can simplify S in the form of the sine to generate the **reflective sine**, rsin. We begin with

$$2i \sin \pi/N \quad \text{☞} \quad (S)<(<S>)>$$
$$2\ \sin \pi/N \quad \text{☞} \quad (<J/2> \ [(S)<(<S>)>])$$

In the case of rsin, $(S) \neq (<S>)$ since negative angles change the polarity of the sine. However, for rsin

$$(S) = <(<S>)>$$

which is supported by the symmetry of the sine function.

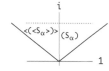

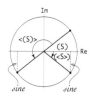

reflective sine

sum of angles

substitute

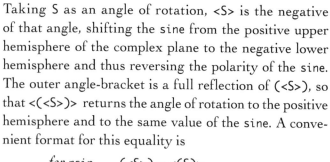

Taking S as an angle of rotation, <S> is the negative of that angle, shifting the sine from the positive upper hemisphere of the complex plane to the negative lower hemisphere and thus reversing the polarity of the sine. The outer angle-bracket is a full reflection of (<S>), so that <(<S>)> returns the angle of rotation to the positive hemisphere and to the same value of the sine. A convenient format for this equality is

$$\textit{for } rsin \qquad (<S>) = <(S)>$$

Although the sine represented by each of these forms is negative rather than positive, they are indeed equal. The redundancy in the trigonometric form is again apparent,

$$2i \; rsin \; S = (S)(S) \qquad \textit{with} \quad S = \pm J/N$$
$$i \; rsin \; S = (S)$$
$$rsin \; S = (<J/2> \; S)$$

The substantive difference between rsin and rcos is the presence of the subform <J/2> which aligns the sine with the cosine by shifting it backward by a one-half reflection. The perspective is that sine is specifically the phase shifted form of cosine,

$$rsin \; S = \quad rcos \; S \; <J/2> = (S \; <J/2>)$$

Since the rsin is now only the phase shifted rcos,

$$rcos \; S = i \; rsin \; S$$

Without relying upon rotational behavior, we can demonstrate the form of rsin purely within the reflective form.

$$\textit{With} \quad S = J/N \quad rsin \; S \quad ☞ \quad (S_{\alpha-\pi/2})$$
$$(S_\alpha \; <S_{\pi/2}>)$$
$$(S \; <J/2>)$$

Read both as Euler exponents and as roots of –1,

$$rsin \; S = (J/N \; <J/2>) \qquad ☞ \qquad Re(e^{i\pi(1/N - 1/2)})$$
$$rsin \; S \qquad ☞ \qquad (-1)^{(1/N - 1/2)} = (-1)^{(1/N)}/i$$

In the example of $\alpha = 30°$, we arrive at the familiar relationship of sin and cos within a right triangle

$$\sin \pi/6 = \cos(\pi/6 - \pi/2) = \cos(-\pi/3) = \cos(\pi/3)$$
$$rsin \; J/6 = rcos \; J/3 = (J/3)$$

Reflective Identities

Taking rcos and rsin to be new trigonometric functions, we'll quickly visit some of the established trigonometric identities. Our starting point is

With $S = J/N$ rcos $S =\partial ef=$ (S)
$\qquad\qquad\qquad$ rsin $S =\partial ef=$ (<J/2> S)
$\qquad\qquad\qquad$ i rsin $S =$ rcos $S =$ (S)

Cosine^2 and Sine^2

Quantized as rational fractions of J *(Section 40.3)*

$\qquad\qquad$ 4 cos^2 S ☞ (2S)(<2S>) oo $\qquad\qquad\qquad$ hybrid

$\qquad\qquad$ 4 sin^2 S ☞ <(2S)(<2S>)> oo $\qquad\qquad\qquad$ hybrid

Reflected as fractions of the unit x-axis *(this section)*
$\qquad$ rcos^2 S = (2S) $\qquad\qquad\qquad$ ☞ $e^{2i\pi/N}$
$\qquad$ rsin^2 S = (<J> 2S) = <(2S)> $\qquad$ ☞ $-e^{2i\pi/N}$

Pythagoras

Quantized $\qquad$ sin^2 S + cos^2 S = 1
Reflected $\qquad$ rsin^2 S + rcos^2 S
$\qquad$ ☞ $\quad$ <(2S)> $\quad$ (2S) $\;=$ *void* $\quad$ ☞ $\quad$ 0 $\qquad\qquad$ cancel

The phase shift of rsin^2 is twice $\pi/2$ which is a full reflection J. The magnitudes of each form are equal, so reflecting by a given magnitude and then reflecting back yields no change. The Pythagorean theorem collapses.

Cosine 2α

Quantized $\qquad$ cos 2S = cos^2 S − sin^2 S
Reflected $\qquad$ rcos 2S =?= rcos^2 S − rsin^2 S
$\qquad$ ☞ $\qquad$ (2S) =?= (2S) $\quad$ <<(2S)>>
$\qquad\qquad$ (2S) $\;\neq\;$ (2S) $\qquad$ (2S) $\qquad\qquad$ unwrap

The double angle (and the half-angle) formulas differ by a factor of 2. This can be traced back to the new relationship between doubling and squaring, which itself is DeMoivre's theorem with sine set to 0.

DeMoivre (sin = 0)

rcos 2S = rcos^2 S

Euler equation

Quantized $\qquad$ (S) = cos S + i sin S $\qquad\qquad$ hybrid
Reflected $\qquad$ (S) =?= (S) $\quad$ (S)

Again the results differ by a factor of 2 due to the phase shifted rsin which no longer cancels the contribution of rcos.

Sum of Angles

Quantized

$$2 \cos \alpha \, \cos \beta = \cos(\alpha + \beta) + \cos(\alpha - \beta)$$

Reflected   For rcos, $S_\beta = <S_\beta>$ so it is sufficient to show

$$([rcos \, S_\alpha][rcos \, S_\beta]) = rcos \, S_\alpha \, S_\beta$$

substitute
$$([\, (S_\alpha) \,][\, (S_\beta) \,]) = (S_\alpha \, S_\beta)$$

clarify
$$(\quad S_\alpha \qquad S_\beta \quad) = (S_\alpha \, S_\beta)$$

Rcos removes the scaling factor of 2 from cos but otherwise does not change its behavior.

Tangent

Quantized

$$\tan S = (<J/2> \; [(S)<(<S>)>]<[(S)(<S>)]>)$$

Reflected

$$rsin/rcos \; ☞ \; ([(<J/2> \, S)]<[(S)]>)$$

clarify
$$(\quad <J/2> \, S \quad < \quad S \quad >)$$

cancel
$$(\quad <J/2> \qquad\qquad) \quad ☞ \quad 1/i$$

$$rtan \, S = (<J/2>) \qquad\qquad i \; rtan \, S = (\,)$$

Since rcos and rsin have the same magnitude S, their ratio reduces to 1 when the phase shift is accounted for. Another way to say this is that the ratio is the phase shift.

In general reflected trigonometry eliminates the duplication that allows Euler's formula to provide concurrent values for sine and cosine. Relations that compare the two (tangent, Pythagoras) collapse without two orthogonal dimensions.

40.7 Remarks

The computational tractability of trigonometric functions is due to Euler's association of exponential functions with trigonometric ratios. In that sense this chapter provides a somewhat convenient notation for the Euler equation. In contrast *reflective trigonometry*, by reducing rotation to reflection, redefines both the Pythagorean theorem and the tangent. It's an experiment that requires further exploration. Next we head off to infinity.

Endnotes

1. **opening quote:** G. Pólya (1963/1977) *Mathematical Methods in Science* p.10.

2. **trigonometric functions, we will focus on the S subforms:** The S form is at this point simply a different notation for the exponent in Euler's equation. It does not offer new insight except within the context of iconic form.

3. **fractional reflection has been doubled to** $2/N$**:** This can also be seen clearly in exponential notation,

$$\cos \ \alpha = \ (e^{i\alpha} + e^{-i\alpha})/2$$
$$\cos^2 \ \alpha = [(e^{i\alpha} + e^{-i\alpha}) \ /2]^2$$
$$(e^{i\alpha} + e^{-i\alpha})^2/4$$
$$(e^{2i\alpha} + 2e^{i\alpha}e^{-i\alpha} + e^{-2i\alpha})/4$$
$$(e^{2i\alpha} + \quad 2 \quad + e^{-2i\alpha})/4$$

4. **summed angles shows S forms in four different combinations:** This form is reminiscent of the tautological expression in logic:

(A and B) or (A and not B) or (not A and B) or (not A and not B) = TRUE

For comparison, here is the product of cosines:

$$(S_\alpha \ S_\beta)(S_\alpha \ <S_\beta>)(<S_\alpha> \ S_\beta)(<S_\alpha> \ <S_\beta>)$$

5. **conversion will come in handy when comparing to cosine:** It is difficult to understand why the exponential expression for sine is often presented in such an obscure format. WolframAlpha acknowledges this alternative form.

6. **two-dimensional rotation, with** $1 \ ☞ \ (\ ), 0 \ ☞ \ (J/2)$ **and** $-1 \ ☞ \ (J)$**:** The ultimate goal is to explore a different way of thinking, not to improve or elaborate upon the well established history of brilliant mathematical advances. The demonstrations in this chapter thus far have been guided by established knowledge. What follows is an experiment with two goals: to exercise the James structural perspective and to construct a formal perspective that is sufficiently unique to be entertaining.

7. **radians of the unit circle. It is fractions:** Radians are of course fractions of a complete 2π rotation.

8. **calling upon the established stepping stone** $J = i\pi$**:** James algebra does not include algorithms such as the iterative evaluation of an infinite series of arithmetic terms. **Numeric methods** are beyond the content of this work. They are incidentally also beyond the content of almost all trigonometry textbooks.

9. that are the n roots of unity: This equation is called the cyclotomic equation with the *cyclo* referring to its conceptualization based on Euler's complex unit circle.

10. on the complex unit circle in a slightly more complicated structure: The location of the roots depends upon whether n is odd or even and whether the root is of 1 or −1. For *odd or even* n one of the roots of 1 will align with 1 on the 1-axis to provide the solution x = 1. The rest will divide the 2π radians around the circle into n sections.

For *odd* n, one of the roots of −1 will align with −1 on the 1-axis. Again the rest divide 2π into n sections. For *even* n, one of roots of −1 will align with i on the complex axis and another will align with −i. The rest distribute evenly.

11. as a *change* in polarity, either 1 ⇒ −1 or −1 ⇒ 1: In electrical engineering the logic of silicon circuits is implemented as changes in the presence of current on a wire, either *hot* or *not*. The direction of the change does not matter, there is no privileged polarity. Similarly the consumption of energy during silicon computation is measured by changes on a wire. Here the type of change does matter since only the change from on to off consumes energy.

12. permit a richer perspective on trigonometry: The *square root* that defines i creates a half-negation but it is not particularly special other than the predisposition of mathematics initiated by Descartes to prefer *right angle orthogonal decomposition*. It is the simplest fraction of polarity but the most important only by *design choice*, perhaps driven by the historical preference of Western philosophy for duality.

Good/bad, true/false, right/left, male/female, etc. are ways to organize thought by partitioning the unified whole of reality. This unfortunately encourages prejudice in the form of us/them and even you/I. Here we have not particularly dispelled this bias, since J J = *void*. The gain in perspective perhaps is that the duality of J-void is defined to be additive rather than opposing (in contrast to the concept of an inverse), and that the duality is defined to be nonexistent.

Chapter 41

Non-numeric

[I feel] engulfed in the infinite immensity of spaces
whereof I know nothing, and which know nothing of me,
I am terrified. The eternal silence
of these infinite spaces fills me with dread.[1]
— Blaise Pascal (1670)

In this chapter, we'll look at what are conventionally considered to be forms of infinity. The chapter lays the groundwork for exploring the iconic interface between a finite and an infinite concept of natural numbers. After observing that many folks believe **infinity** to be a meaningful concept, we'll abandon it in favor of the idea of a distinction that unifies Many into One. Rather than accumulating, the square unit condenses or *unifies* the space it occupies. This apparently isolated change in the behavior of an atomic form percolates throughout the entirety of James algebra, creating two equivalence classes of forms and one class of structural illusions. After reduction by the axioms, James forms can be interpreted either as

$$[\,][\,] \Rightarrow [\,]$$
$$[\,](\,) = [\,]$$
$$(\,)(\,) \neq (\,)$$
$$]\quad] \;=\; void$$

— *numbers*, with the round unit ( ) innermost

— *logics*, with the square unit [ ] innermost

— *void*, omnipresent in the context as potential

Number and numeric form is constructed by the accumulation of round numeric units. Forms composed of round-brackets do not reduce. Logics are constructed by idempotent non-accumulating square units.[2] *Void* is defined by axioms. Within the algebra, the reduced form [A] is numeric only when A itself is numeric but *not* the numeric unit o. When A = o, [A] = *void*. If A is either void-equivalent or contains an empty square-bracket, then [A] is non-numeric. The three algebraic axioms are numeric given that the variables within them are numeric. The Dominion theorem, in contrast, strengthens Void Inversion to include *frames* with *void* content.

$$(\ )<(\ )> = void$$
$$[(\ )] = ([\ ]) = void$$

dominion

$$(A \ [\ ]) = void$$

In the presence of a square-bracket the form A is rendered *indeterminate* by the Dominion theorem, as is the form <A>. Dominion can also be written in a form that emphasizes the *absorptive* capability of [ ].

absorptive dominion

$$A \ [\ ] = [\ ]$$

Demonstration:

cover

$$(A \ [\ ]) = void$$
$$A \ [\ ] = [\ ]$$

Consistent with the empty round-bracket as the round unit, we have called the empty square-bracket the **square unit**. Although its interpretation remains the same, the difference between the square unit and the square operator is fundamental since *the square unit is not a number*. The square operator may generate both numeric and non-numeric forms depending upon its context and its content. In contrast the round operator always generates a number whenever its contents are numeric or *void*.

[ ] *is not numeric*

[o] *is not numeric*

We've been flirting with an interpretation of the unit [ ] as a type of infinity. An alternative interpretation is that [ ] is the Boolean constant 1, which is also called TRUE. Another interpretation is as the logical operator IMPLIES. The inside IMPLIES the outside. Since the Boolean and logical interpretations undermine accumulation, they are not compatible with the axioms of the James arithmetic.[3]

This chapter focuses on some surprising consequences of the square unit, a non-numeric creature that arises naturally out of the void-based axioms of the James algebra. It takes the place of both ±0 and ±∞ in conventional arithmetic, neither of which are numeric. This suggests a fundamental reorientation of the current distinction between what a number is and what it is not. James forms integrate both the numeric and the non-numeric without prejudice precisely because boundary structure is not about numbers. It is about configurations of containers that we can hold, move, count, match, rearrange, map and discard completely.

$$[\ ]\ [\ ] = [\ ]$$
unify

$$(<[\ ]>) = <[\ ]>$$
infinite interpretation

$$[\ ]<[\ ]>$$
indeterminate

Foremost we'll examine some mysterious forms within James algebra, those four stable forms from Figure 20-8 in Chapter 20.4 that we have postponed interpreting until now.

— innermost [ ]	[[ ]], [[[ ]]]	*uninterpreted*
— innermost <[ ]>	(<[ ]>), [<[ ]>]	÷0, *infinite*

We'll interpret [ ] and <[ ]> as negative and positive infinity respectively. This design decision immediately introduces the idea of a polarity of infinity, more generally the **direction of infinity**, which we will consider to be a design problem in a later section. We can understand the iconic behavior of the square-bracket by looking at the rules that incorporate it and by their structural consequences.

Angle-brackets can be eliminated via J-conversion which generates a form containing double-square-brackets, [[ ]].

$$<[\ ]> = (\text{J } [[\ ]])$$
$$(<[\ ]>) = ((\text{J } [[\ ]]))$$
$$[<[\ ]>] = \text{J } [[\ ]]$$

For a more condensed representation, we will continue to use angle-brackets in this chapter. We'll also provide an interpretation of [[ ]] as a type of complex infinity. In Section 41.7 this all changes since complex numbers introduce the option of an infinity of different infinities.

41.1 Infinity

Patrick Suppes
1922-2014

Patrick Suppes traces the history of infinity back to ancient Greece:

> Historically the concept of infinity has played a role in the literature of the foundations of mathematics as important as that of the concept of number.[4]

Anaximander
610-546 BCE

Georg Cantor
1845-1918

Anaximander is credited with introducing the word *aperion* to mean limitless or infinite. Aristotle and his philosophical cohort then had plenty to say about their recently invented idea. During the Dark Ages in the West, the Catholic Church assumed complete authority over the infinite. Then the mathematicians, particularly Cantor, got involved.

By taking [ ] to be a type of infinity, we are interpreting a form that exists. That is, [ ] is not void-equivalent. Regardless of our perspective about the interface between infinite and numeric realities, the square unit is a concrete, manipulable representation with axiomatic behavior. The Unify axiom of the arithmetic defines square units as *not countable*, as signified by a one directional arrow rather than a two-directional equality.

unify

$$[\,][\,] \Rightarrow [\,]$$

Round units describe the Many, the diversity of creation that acquires magnitude via accumulation. Square units describe the unified whole, the One. There's a language trap here: when we generate replicas of square-brackets, it is tempting to use the pronoun *they*, but these replicas are illusory, just like void-equivalent forms. There is no plurality of infinity.

Not Actual, Not Potential

Jorge Luis Borges
1899-1986

Jorge Luis Borges provides a warning:

> There is a concept which corrupts and upsets all others. I refer not to Evil, whose limited realm is that of Ethics; I refer to the infinite.[5]

There have been endless debates among mathematicians about potential and actual infinities. A **potential infinity** is a conceptual unboundedness that is never realized. Failure to realize, of course, is a bound. An **actual infinity** is a concrete mathematical object, at least as concrete as the number 5. Mathematicians back to Aristotle have rejected the actually infinite. The Pythagoreans had two infinities, going large by addition and going small by division. Aristotle distinguished between the two, between number and measure, between the discrete and the continuous. The *discrete* as a collection of units has a lower limit, one single indivisible unit. Aristotle: "What is one is indivisible whatever it may be".[6] There is no upper limit to accumulation of round units. Construction by addition of units is a process and although processes might continue indefinitely they cannot form a permanent, actual infinity. In contrast, the *continuous* as embodied in magnitude has an upper limit but no lower limit since subdivision can always be applied to generate a measure that is smaller still. The One incorporates an actual infinity by unlimited division, shades of Newton's and Leibniz' concept of infinitesimals two millennia later. Here's Aristotle:

Aristotle
384-322 BCE

> It is reasonable that there should not be held to be an infinite in respect of addition such as to surpass every magnitude, but that there should be thought to be such an infinite in the direction of division. For in number there is a limit in the direction of the minimum, and that in the other direction every assigned number is surpassed. In magnitude, on the contrary, every assigned magnitude is surpassed in the direction of smallness, while in the other direction there is no infinite magnitude.[7]

This dual perspective on infinity is perhaps responsible for our historically precarious understanding of the concept. Twenty-three hundred years later, clarifying the meaning of infinity became a primary goal for David Hilbert:

David Hilbert
1862-1943

We must realize that the infinite in the sense of an infinite totality, where we still find it used in deductive methods, is an illusion...the definitive clarification of *the nature of the infinite*, instead of pertaining just to the sphere of specialized scientific interests, is needed for *the dignity of the human intellect* itself.[8]

An alternative reading of infinity is as an **indeterminate object**, one that can take any form but not any specific form. Following the great Carl Gauss, I'll avoid the comparison of countable and uncountable infinities.

Carl Gauss
1777-1855

In mathematics infinite magnitude may never be used as something final; infinity is only a *façon de parler*, meaning a limit to which certain ratios may approach as closely as desired when others are permitted to increase indefinitely.[9]

façon de parler
a manner of
speech

Henri Poincaré strongly supported this viewpoint.

Henri Poincaré
1854-1912

Actual infinity does not exist. What we call infinite is only the endless possibility of creating new objects no matter how many objects exist already.[10]

More recently Alain Connes too supports Aristotle:

Alain Connes
1947-
Fields Medal 1983

Questions about the immeasurably large are idle questions for the explanation of Nature. But the situation is quite different with questions about the immeasurably small.[11]

These mathematicians are referring to the nonexistence of an imaginary infinity within their field, not within the physical world. The debate is more conceptual, about freedom of thought within symbolic rigor. Timothy Gowers comments, "In one way or another, the concept of infinity is indispensable to mathematics, and yet it is a very hard idea to make rigorous."[12] Since James algebra does not incorporate set theory, we will not necessarily run into the thicket of strangeness introduced by Cantor.[13] All interpretations herein that use the word *infinity* are referring to the countable infinity of natural numbers rather than the

Timothy Gowers
1963-
Fields Medal 1998

uncountable infinity of real numbers or the unachievable infinite process. I'll also avoid the controversy of potential and actual infinities by the simple expedient of transferring that discussion to the interpretation.

We usually consider that things infinite have **no boundaries**, no limitations. Standard mathematical concepts include series that continue without limits, processes or values that grow without bound and decimal numbers that never end and never repeat. However there are no concepts within a boundary calculus that are without bound.[14] This was clearly recognized by Jaina philosophers (India, circa 500 BCE), who identified two types of infinite numbers, presaging Cantor by 2500 years. *Aṣmkhyata* is a bounded infinity, an infinity that can be referenced. We would say "infinity is inside". *Ananta* is a boundless infinity, the perspective in which "infinity is outside".

ananta

aṣmkhyata

A representation for the idea of infinity has already been discovered (or designed) within what initially appears to be the arithmetic of natural numbers. Conventionally, ∞ can participate in enumeration (to the limit) and in comparison (the largest object) but not in computation (∞ + 3, NOT!).[15]

Philosopher Penelope Maddy, in discussing the relationship between the countable mathematical infinity of whole numbers and the physical world observes:

Penelope Maddy
1950-

> Embedding the individual facts of elementary arithmetic into the infinitary structure of a standard sequence is an instance of abstract modeling comparable to many others in applied mathematics—introducing falsehoods just as they do, and justified, as they are, when and only when these falsehoods are beneficial and benign. The case of standard arithmetic strikes us as different only because its source lies so deep in our conceptual mechanisms that we don't see ourselves as deliberately choosing to falsify.[16]

Tobias Dantzig
1884-1956

Maddy's perspective is that yes, infinity is not real, but sometimes mathematical departure from reality is justified by expedience. Not all mathematicians are as understanding. Here's Tobias Dantzig:

> The conception of infinity is not a logical necessity and since, far from being sanctified by experience, all experience protests its falsity, it would seem that the application of the infinite in mathematics *must be condemned in the name of reality.*[17]

We'll give Hilbert the last word on this.

> Our principle result is that the infinite is nowhere to be found in reality. It neither exists in nature nor provides a legitimate basis for rational thought — a remarkable harmony between being and thought.[18]

So we have interpretations of the infinite as a sequence without limit, as a value without restriction, as a number without pattern, as a collection without bounds, as a mathematical object, as contraband from philosophy and as the eminent domain of religion. The perspectives of these highly respected mathematicians and philosophers skitter between a semantic infinity (the Nature of Reality) and the mathematical right to make up anything and examine the consequences. The critical distinction is at the interface of *doing* mathematics within physical reality. What bounds apply to imaginary mathematical *acts*? Is there a pragmatic difference between taking ∞ to mean a completed infinite object or action and taking $\Rightarrow\infty$ to mean a never completed approach to the impossible? By design, James algebra cannot make these distinctions. It has no limit process, no quantified domains, no sets, no distinction between object and process and of critical importance, no infinite series. When [ ] occurs, it can be interpreted in any of the ways mentioned. Within James algebra, [ ] is simply an iconic boundary. Since it is empty, it is a type of non-numeric *unit*.

41.2 The Square Unit

What does a non-accumulating distinction within the representation of natural numbers mean? Round-brackets define the natural numbers, and when interpreted functionally as exponentiation, round-brackets exhibit closure; they transform natural numbers into natural numbers. In combination with round-brackets, square-brackets are operators that introduce *irrational numbers* into the James formalism. There are James forms for both *algebraic irrational* and *transcendental irrational* numbers, but only those that can be specified constructively. For example, the algebraic diagonal of a 1 x 1 square is

$$\sqrt{2} \quad ☞ \quad ((\,[[2]]\,<[2]>\,)) \quad ☞ \quad \#^{1/2\,\log_{\#}2}$$

This form represents the real number $\sqrt{2}$ exactly, as does the symbol "$\sqrt{2}$". The transcendental circumference of a unit semicircle is

$$\pi \quad ☞ \quad (<J/2>\,[J]) \quad ☞ \quad \#^{-J/2\,+\,\log_{\#}J}$$

Both conventional algebraic expressions and James forms for irrational numbers are aggregates of natural numbers and operations. To represent the diversity of numbers it is necessary for both notations to mix object and process. But caution is appropriate. We cannot know or record the exact numeric value of $\sqrt{2}$. The token $\sqrt{2}$ stands in place of a completed infinite decimal. Successfully *computing* the square root exactly would require the impossible generation of *completed* infinity.[19] The composite symbol is either a fantasy or a pragmatic approximation, a *potential* infinity, one that we can approach to any desired accuracy (within the limits of pragmatism) but never reach. The dilemma is that $\sqrt{2}$ can be associated with an apparently physical drawing. These composite forms and expressions also suggest a broader attitude, that the distinction between object and process is gratuitous. Boundary forms and symbolic expressions for infinite objects are singularly *both* object and process.

Separation

Conventionally non-numeric expressions are strictly separated from numeric expressions, possibly an historical artifact of myopia in favor of natural numbers, together with confusion about the non-numbers. Non-numbers not only include the non-numeric extensions of numbers such as zero and infinity, they must also include the lawless irrationals, those "numbers" that cannot be described since they have no discernible structure or pattern. As a defining characteristic of our interpretation,

The Non-numeric Form Principle

*All reduced non-numeric forms include
the square unit [ ] within their structure.*

Pattern recognition problems involving [ ] do occur and will require special consideration. A separate non-numeric calculus is tightly integrated within the James numeric algebra. It is not necessary to introduce the word "infinity". We have the luxury of side-stepping the controversies by acknowledging both the utility of [A] for defining multiplication (among other things), and the utility of [ ] for identifying void-equivalent forms without calling [ ] a number or an operation. We are free to examine the *structural* consequences of [ ] and then, after the fact, observe: Gee, so that's what folks call "infinity".

41.3 [ ] as Negative Infinity

Within our current interpretation we'll call the non-numeric square unit *negative infinity*.

negative infinity

$$[\,] \quad \text{☞} \quad \log_\# 0 = -\infty$$

The non-obvious interpretation of a *negative polarity* aligns with the interpretation of the logarithm of an extremely small number approaching 0 as an extremely large negative number. Logarithms identify the magnitude of the *exponent* whenever a number is expressed in exponential notation. By definition the exponential expression of 1 is $\#^0$. Positive numbers larger than 1 have a positive exponent, while positive numbers less than 1 have a negative exponent.[20] Within our interpretation then $\log_\# 1 = 0$ is represented as $[o] = void$. The empty square-bracket $[\ ]$ can be taken to represent the logarithm of the smallest number approaching 0, which itself has an exponent that approaches $-\infty$. The surprising James result is that the logarithm of 0 does not include an inverting angle-bracket as do all other forms that can be interpreted as negative numbers. The angle-bracket is there within the form of the reciprocal.

$$[(<[N]>)] = <[N]> \quad \text{☞} \quad \log_\# 1/N = -\log_\# N \qquad \text{clarify}$$
$$[(<[\infty]>)] = <[\infty]> \quad \text{☞} \quad \log_\# 1/\infty = -\log_\# \infty \qquad \text{hybrid}$$

Section 41.6 provides the transformations necessary to further reduce this hybrid form. We have taken a step along the obviously dangerous path of allowing concepts within the interpretation to suggest properties of boundary forms. With or without interpretation, the square unit is essential for Void Inversion and for Dominion.

$$(\ A \quad [\ ] \ ) \quad \text{☞} \quad \#^{A + -\infty}$$
$$([(A)] \ [\ ] \ ) \qquad \#^A \times 0 \qquad\qquad \text{enfold}$$
$$([(A)][([\ ])]) \qquad \#^A \times \#^{-\infty} \qquad \text{enfold}$$

But how do we reconcile these next two interpretations?

$$([\ ][\ ]) \quad \text{☞} \quad 0 \times 0 \qquad\qquad\qquad \textit{unify}$$
$$([\ ][\ ]) \quad \text{☞} \quad \#^{-\infty + -\infty} \qquad\qquad [\ ][\ ] = [\ ]$$

There is no reconciliation possible within James algebra since there is no structural anomaly to rectify. When there are multiple readings, or interpretations, of the same structure any reconciliation needs to take place within the interpretation.[21] The James form immediately reduces to $void$. We may prefer a limit statement, or we can acknowledge the equality as a definition.

$$\lim\nolimits_{N \to \infty} \#^{-N} = 0 \qquad \textit{alternatively} \qquad \#^{-\infty} =_{def} = 0$$

To move forward, we will also need to address $<[\ ]>$.

41.4 <[ ]> as Positive Infinity

If [ ] is interpreted as negative infinity, then it is reasonable to interpret <[ ]> as *positive infinity*. By construction the Reflection indicated by an angle-bracket is independent of the contents being reflected. The double boundary <[ ]> is then a composite of two different types of containment: [ ] as a non-numeric unit and <A> as reflecting the contents A. This then suggests an interpretation of <[ ]> as "reflected negative infinity", or as positive infinity.

positive infinity

$$<[\ ]> \quad ☞ \quad -(-\infty) = \infty$$

In general, the theorems that apply to [ ] apply equally as well to <[ ]> in place of [ ]. The impact of their structural difference is that the angle-bracket in <[ ]> interferes with clarify reductions such as in the stable form (<[ ]>). <[ ]> also introduces the concept of a **directed or reflected infinity**, an infinity that absorbs magnitude but not polarity. <[ ]> abbreviates a J-frame, (J [[ ]]). For our current context the distinction between positive and negative infinities implies

$$(J \ [[\ ]]) \neq [\ ] \qquad and \qquad J \ [[\ ]] \neq [[\ ]]$$

Non-numeric Reflection

There is a conceptual dilemma with <[ ]>. If the angle-bracket generates an inverse, what does the inverse of a non-numeric form mean? Why should [ ] necessarily be interpreted as *negative* infinity? If we were to call [ ] by an intuitive name, we would probably call it *positive infinity* because our experiences are dominated by positive numbers.[22]

Historically our culture has conceptually identified the *outermost boundary* as the unbounded infinite Universe. But what then is the reflection of this unboundedness? Within the James form, a conceptually unbounded outermost boundary is called *implicit*, in recognition of the idea that there is no accessible infinite extent. Calling an *explicit* outermost boundary "infinity" is not what we do culturally. When we construct and interpret [ ], it *is* an outermost container. The *void* within [ ] is both bounded by a bracket (putting *us* on the outside) and unbounded in that it can accommodate an unlimited but not infinite number of forms as content. It was Aristotle who made the definitive boundary math distinction between the form of a container and its content.

the form ⟶

matter
infinite

> For the matter and the infinite are contained inside what contains them, while it is the form which contains.[23]

Yes, Aristotle appears to be saying that the outermost boundary contains both the content and the infinite, our *void*. We are *within* an apparent unbounded space that is our environment. Aristotle calls the boundary of that environment, **the form**. We must *see* our universe as unbounded precisely because we can see only what is in our commonly shared environment. We see objects as finite and the space that separates them as infinite.[24]

the unbounded
Universe is inside

nothing is outside

Independence of Reflection

But what is the reflection of a *bounded* infinity? The inverse of the square-bracket is the round-bracket not the angle-bracket. ([ ]) is an inversion pair, each boundary provides an operational inverse of the other. The angle-bracket must be a *different type* of inverter. In recognition of this, we have called the angle-bracket a **reflection**. The negative unit, <( )>, and the positive infinity, <[ ]>, are each constructed by the *same* operation of reflection applied to the two fundamental types of unit. Since we have called <o> a reflected-round-unit, we will tolerate calling <[ ]> a *reflected-square-unit*.[25] When we take ( ) as the archetype real and thus positive unit, its reflection might define the imaginary concept of *negative*. When we take [ ] as the archetype imaginary and thus negative unit, its reflection might define the concept of a positive imaginary.

reflection
A <A> = *void*

<o> ☞ −1

template	reflected template ☞ interpretation
unify	$<[\ ]><[\ ]> \Rightarrow <[\ ]>$ $\infty + \infty = \infty$
dominion	$A\ <[\ ]>\ =\ <[\ ]>$ $A + \infty = \infty$
involution	$<<[\ ]>>\ =\quad [\ ]$ $-(\infty) = -\infty$

Figure 41-1: $<[\ ]>$ *theorems*

The important observation is that $<[\ ]>$ is interpreted as *positive* infinity. The J-frame of $<[\ ]>$ stands in place of $<<[\ ]>>$.

$$\log_\# 0 \quad ☞ \qquad\qquad [\ ]$$

wrap $\qquad\qquad < \ < [\ ]> \ >$

J-convert $\qquad\qquad (J\ [<[\ ]>])$

substitute $\qquad\quad ([<o>][<[\ ]>]) \qquad ☞\ -1 \times \infty$

Generalized reflection supports multiple interpretations; we can read the reflection globally, regionally or locally within a form. Each location affords a different interpretation. Addition and multiplication of reflected forms are united into the same operation occurring in different locations. Global locations can be read as subtraction, while regional locations can be read as division and local locations can be read as negation.

global

$<(A\ [B\ [C]])>$

regional

$(A\ <[B\ [C]]>)$

local

$(A\ [B\ [<C>]])$

Think of $<o>$ as a reflection that *shifts* a form from one external perspective to another. Multiplying by -1 reflects direction/polarity, and if we associate numbers with position it reflects numeric magnitude. If we begin looking left, multiplying by -1 reflects our gaze to look right. Adding changes position, *multiplication changes direction*. Multiplying ∞ by -1 does not introduce a new kind of infinity that differs from the positive infinity, rather it provides a different direction from which to observe the same infinity. Quite literally, reflection is required in order to locate our viewing perspective within an infinite potentia.[26] Maintenance of a structural perspective on the infinite however creates substantial technical difficulties for pattern-based computation.

add -1

multiply by -1

$\leftarrow\ \rightarrow$

Unification

Figure 41-1 shows the square unit theorems as they apply to the reflected square unit. Each theorem is easily demonstrated. [ ] and <[ ]> have the same structure within Unify and Dominion, creating reflected versions of each.

$$[] \quad [] \quad \Rightarrow \quad []$$
$$<[]><[]> \quad \Rightarrow \quad <[]>$$

unify

Demonstration:

$$<[]><[]>$$
$$<[] \quad []>$$ join
$$<[] \quad > $$ unify

The two types of Unify engender two types of Dominion.

$$(A \quad [] \quad) = (\quad [] \quad) \quad ☞ \quad 0$$ **dominion**
$$(A <[]>) = (<[]>) \quad ☞ \quad 1/0$$ **dominion II**

Here is the demonstration of reflected Dominion:

$$(\quad A <[]>)$$
$$(<<A> \quad []>)$$ react
$$(< \quad []>)$$ absorb

[ ] absorbs the <A> form, but it does not reduce to *void*. We are heading down a tricky path, since (<[]>) represents divide-by-zero. The two varieties of Dominion represent the extreme of accumulation (adding to the infinite) and the extreme of comparison (dividing the infinite), the same extremes identified by Aristotle.

Square Replication

The Unify axiom asserts that square units do not accumulate. If we enclose Unify in an outer round-bracket, then we have a void-based version of the Unify axiom that has a natural interpretation.

$$([][]) = void$$

$$0 \times 0 \quad ☞ \quad ([][])$$
$$([] \quad)$$ unify
$$void \quad ☞ \quad 0$$ clarify

There is a delicacy here. Transcribing the expression 0×0 imports an idea from conventional arithmetic — that there can be more than one zero — into the James arithmetic for which there is no concept of zero. Transcription constructs an *accidental* James form, just like writing symbolic expressions on a line constructs the accidental appearance of a need for sequential ordering. Multiple square units can also be interpreted as the addition of negative infinity with itself. Adding replicas of infinity does not change infinity.

$$[ ] [ ] \Rightarrow [ ] \qquad \text{☞} \qquad -\infty + -\infty \Rightarrow -\infty$$

Unlike the conventional perspective which permits the free replication of symbols, in James algebra it is a conceptual error to think that the concept of infinity supports symbolic replication. It's a nonsense question to ask for the sum of two infinities, just as it is nonsense to count the number of *void* in a space. The mechanism of void-equivalence permits us to treat some replicated forms as illusory, effectively terminating the multiple-infinity delusion at its core (replication) rather than during an operation (adding "multiple" infinities). From the James perspective, we would say that there are not two infinities although there may be two labels standing in place of the single concept.[27] The point is to have existence rules that reflect the meaning of a concept while permitting tokens to exist only when meaning is maintained. Infinite forms are blind to both cardinality and magnitude. Strictly, this means that we cannot *tally* [ ] units, since Unify defines them to be uncountable.[28] Perception of multiple infinities is an illusion. There is *only one*, by definition.

[ ]
cannot be tallied

$$[ ] [ ] \; \textit{does not support} \; ([[ ]] [2])$$

Consider

violation of
intention

$$[ ] . ._{A} . [ ] = [ ] . ._{A+1} . [ ] = [ ]$$

which shows that two supposedly different tally counts are the same. It is most undesirable to assert that for a numeric count A, for example, that A = A + 1. Similarly 0^A relies on replication of the *token* 0 but not replication of the semantic intention.

41.5 (<[ ]>) as Divide-by-Zero

Perhaps the most sensitive area of common arithmetic is division-by-zero.[29] Although some consider 1/0 to be meaningless, it has definition in the complex realm as complex infinity. Indian mathematician Bhaskar, in his treatise on Vedic mathematics *Lilavati* (1150 CE), identi-fied 1/0 as ∞, although it is ambiguous whether or not he was referring to a limit process (seven hundred years prior to Bolzano's introduction of delta-epsilon limit theory).

Bhaskar
1114-1185

Bernard Bolzano
1781-1848

In his superb historical analysis Alberto Martínez traces the definition of 1/0 from Aristotle to modern computer systems. The current definition, that division-by-zero is *undefined*, is one century old; for the preceding eight cen-turies the definition was that 1/0 equals ∞. Martínez' point is that some mathematical forms are defined by convention rather than by formal proof. Design choices have consequences, but they are still *choices*. Martínez:

> Historically, the expression "undefined" is very appropriate because it is not that the result of the operation has never been defined — actually it used to be explicitly defined — but that later mathema-ticians chose to "undefine" it.[30]

Let's now look at the James form of divide-by-zero.

        A/0   ☞   ([A]<[ ]>)
              (<[ ]>)   ☞   #∞   absorb

Since any numeric form that includes A is absorbed by <[ ]>, the value of A is irrelevant. A is not only *arbitrary*, it is also *indeterminate*. We have no constructive way to know what it is. We can simplify the structure of Dominion II a bit and specify that A = 1.

        1/0   ☞   ([o]<[ ]>)
              (<[ ]>)   ☞   #∞   clarify

(<[ ]>) is in the form of a *unit fraction*, but with the denominator nonexistent. A **unit fraction** stands in place

1/*void*

of a single fragment of a unit that has been divided into N equal fragments. The unit itself is the outer round-bracket. Its pieces are *internal*.

$$1/N \quad ☞ \quad (<[N]>)$$

void reflection

< > = *void*

Surely we cannot divide something into a nonexistent number of pieces as (<[ ]>) requires, no matter what that something is. The problem is the divide operation itself, the concept that we can construct replicas by deconstructing a whole. No pieces of a whole is nothing.

absorb

$$0/1 \quad ☞ \quad ([ ]<[o]>) = ([ ]) = void$$

Let's build the reciprocal of 0/1 by placing it into the form of the unit fraction, (<[A]>).

$$1/(0/1) \quad ☞ \quad (<[\; ([ ]<[o]>) \;]>)$$

clarify

$$(< \quad [ ]< \quad > \quad >)$$

void reflect

$$(< \quad [ ] \qquad >) \quad ☞ \quad 1/0$$

As expected, the form of divide-by-zero is the reciprocal of zero itself. Let's also try

$$0^{-1} \quad ☞ \quad (\; ([[ ]][<o>]) \;)$$

promote

$$(<([[ ]][\; o \;])>)$$

unmark

$$(< \quad [ ] \qquad >) \quad ☞ \quad 1/0$$

(<[ ]>) can be read as a round-bracket that contains the form of positive infinity. Although this interpretation is sound, there has been a subtle change in the intended meaning of #. In particular, if # stands in place of a positive number greater than one, then $\#^\infty = \infty$. If however # is a positive number less than one, then $\#^\infty = 0$. And if # is exactly 1, then the result is indeterminate as will be demonstrated in Chapter 42.2. To examine this change, we can look at the form of 1/0 with an explicit base.

$$B^\infty \quad ☞ \quad ((([B]] \; [\; <[ ]> \;]))_\#$$

enfold

$$((([B]] \; [[(<[ ]>)]]))$$

substitute

$$((([B]] \; [[\quad 1/0 \;]]))$$

The form of 1/0 is embedded within the form of an infinite power, making it independent of any base we might choose. The explicit base-B is the only structure holding this form from clarifying down to 1/0, an expression that does not require a base for interpretation.

Incommensurable

Historically our numeric and our non-numeric mathematical concepts have co-evolved with the definition of number, in particular with the sequential evolution of natural, rational, integer, real and complex numbers. The types of number define different domains. Mathematical operations are taken always to be within a particular domain, a property known as **closure**. The banishment of divide-by-zero comes from the bounded perspective of these numeric domains. We can't divide by zero purely because it lands us outside of what numbers are considered to be. When two domains cannot mix, they are **incommensurable**.

There are other ways to approach the problem of the closure of 1/0. Division, for example, can be *defined* in terms of multiplication.

$$A/B = C \quad means \quad A = B \times C$$
and $\quad 1/0 = C \quad means \quad 1 = 0 \times C$

That's impossible to do within conventional models, there is nothing you can multiply by 0 to get 1. But many things in math are imaginary or impossible. $x^2 = -1$ is impossible, but that does not stop us from defining imaginary numbers such as $x = \sqrt{-1}$ and giving that unit a name: i. Within the definition of division, we could disallow B to be 0. This amounts to disabling the cover operation. The restriction that $B \neq 0$ casts aspersions on the nature of =. If we can name 1/0 (above, that name is C), then we have already granted permission to try to use it, otherwise we will have broken the design of equality.

We know the composite form of C, it is 1/0. Although it may be suspect to set up equations such as

$$0 \times N/0 = N \quad ☞ \quad ([ ][N][(<[ ]>)])$$
$$0 \times 1/0 = 1 \quad ☞ \quad ([ ] \quad [(<[ ]>)])$$

it is certainly OK to identify the boundary form of C as
(<[ ]>). Here is a solution of $0 \times C = 1$ in both languages:

$$([ ][C]) = ( ) \qquad ☞ \qquad 0 \times C = 1$$

compose	$[([ ][C])] = [( )]$		$\log (0 \times C) = \log 1$
clarify	$[ ][C] = void$		$-\infty + \log C = 0$
move	$[C] = <[ ]>$		$\log C = \infty$
cover	$C = (<[ ]>)$		$C = \#^\infty = 1/0$

If we take <[ ]> to be a notation for ∞, then the form of
divide-by-zero is the *same* form as $\#^\infty$. We are constructing an algebra where $1/0$ is not a fundamental problem,
no more than the introduction of infinity. The deeper
problem is that *infinity is not a homogeneous singular concept*. To understand $1/0$, we will need to explore not only
positive and negative infinity, but also complex (directional) infinities and indeterminate forms.

Direction of Approach

After the shock of Leibniz' and Newton's construction of
calculus based on imaginary infinitesimal numbers, the
mathematical community reconstructed calculus based
on limit theory and the idea that we can approach the
non-numbers of 0 and ∞ to arbitrary precision without
having to deal with their inherent structure directly. In
particular limit theory provides a modern grounding for
accepting $1/\infty = 0$:

$$\lim_{n \to \infty} (1/n) = 0$$

This perspective however introduces an unwanted complexity: the *direction of approach*. As n approaches infinity
the unit fraction approaches zero. There is no specific
mention of direction, presumably because we choose
to ignore ± 0. If n approaches negative infinity, then the
result is still zero. The *polarity of the limit* is irrelevant
for the final result although for a very large positive n,
$1/+n$ is a very small positive number, and for a very large
negative $-n$, $1/-n$ is a very small negative number.

As illustrated in Chapter 43.2, the James form of $1/\pm\infty$ is indeed the form of Newton's infinitesimal.

$$1/+\infty \quad ☞ \quad (<[<[\ ]>]>) = <(<[[\ ]]>)>$$

In the following pair of equations for divide-by-zero however an asymmetry shows up.

$$\lim_{n \to +0} (1/n) = \infty$$
$$\lim_{n \to -0} (1/n) = -\infty$$

Polarity offers two apparently different ways to approach infinity. Coming from the positive values, the function approaches positive infinity. Coming from negative values, the function approaches negative infinity. The two polarities of 0 become relevant in the extreme, there cannot be a greater distance than between $-\infty$ and $+\infty$. To summarize the issue with direction of approach,

$$1/\pm\infty = \pm0 \quad with \quad 1/+\infty = 1/-\infty$$
$$while \quad 1/\pm0 = \pm\infty \quad with \quad 1/+0 \neq 1/-0$$

The graph of $1/n$ in the sidebar emphasizes the glaring inconsistency. The asymptotic approach to the x-axis as the *magnitude* of n increases is both from above and from below, yet the limit is taken to be the same non-numeric 0.

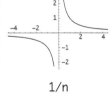

1/n

$$\lim_{n \to +\infty} (1/n) = \lim_{n \to -\infty} (1/n) = 0$$

The asymptotic approach to the y-axis is from the left and the right. The same structure rotated 90° makes the limit infinitely different. This failure of symmetry is the tip of the iceberg that will lead us into complex directional infinities in Section 41.7. From another perspective, accepting

$$1/0 = \infty \quad and \quad 1/\infty = 0$$

is a natural consequence of Riemann's mapping of the complex plane (plus an additional point at infinity) onto a sphere. The North pole of the sphere becomes the point at infinity, while the South pole is at the origin of the complex plane, $\{0,0\}$. Although there are unlimited directions to choose to leave from the Southern origin, these directions all meet again at the *singular* Northern infinity. Transformation of the sphere (such as rotation)

Bernhard Riemann
1826-1866

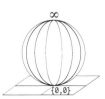

then maps onto transformations applied to complex numbers. This finesse does not absolve arithmetic of all of its monsters at infinity as we will see in Chapter 42.

41.6 Infinite Interpretation

The non-numeric unit [ ] generates the conventional algebraic rules for infinities (with one surprising exception discussed later in the next section). Reduction of compound non-numeric forms such as [<[[ ]]>] is however not supported by the James axioms. To incorporate how we believe non-numerics should behave, we will need to add a new axiom, **Infinite Interpretation**.

infinite
interpretation

$$[<[\ ]>] = <[\ ]> \qquad ☞ \qquad \log_{\#} \infty = \infty$$
$$(<[\ ]>) = <[\ ]> \qquad ☞ \qquad \#^{\infty} = \infty$$

This interpretative axiom again comes with the annoying constraint that the magnitude of # interacts with the polarity of the interpretation. When # is greater than 1, <[ ]> is positive and when # is less than 1, it is negative.[32]

This design decision has been directly influenced by the historical association of divide-by-zero with infinity. It is not really acceptable to place constraints on a James form from the interpretation, so we will indicate the use of this axiom explicitly and use it sparingly. Essentially [[ ]] and other non-numeric forms will not reduce without the Infinite Interpretation axiom. It's a choice between the proliferation of types of compound square units leading to an unlimited number of infinity equivalence classes, or tossing them all together into a small number of classes of infinity.

Each version of Infinite Interpretation can be derived from the other. The demonstration begins with an assertion that was accepted until recently for thousands of years:

$$1/\infty = 0 \quad ☞ \quad (<[<[\ ]>]>) = _{def} = void$$

cover $$[<[\ ]>] \quad = \quad <[\ ]>$$

cover $$<[\ ]> \quad = \quad (<[\ ]>) \quad ☞ \quad \infty = 1/0$$

AXIOMS

```
[ ]  [ ]  ⇒  [ ]
<[ ]><[ ]>  ⇒  <[ ]>
[ ] <[ ]>  ⇒  indeterminate
```

unify

indeterminacy *(Chapter 42)*

HYBRID AXIOM

```
(<[ ]>) = <[ ]>
[<[ ]>] = <[ ]>
```

infinite interpretation

THEOREMS

```
(A  [ ] ) = ( [ ] ) = void
(A <[ ]>) = (<[ ]>) = <[ ]>
(A [[ ]]) =    [ ]
   [[ ]]  = J <[ ]>
```

dominion
dominion II
dominion III
double-square

Figure 41-2: *Axioms and theorems of* [ ] *and* <[ ]>

Progress

Chapter 20.4 identifies eight three-boundary forms that are stable from the perspective of the three James axioms. Four are numeric. The four non-numeric forms are:

$$[<[ ]>] \quad (<[ ]>) \quad [[ ]] \quad [[[ ]]]$$

Infinite Interpretation reduces the first two of these non-numeric forms to <[ ]>. The double-square-bracket is directly implicated in the J-frame form of <[ ]>.

$$<[ ]> = (J [[ ]])$$

J-convert

But as described earlier, the reduction of [[ ]] takes us into new territory that will leave us with the axioms and theorems of infinite forms presented in Figure 41-2.

41.7 Complex Infinity

There is another, relatively new description of the behavior of the infinite: **complex infinity**. Complex numbers such as $a + bi$ have two components, a real part a and an imaginary part bi. Complex infinity can have either component infinite. An infinite real component can be visualized as a ray extending out to infinity but in a known direction. A *finite* imaginary component can be visualized as a specific rotation or as a direction. When only the imaginary component is infinite, a finite real component extends a specific distance in an indeterminate direction on the complex plane.

Complex infinity then is a known or an infinite distance in a known or an unknown direction. An **infinite real component** is a *without bound* type of infinite, whereas an **infinite imaginary component** is a *without direction* type of infinite. The James approach is to condense the diversity of interpretations into one empty container [ ] and then let context determine the available varieties of interpretation. For now it has be sufficient to consider perhaps the simplest version of a *countable infinity with polarity*. The problem to wrestle with is exemplified in the comparison of a ray to a line. A **ray** resembles the inductive ladder of Peano numbers: there is choice of direction but there is also an obvious origin. Progressing from an arbitrary point *toward the origin* is finite, the process is recursion. *Away from the origin* is infinite, the process is induction. The origin itself is unambiguous while toward and away carry polarity. A **line** suggests two opposite directions but offers no metric, no way of knowing an extent in either direction. Both directions are infinite, both are indistinguishable except in contrast to one another. Identifying the polarity of the two infinities is equivalent to identifying an origin, otherwise there is no way to know which way is which. Only when an *origin* is added to the line from an external source can we determine polarity. The singular point from which two infinite rays emanate cannot itself *have* a location, it can only define a location for other points, *as does any other point* on an infinite line. Still we cannot discern which direction is which. We need to add a label: original and reflected, positive and negative, right and left, toward and away, marked and unmarked. Infinity gains

varieties of infinity

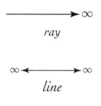

ray

line

complex: ∞ + b i

complex: a + ∞ i

complex: ∞ + ∞ i

direction from a binary choice of polarity introduced by
distinguishing two infinite sides of the arbitrary point
coupled with a design decision to maintain multiple types
of infinity.[31] **Reflected infinity** has infinite magnitude
and binary polarity. It is manifest in James form as [ ]
and its reflection <[ ]>. *Other directions are simply partial
polarities.* As a subtle point, there is no implicit distinction
requiring the "opposite" directions to align once the point
serves to cut a line into rays. Reflection is not necessarily
co-defined with *straightness.*[33]

Only when a second point is added can we establish a
unit and measure magnitude or distance. One arbitrary
point gives us a complex direction bi, two points give us
a complex magnitude a.

[[ ]] as Complex Infinity

It seems as though [ ] is quite useful and offers little
confusion (other than its interaction with <[ ]>, discussed
in the next chapter). The double-square-bracket, [[ ]],
is another story. Not only does interpretation of [[ ]]
suggest infinity, it also incorporates the interpretative
question of a negative logarithm. The **double-square-
bracket** is both non-numeric and complex since negative
logarithms have been defined to be complex numbers.

$$[[ ]] \quad \text{☞} \quad \log\log_\# 0 = \log_\# -\infty$$

We can partition the "negative" aspect from the "infinite"
aspect using J to explicitly separate concepts associated
with the angle-bracket (negation, inverse, direction,
reflection) from concepts associated with the square-
bracket (logarithm, infinity, unity). We can then begin
to anchor the thus far undefined form [[ ]].

<[ ]> = (J [[ ]])	J convert
[ ] = <(J [[ ]])>	cover
[ ] = (J [<[ ]>])	demote
[[ ]] = J <[ ]>	cover/infinite

$$\text{☞} \quad \log_\# -\infty = \log_\# \infty + \log_\# -1$$

It should come as a surprise that an infinite form remains sensitive to polarity. Why doesn't the infinite <[ ]> also *absorb* direction? The issue is that J is interpreted as a complex number while [[ ]] is a *complex infinity*. The introduction of the complex plane over two centuries ago *legitimized* direction and rotation as structurally different than magnitude. Perhaps a good design decision in light of the importance of geometry, but no more essential than could have been the legitimization of sound or color or roughness into the structure of mathematics.[34]

We'll need a theorem to preserve the nature of the double-square for later use.

double-square

$$[[ ]] = J <[ ]>$$

The double-square theorem also provides an extension of Dominion that will be useful in Chapter 43.

dominion III

$$(A [[ ]]) = [ ]$$

In this demonstration A is positive real and can be absorbed. A severe restriction, to be discussed next, is that A cannot be in the form of J. It takes careful juggling of angle-brackets maintains polarity:

	(A [[ ]])
double-square	(A J <[ ]>)
absorb/enfold	(J [(<[ ]>)])
J-convert	<(<[ ]>)>
infinite	< <[ ]> >
unwrap	[ ]

The following demonstration *erroneously* absorbs the angle-bracket within J.

	1 x ∞ ☞ ([o][<[ ]>])			
wrap	<<([o][<[ ]>])>> ☞	- -(1 x ∞)	
demote	< ([<o>][<[ ]>]) >		-(-1 x ∞)	
infinite	< ([<o>] <[ ]>) >		-(-1 x #$^\infty$)	
absorb ERROR	< (<[ ]>) >		- #$^\infty$	
infinite	< <[ ]> >		- ∞	
unwrap	[ ]		-∞	NOT

A defensive posture is to promote any angle-bracket out of the scope of square-bracket absorption. That is, numeric forms can assure that the effect of < > is independent of the effect of [ ] by giving < > priority to be outermost.

Absorption of J

Using J to indicate polarity is *non-standard*. Using it to indicate infinite polarity generates non-standard results. Consider [<[ ]>]:

$$
\begin{aligned}
[<[\ ]>] &= [(J \quad [[\ ]])] & \text{J-convert} \\
&\quad J \quad [[\ ]] & \text{clarify} \\
&\quad J\,J<[\ ]> & \text{substitute} \\
&\quad <[\ ]> & \text{J-void object}
\end{aligned}
$$

This result is consistent with the Infinite Interpretation axiom. Here is the comparison:

$$
\begin{aligned}
[<[\ ]>] &= <[\ ]> & \text{☞} & \quad \ln \infty &= \infty \\
[\ [\ ]\ ] &= <[\ ]>\ J & \text{☞} & \quad \ln -\infty &= \infty + J
\end{aligned}
$$

The presence of J above indicates a negative argument to the logarithm function, however the conventional logarithm is blind to the polarity of infinity.[35]

$$
\ln +\infty = \ln -\infty \quad \textit{while} \quad [<[\ ]>] \neq [[\ ]] \qquad \textit{anomaly}
$$

The contextual anomaly can be seen clearly in the behavior of J within the Dominion III theorem. When A = J

$$
(J \ [[\ ]]) = <[\ ]>
$$

Complex mathematics locates log −N on the complex plane as {N, π}, with the positive magnitude of N expressed along the *positive* x-axis and the imaginary rotation of iπ expressed vertically along the i-axis. J is located at {0, π}. As the magnitude of N increases, the ratio of the real to the imaginary coordinates decreases. At infinity, {∞, π}, the imaginary component is effectively 0. The magnitude component remains at positive infinity while the influence of the negative aspect of −∞ vanishes. *Negative infinity merges with positive infinity.* The James form of the logarithm however separates magnitude from polarity, storing

positive

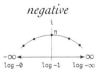

negative

the "negative" aspect as J. $\log_{\#} -\infty$ as $[[\ ]]$ has an infinite magnitude while maintaining its negative polarity. Were an infinite form able to *absorb* J so that

$$<[\ ]> J = <[\ ]> \quad \text{☞} \quad \ln -\infty = \infty \qquad \text{NOT}$$

then the James concept of infinity would be forced into bipolarity.[36]

$$<[\ ]> = [\ ] \quad \text{☞} \qquad \infty = -\infty$$

Sign-Blind Absorption

We have accumulated several absorptive non-numeric forms. An **absorptive form** renders numeric forms within its context void-equivalent. Such forms lose both the polarity and the magnitude of A. A cannot then be in the form of J.

absorptions

$$[\ ] \quad A = \quad [\ ]$$
$$<[\ ]> \quad A = \quad <[\ ]>$$
$$[[\ ]] \quad A = \quad [[\ ]]$$
$$[<[\ ]>] \quad A = [<[\ ]>]$$
$$(<[\ ]>) \quad A = (<[\ ]>)$$

Dominion sends magnitude and polarity, and more generally rotation, into *void*. Prior to the introduction of directional infinity we did not need to be concerned about absorbing polarity. After all, $0 \times -A = 0 \times A$. Both versions of Infinite Interpretation too are *sign-blind* however conventional ∞ is not sign-blind because polarity is confounded with rotation. The magnitude ∞ can be *multiplied* by -1 or it can be *rotated* by π to reach $-\infty$. But logarithms of negative numbers rotate past the i-axis into negative values only if they larger than -1 (i.e. between -1 and 0), since $\log -1$ lies on the i-axis. This then leaves $\log 0 = -\infty$ and $\log -\infty = +\infty$.

infinite interpretation

$$(<[\ ]>) = <[\ ]>$$
$$[<[\ ]>] = <[\ ]>$$

Here is a conventional demonstration of a contradiction that relies upon the sign-blindness of 0.

$$+ 1/0 = 1/+0 = 1/-0 = - 1/0$$

Of course, there are conventional rules in place that forbid us from changing the sign of an expression by changing the sign of zero. It is inappropriate within a conventional interpretation even to consider the sign of $1/0$ in isolation.

Here is the analogous James demonstration.

$$
\begin{array}{ll}
\text{(<[\quad]>)} \quad \text{☞} & +1/0 \;\Rightarrow\; \#^{\infty} \\
\text{(<[< >]>)} \quad\bigg| & 1/-0 \\
\text{<(<[\quad]>)>} \quad\bigg| & -1/0 \;\Rightarrow\; -\#^{\infty}
\end{array}
$$

The James constraint would be associated with the second step. The apparently benign insertion of < > into the interior of a square unit can change the polarity of the infinite.

Although absorption is the behavior of infinities, the consequences of failure to *absorb* polarity leads to substantive exceptions to this behavior for complex numbers.

Reflection of Infinity

Thus far our design choices have been limited to those supported by the James forms. The introduction of complex infinity permits an unlimited number of choices about how to structure infinite concepts. There are also an unlimited number of forms that may take on various interpretations should we wish to modify Infinite Interpretation. These choices, which we will not explore here, revolve around the concept of a directional infinity. The technical term is **compactification**, which basically addresses how we may wish to define various dimensions (directions, rotations, reflections) and various types of infinities. The Riemann compactification mentioned earlier conjoins the polarized $+\infty$ and $-\infty$ into a single point, a single infinity. That would be equivalent to asserting [ ] = <[ ]>, a design decision that makes sense when dealing with infinite complex numbers but not for the content of high school algebra. Here we'll briefly consider a compactification that conjoins all complex directional infinities into one direction, the $\pi/2$ rotation/reflection named i. We're left with four infinite directions, $\{+1\infty, -1\infty, +i\infty, -i\infty\}$. James reflective trigonometry in Chapter 40.6 constructs an unlimited number of **quantized reflective infinities** determined by the J/N fractional reflections. Abstract mathematics is largely about making and justifying exotic design choices.

If J = iπ, then a rotation of iπ would land on the real number line at −1 rather than at i. This behavior is undermined when a multiplication by a directional infinity is involved. The anomaly is due to complex infinity distinguishing magnitude from direction. Infinite Interpretation becomes dubious when applied to complex numbers. We saw the origins of this issue in the last section, a particularly sensitive issue since J is interpreted as an imaginary number.

$$\log -\infty \quad ☞ \quad [[\ ]] = <[\ ]> J \quad ☞ \quad \infty =?= \infty + J$$

Complex infinity can be defined to *absorb* numeric magnitude but not i as a *rotation*. Multiplying a complex number by infinity then generates unexpected James behavior due to Euler's conventional resolution of the meaning of J as a complex number. Considering only the imaginary component ib, one approach absorbs the magnitude of a rotation b but not the rotation into the imaginary axis itself, i. That is, infinity absorbs the π in iπ and leaves the i. The imaginary component is converted into a *half-reflection*. For example

$$(0 + \quad i) \times \infty = i \times \infty$$
$$(0 + \quad i\pi) \times \infty = i \times \infty$$
$$(0 + 2i\pi) \times \infty = i \times \infty$$
$$(0 + i\pi/4) \times \infty = i \times \infty$$

Expressed respectively as James forms,

$$(J/2 \ [<[\ ]>]) = (J/2 \ <[\ ]>)$$
$$(J \quad [<[\ ]>]) = (J/2 \ <[\ ]>) \qquad \text{NOT}$$
$$(J \ J \ [<[\ ]>]) = (J/2 \ <[\ ]>) \qquad \text{NOT}$$
$$(J/4 \ [<[\ ]>]) = (J/2 \ <[\ ]>) \qquad \text{NOT}$$

In multiplying a rotation by an infinite magnitude, the rotation is normalized to i regardless of magnitude. The situation degrades further when a *complex number* is multiplied by an infinity since the normalization process now incorporates the real component.

$$(1 + i) \times \infty = ((1 + i)/\sqrt{2}) \times \infty$$
$$(1 + J) \times \infty = ((1 + J)/\sqrt{(1 + \pi^2)}) \times \infty$$

These expressions could be transcribed into James forms but they wouldn't make much sense with our current axioms.

expression	value ☞	James form	reduction
∞ ± n	∞	<[ ]>　n　= <[ ]>	*dominion II*
∞ + ∞	∞	<[ ]><[ ]> ⇒ <[ ]>	*unify*
∞ x ±n	±∞	([<[ ]>][n]) = <[ ]>	*dominion II*
∞ x ±∞	±∞	([<[ ]>][<[ ]>]) ⇒ <[ ]>	*unify*
n ÷ 0	∞	([n]<[ ]>) = <[ ]>	*dominion II*
∞ ÷ ±n	±∞	([<[ ]>]<[n]>) = <[ ]>	*dominion II*
∞ ÷ 0	∞	([<[ ]>]<[ ]>) ⇒ <[ ]>	*unify*
∞ ^ n	∞	(([[<[ ]>]][n])) = <[ ]>	*dominion II*
∞ ^ ∞	∞	(([[<[ ]>]][<[ ]>])) ⇒ <[ ]>	*unify*
n ÷ ∞	0	([n]<[<[ ]>]>) = *void*	*dominion*
0 ÷ ∞	0	([ ]<[<[ ]>]>) = *void*	*unify*
0 ^ ∞	0	(([[ ]][<[ ]>])) = *void*	*unify*
∞ − ∞	*indet*	<[ ]>[ ]	*Chapter 42*
∞ x 0	*indet*	([<[ ]>][ ])	*Chapter 42*
∞ ÷ ∞	*indet*	([<[ ]>]<[<[ ]>]>)	*Chapter 42*
0 ÷ 0	*indet*	([ ]<[ ]>)	*Chapter 42*
∞ ^ 0	*indet*	(([[<[ ]>]][ ]))	*Chapter 42*
0 ^ 0	*indet*	(([[ ]][ ]))	*Chapter 42*
1 ^ ∞	*indet*	(([[( )]][<[ ]>]))	*Chapter 42*

Figure 41-3: *Operations on non-numeric expressions*

41.8 Arithmetic of Infinity

Figure 41-3 shows operations on ∞ and their associated James forms. When Infinite Interpretation is included as an axiom, all forms containing [ ] reduce to the form of infinity or its reflection. All but the top two expressions in the figure require Infinite Interpretation for reduction. Both Infinite Interpretation axioms incorporate an angle-bracket, which is a proxy for the double-square unit that we are interpreting as a complex infinity.

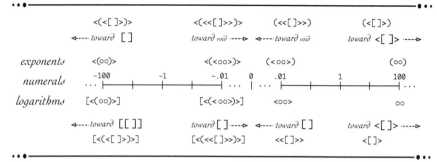

Figure 41-4: *Types of infinity on the composite number line*

After a form is reduced the types of nested boundaries remaining identify the type of conventional expression. The following listing is exhaustive, all possible forms can be classified uniquely into one of these six types.

type	archetype
void-equivalent	([ ])
real numeric	( ), *no* [ ]
imaginary numeric	[<( )>]
infinite non-numeric	[ ]
indeterminate (Chapter 42)	[ ]<[ ]>
unresolved (Chapter 42)	([[<A>]][ ])

The Infinite Number Line

The composite number line in Figure 41-4 resembles those in Chapter 38.6. It shows a spatial array of eight different approaches to some type of James infinity:

— {-, +} left from the center 0 is -, right is +
— {#ⁿ, log n} top is exponents, below is logarithms
— {<1, >1} left scale centers on -1, right on +1

The 2x2x2 array contains eight arrows, each pointing to a different approach to infinity. The infinite form for each is generated by substituting <[ ]> for the infinite accumulation of units that approaches limits on the left (as conventional negative infinity), at the center (as negative and positive infinitesimals), and on the right (as positive infinity). The non-reduced James forms border the top and bottom of the arrows, while the arrows identify the reduced James form that each limit defines.

When Infinite Interpretation is taken as an axiom, four types of infinity are generated. <[ ]>, *void* and [ ] have conventional interpretations as positive infinity, zero and negative infinity respectively. [[ ]] is non-standard; by the double-square theorem it is positive infinity with an irreducible J appended. However both [ ] and <[ ]> structurally *absorb* J via J-transparency, making infinity bipolar within the James form.

```
      J       [ ]              J          <[ ]>
   [<(   )>] [ ]          [<(        )>] <[ ]>       substitute
   [<([ ])>]               [<(<[   ]>)>]             J-transparent
   [<    >]                [ (<[< >]>) ]             clarify--demote
   [      ]                  <[   ]>                 void cancel--clarify
```

And here we run into a recurrent controversy. If infinity is absorptive of finite numbers, why does it not *absorb* −1? Alternatively why should negative infinity *absorb* or not *absorb* J? The conventional decision to imbue polarity with significance greater than that of the infinite colors all of elementary and complex arithmetic. It complicates the James form with potential absorption, sign-blind and tally failure contradictions. An alternative mechanism is to mimic Euler: there is but one bipolar $\pm\infty$.

41.9 Remarks

Chapter 27 in Volume II proposes that infinity should be abandoned as a meaningful concept. Here we have continued to use the word infinity as a metalinguistic convenience to associate a conventional meaning with <[ ]>. The frame-type J, of course, can be read as times −1, making it easier to see that absorption of J means absorption of polarity. We next continue with the exploration of square-bracket forms, in particular identifying forms that are inherently *indeterminate.*

Endnotes

1. **opening quote:** B. Pascal (1670/1966) *Pensées*. XV. From knowledge of man to knowledge of God. A. Krailsheimer (trans.) (2011).

2. **constructed by idempotent non-accumulating square units:** Figure 15-1 in Volume I shows that the structure of *logic* is exposed by converting the three types of James numeric bracket into one type without changing their relative nesting structure. The single type of bracket does not accumulate. Numerics adds a new bracket *type* to logic, to yield a boundary unit that accumulates and one that absorbs. Further, polarity adds the new imaginary constant J to logic, effectively creating a modal logic with shades of truth.

3. **not compatible with the axioms of the James arithmetic:** The mathematical study of discrete objects is *combinatorics*, while the study of continuity is *analysis*. Ordinarily the two do not mix. But we find ourselves here mixing the two foundational ideas, discrete unity ( ) and continuous infinity [ ].

4. **as important as that of the concept of number:** P. Suppes (1960) *Axiomatic Set Theory* p.2.

5. **whose limited realm is that of Ethics; I refer to the infinite:** J.L. Borges (1962) Avatars of the tortoise. *Labyrinths: Selected stories & other writings.*

6. **what is one is indivisible whatever it may be:** Aristotle (350 BCE) *Physics* Book III Part 7. R. Hardie & R. Gaye (trans.). Online 4/18 at http://classics. mit.edu/Aristotle/physics.3.iii.html#485

7. **while in the other direction there is no infinite magnitude:** Aristotle Book III Part 7.

8. **is needed for *the dignity of the human intellect* itself:** D. Hilbert (1925) On the infinite. In P. Benacerraf & H. Putnam (eds.) (1983) *Philosophy of Mathematics* 2nd ed. p.185. Emphasis in original.

9. **while others are permitted to increase indefinitely:** C. Gauss, quoted in M. Kline (1980) *Mathematics The loss of certainty* p.200.

10. **new objects no matter how many objects exist already:** H. Poincaré, quoted in Kline p.233.

11. **quite different with questions about the immeasurably small:** A. Connes (2010) *A View of Mathematics*. p.13. Online 11/18 at http://www.alain-connes.org/en/downloads.ph

12. **yet it is a very hard idea to make rigorous:** T. Gowers (2002) *Mathematics: A very short introduction* p.56.

13. **the thicket of strangeness introduced by Cantor:** Cantor, circa 1880, constructed a hierarchy of types of infinity within the theory of sets, a result strongly supported by Hilbert. Hilbert sought to resolve the criticisms of his one-time teacher, Leopold Kronecker, who is attributed as saying, "I don't know what predominates in Cantor's theory - philosophy or theology, but I am sure that there is no mathematics there." This quote, widely circulated, is no doubt representative of Kronecker's opinion, however other than Wikipedia (https://en.wikipedia.org/wiki/Controversy_over_Cantor%27s_theory), there appears to be no source for it.

14. **no concepts within a boundary calculus that are without bound:** The atomic action, *distinction*, creates a boundary that distinguishes one side from the other. The inside is naturally bounded. The outside is naturally unbounded only in the case that the outside is otherwise empty, since distinctions within an unbounded space are required to have an outermost boundary. That which is outside of the outermost boundary is *void*, which is not a concept, since *void* has no properties. Abandoning the No Properties constraint of *void* often leads to long, sometimes confusing, self-referential philosophical ruminations.

15. **in comparison (the largest object) but not computation ($\infty + 3$, not!):** The sign for infinity, ∞, is a corruption of the Roman icon for 1000, CIƆ. The icon is not composed of letters, rather it is a circle split in half. J. Conway & R. Guy (1996) *The Book of Numbers* p.19.

16. **don't see ourselves as deliberately choosing to falsify:** P. Maddy (2014) A second philosophy of arithmetic. *The Review of Symbolic Logic* 7(2) p.247.

Maddy, on page 245, provides some examples:

> We treat the ocean as infinitely deep when analyzing waves on its surface; we treat discrete items, like incomes or test scores, as continuous variables in statistical analyses; we treat fluids as continuous substances in fluid dynamics. In each of these cases and many more, a finite worldly phenomenon is embedded in an infinitary mathematical

setting — much as we embed the worldly facts of elementary arithmetic in the infinitary structure of standard arithmetic.

17. *must be condemned in the name of reality*: T. Dantzig (1930) *Number* p.248. Emphasis in original.

18. **a remarkable harmony between being and thought:** D. Hilbert (1925) On the infinite. In P. Benacerraf & H. Putnam (eds.) (1983) *Philosophy of Mathematics* 2nd ed. p.201.

19. **would require the impossible generation of a *completed* infinity:** This is the essence of Wittgenstein's rejection of real numbers. Irrational numbers must be rules rather than objects. However with probability 1 a randomly selected real number is *lawless*, having no rule that identifies it. So Wittgenstein concludes that real numbers cannot exist. They are certainly not *knowable*. The same can be said for *random numbers*. There are physical techniques that produce random numbers but they cannot be produced by any mathematical algorithm without rendering them non-random. See:

J. vonNeumann (1951) Various techniques used in connection with random digits. In A. Householder, G. Forsythe & H. Germond (eds) *Monte Carlo Method*.

G. Chaitin (2004) *Meta Math!*

20. **while positive numbers less than 1 have a negative exponent:** See Figures 38.6 and 38.7 for an illustration of this conventional notation.

21. **reconciliation needs to take place within the interpretation:** Functional thinking generally forbids expressions that have multiple structural readings. Conventional mathematics strives to embody different readings in different syntax. The theory of semantics asserts that conventional symbolic structure supports an unlimited number of *interpretations*. Boundary forms too enforce different structural readings for different containment configurations. The anomaly here is that conventional notation harbors many notational redundancies that the James form has eliminated.

22. **because our experiences are dominated by positive numbers:** We can convert [ ] into a positive (non-reflected) form by using the two bracket James algebra described in Chapter 20.5. $[\![A]\!] =def= <[A]>$

23. **while it is the form which contains:** Aristotle Book III Part 7.

24. and the space that separates them as infinite: The *unbounded universe* must necessarily be a fantasy that we create inside of us, so that we can see it by imagining that we are outside of it. The square-bracket is simply making our fantasy explicit. When we examine the reflection of a square unit, <[ ]>, the square-bracket is clearly no longer outermost. The form of <[ ]> shows explicitly our "eyes" looking at each side of a bounded universe. Iconically we are outermost. By taking the angle-bracket as outermost, we are changing our reading perspective. We have changed the relative location of the infinite by providing ourselves (our imagination) as the boundary of the observable. We are both reflecting our location and reflecting upon our location.

25. tolerate calling <[ ]> a *reflected-square-unit*: Reflection requires us as Agents to turn around, to look the other way. However the concept of direction is not within James forms, since < > = *void*. Viewpoints are instead outside, an action we take to generate the polar alternative direction. When reflection is applied to the accumulating unit we generate <o>, which then allows the construction of imaginaries such as [<o>] and void-equivalent forms such as o<o>. The indiscretion of accepting −1 as a foundational concept percolates throughout mathematical form, causing headaches not only for units but for infinities as well.

26. viewing perspective within an infinite potentia: That void reflection is void-equivalent is recognition that to orient ourselves within *void* we need an external object, thus negating the void. The situation is slightly more complicated, since the void is not empty when we place ourselves in it in order to attempt to view the nothing (other than us) that is (not) there. Recursively embedded forms support a "spatial" environment of fractal dimensions.

27. there may be two labels standing in place of the single concept: Duplication of infinities is conventionally suppressed by an assortment of counter-intuitive reduction rules.

28. since Unify defines them to be uncountable: More specifically, if we do tally a form that does not accumulate then we end up defining all whole numbers as the same number. The tally is degenerate and if not contained it is also degrading.

29. of conventional arithmetic is `division-by-zero`: "Dividing by zero is the closest thing there is to arithmetic blasphemy." William Dunham (1994) *The Mathematical Universe*. Quoted in K. Cole (2001) *The Hole in the Universe* p.47.

30. later mathematicians chose to "undefine" it: A. Martínez (2012) *The Cult of Pythagoras* p.85.

31. a design decision to maintain multiple types of infinity: Perhaps the deeply embedded priority that creates the impression of two infinities (positive and negative) comes from Euclid's geometry and optics of 2500 years ago. Should we place a point on a line, the line heads off to infinity in two directions. But placing a point should not necessarily change *infinity itself.* The two directions that each heads toward is the same infinity. Polarity somehow acquired two different names while infinity itself was demoted to serve dichotomy. Rather than maintaining its absorptive power to render negligible all magnitudes, infinity was required not to absorb direction. This perspective might also find its formal roots in Euler's association of imaginary exponents with infinite angular rotation.

32. when # is less than 1, it is negative: A base of precisely 1, i.e. # = 1, throws forms into the exotic realm of indeterminate values. See Chapter 42.

33. Reflection is not necessarily co-defined with straightness: The number *line* supports nearly universal confusion that the ordering of numbers is somehow geometrically *straight*. Straight lines have no embedded counting metric of "distance", while the unitary distance between natural numbers does not necessarily embed geometric linearity.

34. legitimization of sound or color or roughness into the structure of mathematics: Sound through the vehicle of music was integrated into mathematics within the curriculum of the quadrivium circa 500 BCE to 1500 CE. Color has recently been incorporated into mathematics through computer graphics. Roughness is a central topic of the mathematics of fractals.

35. conventional logarithm is blind to the polarity of infinity: Conventional behavior here is taken to be the output of the knowledge engine *Mathematica*.

36. the James concept of infinity would be forced into bipolarity: This in itself may be a very good idea. There are mathematical systems such as projective geometry that incorporate bipolar objects but it is difficult to reconcile unlimited accumulation with bipolarism. The consequences of one unified infinity that absorbs polarity have yet to be explored.

Chapter 42

Indeterminate

In short, science rejects the indeterminate.[1]
— *Claude Bernard (1865)*

The square-bracket, [ ], is a unit that we have elected to interpret as negative infinity. Since angle-brackets act independently of their contents, <[ ]> is a reflected negative infinity, what we call positive infinity. But what about the other non-numeric forms? In a rather brash move, we have called upon the *interpretation as infinity* to suggest how to handle some non-numeric boundary forms.

infinite interpretation

$$(<[ ]>) = <[ ]>$$
$$[<[ ]>] = <[ ]>$$

Unlike the three numeric James axioms the design decision to allow <[ ]> to absorb its *container* is motivated by conventional equations outside of the James form. Yes, this does lead to difficulties. For example reflection boundaries that are taken to represent positive and negative polarity or direction can be absorbed, making the Infinite Interpretation axiom sign-blind. And yet [ ] and <[ ]> are not behaviorally equivalent. The primary result of this chapter is to identify the form [ ]<[ ]> as a new *indeterminate* ground unit with special behavior.

42.1 Indeterminate Variables

Timothy Gowers paints a dark picture when infinity becomes a symbolic concept:

> At first there seems to be nothing stopping us: infinity should mean something like 1 divided by 0, so why not let ∞ be an abstract symbol and regard it as a solution to the equation $0x = 1$? The trouble with this idea emerges as soon as one tries to do arithmetic.[2]

As an example Gowers contrasts the associative law of multiplication with the number fact $0 \times 2 = 0$.

$$1 = 0 \times \infty = (2 \times 0) \times \infty = 2 \times (0 \times \infty) = 2 \times 1 = 2$$

> What this shows is that the existence of a solution to the equation leads to an inconsistency. Does that mean that infinity does not exist? No, it simply means that no natural notion of infinity is compatible with the laws of arithmetic.[3]

Well, alternatively it means that arithmetic is better described with different laws. Let's see how the James form handles Gowers' challenge.

```
 1 = ([                ][<[ ]>]  )    ☞          0 x ∞
emit      ([([2]  [ ])][<[ ]>]  )          (2 x  0) x ∞
clarify   (  [2]   [ ]  [<[ ]>]  )           2 x  0  x ∞
enfold    (  [2][([ ]  [<[ ]>])])           2 x (0  x ∞)
ERROR     (  [2][        o       ])          2 x     1
```

Although ∞ is a solution to the equation $0x = 1$, it is also a solution to the equation $0x = A$. The situation is reminiscent of the equation $x^2 = 1$, for which there are two solutions. Here there are an unlimited number of different equations with the same solution. The solution is **lossy**, the numeric magnitude of A no longer matters. As well, depending on design preferences, polarity can also be lost.

$$-A \times 0 = +A \times 0$$
$$-A \div \infty = +A \div \infty$$

Like self-multiplication *the sign of* A *might also be absorbed.* This conundrum creates a difficulty for the maintenance of positive and negative infinities. That is,

$$-1/0 =?= +1/0$$
$$1/-0 =?= 1/+0$$

Functional thinking is not well suited for many-to-one relationships. The problem is not within the laws of arithmetic however, it is within the behavior of equality when a disjunctive result is possible. Gowers' example makes the functional assertion that $\infty \times 0$ *only* equals 1. The **relational mapping** of pattern-matching systems requires a different perspective on substitution.[4]

An **indeterminate variable** does not indicate a value and does not behave like a conventional variable. The value of an indeterminate variable within an equation cannot be determined. Doing so can result in a contradiction. Whether or not a variable is indeterminate depends upon the structure of its *context*, not its assigned value. This is in contrast to a universally quantified variable, which can legitimately take on any value within a specific domain. In the equation $N \times \infty = \infty$ we cannot determine or solve for a value of N. In the example of N/0, it does not matter what the value of the numerator N is. In both cases, N is an indeterminate variable. An implication is that *infinity cannot be tallied.* Just like *void*, it is not possible to accumulate more than one infinity (of a given type). Unlike *void*, it *is* possible to have one infinity. Although we can construct an expression that looks like an accumulation of multiple infinities, it is a meaningless expression. That's the message of Dominion: a container with [ ] or <[ ]> within its contents *does not support* numeric contents or cardinality. The label A within the form of Dominion is indeterminate. Dominion renders indeterminate forms contextually void-equivalent, *except now for their polarity.*

$\infty+\infty+\infty =?= 3 \times \infty$

dominion

$(A [ ]) = void$

James algebra includes a Principle that clearly indicates when an indeterminate form is present.

Principle of Indeterminacy

Any numeric form in the same container
as a square unit is indeterminate.

Here is an example of a context that disguises an indeterminate form A as apparently meaningful. First let's
construct a simple void-equivalent form.

		void	☞	$\emptyset$
create	$<($ $)> $ o			$-$ 1 $+1$
create	$<([B]<[$ B $]>)> $ o			$-(B/B) + 1$
demote	$([B]<[<B>]>)$ o			$B/(-B) + 1$

Now we'll place it into the form of Dominion.

$(A\ [$ $])$ ☞ $\#^A \times \emptyset$

void substitution $(A\ [([B]<[<B>]>)\ o])$ ☞ $\#^A \times (B/(-B) + 1)$

This entire expression is in fact void-equivalent, and yes
that is fairly easy to see within the conventional notation.
The difference, though, is that we usually treat the conventional variable A as having meaning that is lost when
it is multiplied by $\emptyset$. The variable A might begin with a
value, say 5. Later we discover that value to be irrelevant.
But surely the value of A should not depend upon when
we look at it. As a default we also tend to believe that
variable B has a potential value, even though in this case
B was intentionally constructed to be meaningless.

An alternative perspective, encouraged by Dominion,
is that the variables A and B are indeterminate and *never*
had a meaning within their context even if we were to
discover the nature of that context after we assign a
specific value to either. If A is taken to be universally
quantified, then the entire *domain* is indeterminate. We
are accustomed to viewing all conventional expressions as
within the domain of real numbers, however the inclusion
of $\emptyset$ in that domain can undermine the domain itself. We
then classify undermined expressions as exceptions or
exclusions. Both algebra and physics are rife with these
exclusions. Abstract expressions that contain $\emptyset$ or ∞ serve
as examples:

— $N/0$, $N \times 0$, N^0

— N/∞, $N \times \infty$, N^∞

— $\log_N 0$, 1^∞, 0^0

More generally any expression that may involve either extremely large or extremely small magnitudes might be confounded with infinity and zero respectively. A critical distinction is whether a variable stands in place of a precise measurement (physics) or an exact abstract number (mathematics).

From the perspective of James algebra, *void* (zero) and [ ] (negative infinity) are very close to the same thing. In this chapter we'll introduce an axiom to differentiate them by limiting the reductive power of Reflection to numeric forms only. However we must be aware that when indeterminate variables are absorbed by their context, if they are treated as though they are numeric, they are capable of carrying both polarity and magnitude into the absorption. In question is the role of −1 as an indeterminate value.

Indeterminate Expressions

Expressions such as $\infty + \infty$ from the iconic perspective are worse than meaningless, they are conceptually muddled. The source of the confusion is a belief that replication of symbols is free, without consequence and independent of meaning. This in turn comes from the construction of an artificial syntax/semantics barrier. For students in particular a notation should not support semantically confused expressions.

An **indeterminate expression** is a conventional expression that does not obey the conventional rules of arithmetic. A single indeterminate expression poisons any numeric expression it is part of. Is there a coherent way to organize the diversity of indeterminate expressions? Conventionally indeterminate expressions reduce to different non-equivalent structures depending upon either context or choice of rule application. For example, in the theory of limits, indeterminate expressions are generated whenever 0/0 occurs.

$$\lim_{n \to 0} F(n) = 0$$
$$\lim_{n \to 0} G(n) = 0$$
$$\lim_{n \to 0} F(n)/G(n) = 0/0$$

Although the N in N/0 is an indeterminate variable, the expression N/0 is *not* considered to be indeterminate because it is possible to introduce an equivalent expression, N/0 = ∞, in a way that conforms to the rules governing algebraic limit processes. In particular,

$$\lim_{n \to 0} A/n = \infty$$
$$\lim_{n \to \infty} A \times n = \infty$$

When extended to include complex numbers, N/0 is a specific type of infinity. The corresponding boundary form simplifies and can be interpreted.

```
          N/0      ☞  ([N]<[ ]>)
absorb               (   <[ ]>)
infinite              <[ ]>      ☞    ∞
```

Similarly

```
          N x ∞    ☞  ([N][<[ ]>])
infinite             ([N] <[ ]> )
absorb               (    <[ ]> )
infinite              <[ ]>      ☞    ∞
```

Infinite Interpretation asserts that N/0 is equivalent to ∞. However, different approaches to division by zero as a limit lead to different results. For example,

$$\lim_{n \to 0+} 1/n = \infty$$
$$\lim_{n \to 0-} 1/n = -\infty$$
$$\lim_{n \to 0+} -1/n = -\infty$$
$$\lim_{n \to 0-} -1/n = \infty$$
$$\lim_{n \to 0} 0/n = 0$$
$$\lim_{n \to 0} n/n = 1$$

The first two examples illustrate the interaction of the direction of approach with the polarity of the result. The conventional explanation is that polarity depends upon how a value is approached. This explanation relies upon a geometric physical metaphor that can be more succinctly explained by the absorptive properties of specific operations. We do not, after all, say that the value of $\sqrt{4}$ depends upon the direction we approach it from. Approaching the negative expression $-(1/n)$ flips the polarity of infinity. And here is where a tension arises. If N is negative, and if the polarity of N were maintained in spite the indeterminate nature of N, then the polarity of infinity changes. The standard design choice is to respect polarity above both infinity and indeterminism, and thus the bewildering array of approach-to-zero problems.

$$\sqrt{4} = \pm 2$$

The case of $0/n$ shows that an approach to 0 itself can differ from being at 0. The case of n/n shows an approach to a limit depends upon the context of the limit variable. The point is that even using limit processes, division by zero can result in different values.

$1/0 \Rightarrow \infty$ *directional infinity*
$-1/0 \Rightarrow -\infty$ *directional infinity (other direction)*
$0/0 \Rightarrow 1$ *by fiat or by definition, indeterminate*

Divide-by-zero is certainly *not* undefined. Only in unusual cases is it indeterminate. There are no algebraic rules to suggest that $0/0$ might have a value or even a non-numeric interpretation. In other words, the expression itself cannot be unambiguously defined. This is indeed what Euler concluded, $0/0$ can have any value.[5]

Assimilating Infinity

In the classification of reduced James forms, all non-numeric forms include the [ ] unit. There are two varieties:

type	structure includes
infinite	[ ] *or* <[ ]>, *not both*
indeterminate	*both* [ ] *and* <[ ]>

An opportunity to remove the confusing idea of infinity has presented itself.[6] Rather than defining <[ ]> as infinity, we can return to pure James forms without the word "infinity". Dominion adequately integrates the

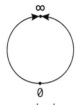

projective

conformal

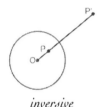

inversive

L'Hôpital's Rule

$\lim_{x \to c} f(x)/g(x)$
=
$\lim_{x \to c} f'(x)/g'(x)$

square-bracket into the numeric calculus. Contingent upon the Infinite Interpretation axiom, [ ] can be considered to be a new type of number, rather than the non-numeric concept of infinity.

This is precisely what **projective geometry** does in adding new points (and lines, etc.) "at infinity" to standard geometry. These new points are where parallel lines meet. This greatly simplifies things like perspective calculations and matrix multiplication to achieve 3D motion.

Conformal geometry studies transformations that conserve angles and orientations. It adds a single point at infinity. **Inversive geometry** also adds a point at infinity to accommodate geometric reciprocals. It is *anticonformal*, conserving angles but reflecting orientations. Arithmetic in inversive geometry includes $1/0 = \infty$ since 0 is mapped onto ∞ and ∞ is mapped onto 0.

42.2 Indeterminate Forms

Figure 42-1 shows the seven conventionally acknowledged indeterminate expressions and their James representation after literal transcription and after reduction. Remarkably, after reduction the James forms for this diverse collection of indeterminate expressions all contain the same structure, [ ]<[ ]>.

By treating 0 and ∞ as the value of a function at a limit, it is possible to convert each of the seven indeterminate forms into the others, with $0/0$ and ∞/∞ as archetypes for limit expressions. The archetypes are in the form of division since the application of L'Hôpital's rule for resolving indeterminacy happens to be expressed as a division of functions, $f(x)/g(x)$.

From the James perspective the archetype indeterminate form is $\infty - \infty$.

$$[\ ]<[\ ]> \quad \text{☞} \quad -\infty + \infty$$

indeterminate expression	James form	reduced James form
∞ − ∞	<[ ]> <<[ ]>>	[ ]<[ ]>
0/0	([] <[ ]>)	([ ]<[ ]>)

reduction includes use of the Infinite Interpretation Axiom

0^0	(([] [[]]))	([ ]<[ ]> ⅃)
0 × ∞	([] [<[ ]>])	([ ]<[ ]>)
1^∞	(([[o]] [<[ ]>]))	(([ ]<[ ]>))
∞/∞	([<[ ]>] <[<[ ]>]>)	([ ]<[ ]>)
∞^0	(([] [[<[ ]>]]))	(([ ]<[ ]>))

Figure 42-1: *The James form of indeterminate expressions*

Under interpretation the sum of positive and negative infinity is indeterminate. Within the James arithmetic when a container has both [ ] and <[ ]> as contents (together with any numeric forms), James reduction becomes indeterminate.

The indeterminate forms in Figure 42-1 are separated into two groups. The first group reduces directly to the indeterminate form [ ]<[ ]>. Each form in the second group contains the subform [<[ ]>]. This form can be reduced by Infinite Interpretation:

1^∞ ☞ (([[o]] [<[ ]>]))
     (([ ] [<[ ]>]))   clarify
     (([ ] <[ ]>)) ☞ *indeterminate* infinite

Negotiable Indeterminism

The value of 0^0 is a controversial topic. Conventionally this expression is indeterminate but many mathematicians say that $0^0 = 1$ simply as a convenience definition. Here

Donald Knuth
1938-
Turing Award 1974

we are looking for a structural justification for this choice but fail to find one. Donald Knuth insists

> Some textbooks leave the quantity 0^0 undefined, because the functions x^0 and 0^x have different limiting values when x decreases to 0. But this is a mistake. We must define
> $$x^0 = 1, \textit{ for all } x,$$
> if the binomial theorem is to be valid when x = 0, y = 0, and/or x = -y. The theorem is too important to be arbitrarily restricted! By contrast, the function 0^x is quite unimportant.[7]

Knuth's quote is a great example of a mathematical design decision. The *utility* of a definition is as important as its mathematical consistency. That such an illustrious computer scientist would feel free to change the status of one indeterminate form indicates that there is no well-formulated theory of how indeterminate forms relate to each other and to the structure of numeric arithmetic.[8]

Unfortunately, the James form of 0^0 is in the indeterminate family and changing it would impact all other indeterminate forms.

$$0^0 \quad ☞ \quad ((\texttt{[[]][ ]}))$$

double-square
$$((\texttt{J <[ ]>[ ]})) \quad ☞ \quad \textit{indeterminate}$$

There are no remaining undefined forms, but there is another complexity. In the case of an infinite form and [<o>] in the same container, we enter into a new variety of infinities, the complex infinities with infinite extent but also with a specific orientation, as explored in Chapter 41.7.

Design Choices

James algebra is independent of its numeric interpretation, it is simply a collection of nesting patterns and permitted structural transformations. Nominating particular forms as undefined or irreducible is a design choice. However there are still some traditional preferences to maintain. Basically we want **substitution** of equals for equals to remain valid at all costs, otherwise the entire endeavor of transformation by pattern-matching becomes suspect.

The form of divide-by-zero, for example, would not be problematic if we did not know that (<[ ]>) leads to difficulties within the interpretation. We have also enlisted an interpretation of [ ] as "negative infinity". The potential structural contradictions being addressed by the concept of an indeterminate form have nothing to do with the interpretation, it is inherent in the ambiguity of having more than one James transformation rule that applies to the same form and more importantly, that applying different rules leads to different results. From the rewriting perspective we want substitutions to be confluent, to arrive at a single unique reduced form.

0/0 exemplifies the design choices embodied in the problematic [ ]<[ ]> James form. The structure of [ ]<[ ]> implicates both Dominion and Reflection, providing a choice for continued reduction.

$$([ ]<[ ]>) \Rightarrow \textit{void} \qquad or \qquad ([ ]<[ ]>) \Rightarrow ( ) \qquad \text{absorb--cancel}$$

The essential indeterminacy is this: which of Dominion or Reflection should apply? We cannot know. Here are three possible outcomes depending upon how we define transformations involving square unit forms.

$$0/0 ☞ ([ ]<[ ]>) \Rightarrow (\qquad) \qquad ☞ 1 \qquad \textit{cancel}$$
$$0/0 ☞ ([ ]<[ ]>) \Rightarrow ([ ]) \qquad ☞ 0 \qquad \textit{absorb}$$
$$0/0 ☞ ([ ]<[ ]>) \Rightarrow (<[ ]>) = <[ ]> ☞ \infty \qquad \textit{absorb II}$$

It is appealing that these choices lead to the three fundamental grounding concepts of arithmetic, $\{0, 1, \infty\}$. However we must choose only one if we hope to freely use empty square-brackets during computation. Should we accept Reflection applied to [ ]<[ ]>, or is Dominion perhaps a better choice? If Dominion, then which form is being absorbed? Figure 42-2 summarizes these choices.

design decision	*transformation rule*
[ ] <[ ]> =?= *void*	*reflection*
[ ] <[ ]> =?= [ ]	*dominion*
[ ] <[ ]> =?= <[ ]>	*dominion II*
[ ] <[ ]> =?= [ ] <[ ]>	*does not reduce*

Figure 42-2: *Design decisions to suppress ambiguity*

Unfortunately contradiction is *unavoidable* when the two forms [ ] and <[ ]> sharing a container are reduced. We should expect this if indeed [ ]<[ ]> indicates indeterminacy. Dominion relies upon Reflection for its validity so accepting either version of Dominion will contradict the Reflection axiom. It is appropriate then that the structure of Dominion be seen as derivative.

One way of suppressing contradiction is to constrain allowable transformations by limiting their application. We could, for example, nominate specific exceptional forms for which the James axioms do not apply. We could impose, for example, a restriction that Reflection cannot be applied to the special form [ ]<[ ]>.

This then leads to yet another consideration. We could make some rules *context-dependent*. For example, rules that would apply to specific content can be defined to depend upon a specific type of container. We might say that Dominion applies to the content of a round-bracket, while Reflection applies to the content of a square-bracket. It would look like this:

round-bracket dominion   ([ ] <[ ]>) ⇒ ([ ]) = *void*

square-bracket reflection   [[ ] <[ ]>] ⇒ [ ]

Choosing to accept these *situated transformations* is difficult since such choices are rather unmotivated. As well, there are no situated axioms within a conventional interpretation, common arithmetic does not embrace this idea. None of the other James axioms depend on context. Finally, context-dependency places severe (and unacceptable) limitations upon the functioning of pattern-matching and substitution.

We are left with one final choice to consider, which is to *do nothing*, following a design decision of avoiding contradiction by freezing potential difficulties. In the interpretation we would say that infinity is not a number and thus does not trigger pattern-matching.

The safest route is to refuse to reduce ambiguous forms. This leaves us with an incomplete system, but it's a small price to pay since what we are giving up, in the interpretation at least, are rarely used rules about how infinities interact. This is the same kind of issue that took mathematicians a century to resolve with regard to infinitesimals within the Newton/Leibniz calculus.

Gödel's point is that within an arithmetic we must choose between completeness and consistency and we cannot have both. **Completeness** refers to the idea that we can transform *all* James forms into their simplest configuration. **Consistency** is the idea that when we implement a transformation we do not generate a contradiction. In our current mathematical culture consistency is far more important than completeness. Accepting any of the first three interpretations in Figure 42-2 leads to an inconsistent system. By making the fourth choice of identifying and freezing indeterminate forms we are explicitly accepting an incomplete system.[9]

Kurt Gödel
1906-1978

42.3 Indeterminate Series

If an infinity of objects (say an infinite set) were matched one-to-one with an infinity of matching inverse objects so that all mutually reduce in pairs, then we would expect

$$\infty + -\infty = 0 \quad \text{☞} \quad <[\ ]>[\ ] \Rightarrow \textit{void}$$

We might for example match every positive number with its inverse negative number. In that case, the sum of all the integers is zero. However there is only one match of this sort. With infinity we can also have one-to-one correspondence with any infinite subset of the infinite set. We might for example build a set of all natural numbers and a set of all even natural numbers. We could remove the even set from the set of all numbers, and still have an infinity of odd numbers remaining. So it is tempting to say that

$$\infty + -\infty = \infty \qquad ☞ \qquad <[\ ]>[\ ] \Rightarrow <[\ ]>$$

But what about the case of removing all natural numbers that do not include a string of 34 sevens in a row? There is still an infinity of these special numbers and they would continue to be in one-to-one correspondence with the natural numbers. Infinity is big!

Subtracting two infinities can leave *an arbitrary remainder*. Infinite series are not included in this analysis but there is one example that nicely illustrates the dilemma of indeterminate series.

indeterminate

$$1 + -1 + 1 + -1 + 1 + -1 + 1 + \dots$$
$$(1 + -1) + (1 + -1) + (1 + -1) + (1 + \dots = 0$$
$$1 + (-1 + 1) + (-1 + 1) + (-1 + 1) + \dots = 1$$

Different groupings of alternating units yield different results. Below splitting the sequence into two components yields an indeterminate result.

infinite oscillation

$$1 \qquad + 1 \qquad + 1 \qquad + 1 + \dots = \infty$$
$$+ -1 \qquad + -1 \qquad + -1 \qquad + \dots = -\infty$$
$$1 + -1 + 1 + -1 + 1 + -1 + 1 + \dots = \infty + -\infty$$

Even forms that generate zero, like $1 - 1$, are untrustworthy if left to run on forever. The net result is that we need to be very careful about our concepts and about our interpretations.[10] In particular the above examples are about *sets* not about numbers and we certainly do not want to suggest that James forms are sets.

42.4 Form of Indeterminacy

Dominion and the indeterminate form are sufficient to eliminate the concept of infinity from James forms. Of course the *idea* of infinity is wedded to modern mathematics in the fields of real and complex analysis. It suffices for our purposes to show that infinity is not necessary for school arithmetic.[11]

Due to Infinite Interpretation, when [ ] and <[ ]> are both anywhere within the same form they will condense into the same container, unless [ ] is eliminated by Void Inversion, or unless the angle-bracket of <[ ]> is eliminated by Involution or Promotion. The presence of both within the same form is *insufficient* to conclude that the form is indeterminate. It could be simply infinite. It could be void-equivalent. Reduction by Infinite Interpretation however will identify the non-numeric type.

Here we'll elect a conservative path by defining one particular non-numeric form that is not responsive to any reduction rules.

> [ ]<[ ]> ☞ *indeterminate*

indeterminacy

The form of indeterminacy unifies the diversity of conventionally indeterminate expressions without relying upon the theory of limits and without the mechanisms of differential calculus. This new ground form, [ ]<[ ]>, explicitly acknowledges that it's undesirable to let infinities propagate throughout symbol systems. Without calling upon Infinite Interpretation we can now identify other forms that are by nature indeterminate. In particular, earlier we established by transformation that

$$(A [[ ]]) =$$
$$<(A [<[ ]>]) >$$

0 x −∞   ☞   ([ ][[   ]])
           ([ ] J <[ ]>)   ☞   *indeterminate*   substitute

The indeterminate form is not so much an axiom as it is an unavoidable stopping point for reduction. Reduction stops when no further axioms apply, so indeterminacy is the observation that we must stop without arriving at a result that can be interpreted.

Restrictions on Dominion

The James indeterminate form <[ ]>[ ] provides a singular perspective on what to do when we find non-numeric reflection pairs in the same container. The decision to freeze the James indeterminate form places a *restriction* on the two versions of Dominion.

conditional
dominion

$$(A \ [\ ] \ ) = (\ [\ ] \ ) \qquad when \ A \neq <[\ ]>$$
$$(A <[\ ]>) = (<[\ ]>) \qquad when \ A \neq \ [\ ]$$

We have actually refined the prior restriction that A is not harboring a change in polarity in the form of J. Now we must also avoid construction of the James indeterminate form [ ]<[ ]>. These restrictions pose a computational problem in that the reduced form of A must be known prior to invoking Dominion. We could imagine an extremely complicated form that would be absorbed immediately should it be numeric, but cannot be absorbed until it is known to be numeric. Indeterminism imposes a heavy pragmatic cost. The cost of restricting Dominion to non-imaginary values of form A is knowing ahead of time that A is a conventional numeric form (or at least a *matching* type of infinity). Not only can the polarity of infinity be changed, so can the capability of identifying infinity in the context of indeterminism.

42.5 Remarks

It is fascinating that these complexities occur naturally in the process of juggling around containers by following three numeric axioms that themselves do not incorporate complexity. It appears that *computational complexity is an emergent property of the accumulation of units*. We next explore some exotic conventional expressions to see Infinite Interpretation at work.

Endnotes

1. **opening quote**: C. Bernard (1865/1957) *An Introduction to the Study of Experimental Medicine*. Chapter 1 Section 7.

2. **this idea emerges as soon as one tries to do arithmetic**: T. Gowers (2002) *Mathematics: A very short introduction* p.32.

3. **infinity is compatible with the laws of arithmetic**: Gowers p.32.

4. **requires a different perspective on substitution**: Another subtle bias that has slipped into Gower's example is to treat 0 as numeric and ∞ as non-numeric. The guard against this type of bias is to require *type consistency*, a computational constraint that mirrors mathematical closure. $2 \times 0 = 0$ is TRUE not only by rule but also by the necessity of having the same type of object on both sides of the equal sign. It is the 2 that is in type violation, so it is deleted rather than multiplied. Similarly in the associative sequence $2 \times 0 \times \infty$, the introduction of 2 is a type violation. The "multiplication" by 0 converts the 2 into an indeterminate value so it no longer carries a value into the rest of the computation.

5. **Euler concluded, $0/0$ can have any value**: M. Kline (1980) *Mathematics The loss of certainty* p.147.

6. **the confusing idea of infinity has presented itself**: I've included this excursion as an example of a common occurrence in learning. We build upon our prior knowledge in order to get to a point that we can see that the prior knowledge is not only unnecessary but also misleading.

7. **By contrast, the function 0^x is quite unimportant**: R. Graham, D. Knuth & O. Patashnik (1989) *Concrete Mathematics: A foundation for computer science* p.162.

8. **and to the structure of numeric arithmetic**: There is a broader case in support of Knuth's suggestion. We can write polynomials in the form (I'm using the generic cubic as an example here)

$$y = ax^3 + bx^2 + cx^1 + dx^0$$

The final coefficient d usually stands alone. In our base-10 number system we could for example write the units column as 10^0 and in the cubic equation above as dx^0. This is, in fact, part of the reason for defining $x^0 = 1$ for any

x. In the case of the y-intercept, when $x = 0$, we certainly wouldn't want to lose the value of d. So in this case we would want to stick with $0^0 = 1$.

9. **we are explicitly accepting an incomplete system:** Although consistency is highly valued within mathematical culture, it is not necessarily of critical importance for philosophy. We might first recognize that language is built to embrace inconsistency and interdependent webs of contextual meaning. The logical crux is that any proposition can be derived from contradictory premises. But this is too broad. The **paraconsistency** community limits what can be concluded from false beginnings. I once implemented a logical inference system in which contradictions were identified, isolated and then used as information rather than as the source of complete degradation. In an expert system, for example, rules might be collected from several expert sources. But experts do disagree. A contradiction arising from two expert opinions should not invalidate information from other experts, nor should it necessarily invalidate other information from the two experts in question. The source of the disagreement is itself valuable information. There's a similar situation here with the indeterminate kernel [ ]<[ ]> which can be used for information about a portion of a computation without necessarily destroying all results. In 1930, Wittgenstein wrote:

> Indeed, even at this stage, I predict a time when there will be mathematical investigations of calculi containing contradictions, and people will actually be proud of having emancipated themselves from consistency. *Philosophical Remarks* (1930/1980) p.332.

10. **about our concepts and about our interpretations:** We have built the concept of counting on a basis of one-to-one correspondence, but the concept of counting breaks down completely when we introduce infinite sets. The infinite set of natural numbers is called a *countable infinity*, continuing the mathematical tradition of naming concepts with words that mean exactly the opposite. It comes as no surprise that the set of counting numbers is countable, but it takes a conceptual disconnect to believe that it is possible to count to infinity. The countable infinity is simply not countable in any operational sense of counting. Basically potential infinity (trying to *do* the impossible) is less credible than actual infinity (labeling an impossible object).

11. **infinity is not necessary for school arithmetic:** I'll make an *explicit pedagogical suggestion* that the concept of infinity should be eliminated from mathematics education until a student declares a major in mathematics.

Chapter 43

Exotics

*Mathematics as we know it and as it has come to shape
modern science could never have come into being without
some disregard for the dangers of the infinite.*[1]
— *David Bressoud (2007)*

Conventional arithmetic works very nicely so long as
you don't look at the edges. The edges are occupied
by two very special non-numeric creatures, 0 and ∞.
They both have a strong influence on making 1 special
too. If we consider {0, 1, ∞} to be the fundamental objects
of arithmetic, then arithmetic is dominated by the exotic.
Exotics are not rare, they are just strange. They don't fit
in. There are fences built around them, forbidding various
operations on specific entities. The history of arithmetic is
permeated with discovery and with growth. That growth
has never been tidy. The more exceptions the harder a system is to remember and to understand. The weakness is
that our conventional concepts and terminology leave an
indelible impression on our ability to see difference. The
initial objective of this chapter then is explore what it would
be like if the three basic objects in arithmetic {0, 1, ∞} were
completely compatible with the basic operations of arithmetic {+, ×, ∧} and their inverses {−, ÷, log}. With iconic
arithmetic we have a unique opportunity to explore the
formal structure of non-numeric forms.

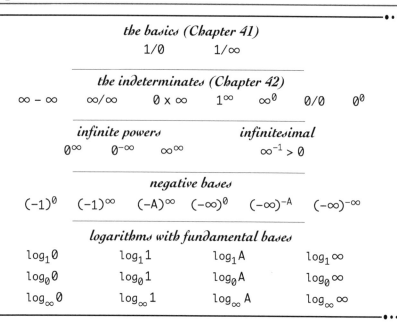

the basics (Chapter 41)

$$1/0 \qquad 1/\infty$$

the indeterminates (Chapter 42)

$$\infty - \infty \qquad \infty/\infty \qquad 0 \times \infty \qquad 1^\infty \qquad \infty^0 \qquad 0/0 \qquad 0^0$$

infinite powers   *infinitesimal*

$$0^\infty \qquad 0^{-\infty} \qquad \infty^\infty \qquad\qquad \infty^{-1} > 0$$

negative bases

$$(-1)^0 \qquad (-1)^\infty \qquad (-A)^\infty \qquad (-\infty)^0 \qquad (-\infty)^{-A} \qquad (-\infty)^{-\infty}$$

logarithms with fundamental bases

$$\log_1 0 \qquad \log_1 1 \qquad \log_1 A \qquad \log_1 \infty$$
$$\log_0 0 \qquad \log_0 1 \qquad \log_0 A \qquad \log_0 \infty$$
$$\log_\infty 0 \qquad \log_\infty 1 \qquad \log_\infty A \qquad \log_\infty \infty$$

Figure 43-1: *Some of the exotics*

Figure 43-1 lists some of the non-standard conventional expressions that we have considered in the previous two chapters and those that we will consider in this chapter. Chapter 41 explored the basics, with the Infinite Interpretation axiom providing a ground for $1/0$ and its sister $1/\infty$. The indeterminates were organized in Chapter 42, all have $[\ ]<[\ ]>$ at their core. We have remaining four additional categories of exotics: more infinite powers, infinitesimals, negative bases and logarithms with bases that are the fundamental objects of arithmetic.

infinite interpretation

$$(<[\ ]>) = <[\ ]>$$
$$[<[\ ]>] = <[\ ]>$$

In this chapter we'll try to find structure in exotic non-numeric forms. There are two philosophies, for example, to finding a comfortably defined and meaningful context for 0^0. School mathematics is currently taking the low road by treating the exotics like invaders that wreak havoc while insidiously undermining the *rules*. It's difficult to form a rigorous system when its edges are ragged. The alternative high road values exotics as lights shining upon rules, exposing their biases and their weaknesses.

concept	form	structure	interpretation	symbol
void		absence	zero	$\emptyset$
whole	( )	bound	one	1
dominant	[ ]	unify	negative infinity	$-\infty$
inversion	[( )]	illusion	logarithmic zero	$\log_{\#} 1$
inversion	([ ])	illusion	exponential zero	$\#^{-\infty}$
reflection	<( )>	reflected	negative polarity	-1
reflection	<[ ]>	reflected	positive infinity	∞

Figure 43-2: *Concepts that ground James algebra*

In the virtual world of mathematics we can generalize standard concepts by broadening their definitions, like Hausdorff, and later Mandelbrot, did in converting integer dimensions into logarithmic fractal dimensions. Looking back we can now see that the smooth flat geometry of Euclid was a limitation that obscured the geometry of Nature with an imposed simplification that dimension must be a whole number. People love Euclid's simplicity so much that we surround ourselves with it. Flat floors, flat walls, flat tables, flat paper, flat screens. Step outside and the dimensions of Nature are not whole numbers.

Felix Hausdorff
1868-1942

Benoit Mandelbrot
1924-2010

dimensions
0,1,2,3!

We're not proposing that James algebra is an extension of the conventional algebra of numbers. The proposal is that any model of arithmetic that excludes a basic element from full participation in all operations does not provide a sufficiently robust core onto which an extension can be confidently added. We should begin with a calculus that permits everything and then constrain permissible transformations within our universe of all possibilities. We need a world in which $\emptyset^{\emptyset}$ feels at home.

$\emptyset^{\emptyset}$ ☞ (([[ ]][ ]))

Figure 43-2 summarizes the ground upon which James algebra is constructed. This ground itself is exotic since it includes absence and illusion. In the logarithm of zero, [ ], we are not looking directly at infinity, but rather

operation	expression	form	reduced form
division	$0/0$	$(\ [\ ]\ <[\ ]>)$	indeterminate
power	0^0	$((\ [[\ ]]\ \ [\ ]\ ))$	indeterminate
root	$A^{1/0}$	$((\ [[A]]\ <[\ ]>))$	$<[\ ]>$
	$0^{1/0}$	$((\ [[\ ]]\ <[\ ]>))$	void
logarithm	$\log_B 0$	$(<[[B]]>[[\ ]])$	$[\ ]$
	$\log_0 A$	$(<[[\ ]]>[[A]])$	void
	$\log_0 0$	$(<[[\ ]]>[[\ ]])$	indeterminate

Figure 43-3: *Problematic operations on zero*

at its containment. Indeed, to look at infinity requires us to be outside of that infinity. What we look at as the interior of both the square unit and the round unit is the unlimited depth of nothingness. If we put a limit on the *capacity* of a container, we declare both that we are outside of that container (as is the limit!) and that the space inside is limited. And by rule, some configurations of apparent containers are transparent and illusory.

An ecological observation is that thinking in terms of infinite capacity works quite nicely for virtual realities and quite horribly for physical realities. With finite containers that possess unlimited capacity the concept of infinity goes away completely but the concept of *void* remains. A bounded *void*, i.e. ( ), represents unity, while the inversion of that unity, [( )], returns to *void*. This defines unity to be the same as the original Greek concept of One as *everything*, not a number but a whole. It is only the outermost container that permits us to look or to intercede. We must put some modest computational limits on the depth to which we are descending into abstraction, otherwise the virtual will permit us to manifest anything we desire, limited only (as the saying goes) by our imagination. And we are limited by available time, another insistent physical bound.

43.1 Zero or Nothing

A theme is that *zero is non-numeric*. Figure 43-3 shows several problematic operations on zero. (In these forms capital letters like A are assumed to be numeric and greater than one.) Conventional operations on zero lead to nothing, or to one of the infinities, or to an indeterminate form. That is, zero behaves more like a non-numeric than a numeric concept. It is associated with several different constraints or exceptions to the behavior of common operations.

The three frame-based algebraic axioms can each be expressed as transformations on empty containers. At the foundations of James *arithmetic* all axioms are void-equivalent.

$$([\ ]) = [(\ )] = void \qquad \textbf{void inversion}$$

$$(A\ [\ ])\ (A\ [\ ]) = (A\ [\ ]) = void \qquad \textbf{void arrangement}$$

$$<\ > = void \qquad \textbf{void reflection}$$

Sum of Nothing

It's fairly safe to agree that *adding up* lots of zeros results in zero. Except if we add zero to itself infinitely the value turns indeterminate! Too many conventional zeros creates confusion. Here we have a case in which successive addition fails to qualify as a form of cardinality, finite or infinite. With the exception of the sum at infinity, cardinality is essentially a numeric concept, it does not generalize to non-numeric forms.

We have a prototype axiom for non-addable forms, Unify. The square unit does not support the property of cardinality. An infinite degree of nonexistence does not bring something into existence, nor does it make the nonexistent indeterminate. *Summation* of what zero represents is **not** indeterminate, it is nothing, because addition cannot be applied to things that do not accumulate.

unify

$$[\ ][\ ] \Rightarrow [\ ]$$

What converts $\infty \times 0$ from nothing to indeterminacy is the structure of *multiplication*, not the structure of addition.

$$0 + .._{\infty}.. + 0 \quad \text{☞} \quad void$$

$$\infty \times 0 \quad \text{☞} \quad ([<[\,]>][\,])$$

infinite

$$(\ <[\,]>\ [\,]) \quad \text{☞} \quad indeterminate$$

The product of 0 and ∞ is indeterminate not because we cannot know the numeric value of the result but because the presumption of a multiplicity of nothing(s) is a **conceptual confusion**. Bluntly, we can have potentially infinite *representations* of zero but not a potentially infinite number of zeros.[2] This is a weakness in symbolic mathematics: symbols are treated as if they were concepts and concepts are thought to be arbitrarily capable of being symbolized.

The form of multiplication arises from the Replication theorem, which as a prerequisite requires Indication and prior to that, Dominion. Attempting to indicate *void* generates a deception. Attempting to mark *void* generates the form of Dominion. We have been reading Dominion as an absorption property of [ ], it can also be seen as an attempt to accumulate *void*.

$$([\,][N]) = void$$

Dominion is the ground form of accumulation, prior to multiplication not as a result of multiplication. It is strangely conceivable to collect an infinite number of replicas of a specific form, that is if we grant the possibility to generate an infinite tally.

$$([A][o.._{\infty}..o]) = A.._{\infty}..A$$

It is doubly strange to attempt to replicate nothing infinitely. Here's what the form of infinite nothings might look like.

an attempt to mark void

$$([\,][o.._{\infty}..o]) = ([\,][<[\,]>]) \quad \text{☞} \quad indeterminate$$

The problem, as we can see, is deeper than replication. In the notation we end up knowing the count but not the counted. The representation for an infinite sum of *void* is itself an infinite number of *type errors*, confusing nothing with its mark of existence not just once but without end.

An equal sign asserts a relationship between two members of a given domain. The relation is FALSE when the *values* of the members differ. A **type error** asserts an equality relation between members of *different* non-comparable domains, here infinite and indeterminate, a *conceptual* rather than algebraic error.[3]

type error

$5 = cat$

Self-multiplying Nothing

Intuitively *multiplying* nothing together many times should also result in nothing, but we should ask: Why believe this intuition? We know that *dividing* by zero creates a major problem, where does that problem go when we multiply by zero? We can sneak up on this question by *self-multiplying* zero a specific number of times. What is 0^A? When $A = 1$, we have

0^1 ☞ $(([[ ]][o]))$ ☞ $\#^{-\infty} \times 1$
   $(([[ ]]\quad))$ clarify
       void   clarify

When $A = 2$, we cannot call upon Inversion directly and accumulation of [ ] is prohibited. The direct transcription carries accidental structure over from the symbolic system: it looks as though *void* is being tallied. We'll immediately rewrite it.

0^2 ☞ $(([[ ]][2]))$ ☞ $\#^{-\infty} \times 2$
   $(\ [ ]\quad\quad)$ absorb III
       void   ☞ 0 clarify

Here is zero to a negative power, first erroneously:

0^{-A} ☞ $(([[ ]][<A>]))$ ☞ $\#^{-\infty} \times -A$
   $(\ [ ]\quad\quad\quad)$ absorb III ERROR
       void   ☞ 0 NOT   clarify

Mishandling the angle-brackets above can lose polarity information, sometimes for example converting $([ ])$ to $(<[ ]>)$. In this example, the angle-bracket containing A has been erroneously absorbed. The lost angle-bracket here changes magnitude in the extreme, from infinity to *void*. This example thus illustrates how close zero and infinity are to being the same thing.

Here the polarity information is correctly preserved via Promotion, yielding the correct divide-by-zero.

```
0⁻ᴬ  ☞   ( ([[ ]][<A>]) )
promote        (<([[ ]][ A ])>)
absorb III     (<  []        >)
infinite        <[ ]>              ☞    ∞
```

Now we'll consider the product of infinite zeros. We'll be mixing two absurdities to reach the idea of an **infinite dimensional empty space**.

```
0^∞  ☞  ( ([   []] [<[ ]>]) )
promote          (<([   []] [ [] ])>)
double-square    (<(J <[ ]> J <[ ]>)>)
J-void/unify     (<( <[ ]>         )>)
infinite         (<  <[ ]>          >)
unwrap/clarify          void            ☞    0
```

To more closely examine the form of infinite multiplication, we can consider raising zero to negative infinity which leads to a variety of divide-by-zero. The difference between raising to a positive power vs a negative power is a single strategically placed angle-bracket. The polarity of angle-brackets again plays a central role.

```
0⁻^∞  ☞   (([ [] ] [ [] ]))
double-square    ((J <[ ]> J <[ ]>))
J-void/unify     ((  <[ ]>        ))
infinite          <[ ]>              ☞    ∞
```

43.2 Infinitesimals

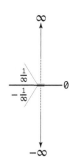

An **infinitesimal** is a quasi-numeric form so small that it is effectively zero but it is not equal to zero. Both Leibniz and Newton built the calculus on this ephemeral. Infinitesimals presume a *continuity* that lets us take as small a step as desired without encountering some form of quanta.[4] But infinitesimals *act like* quanta, suggesting a conceptual confusion, one that mathematicians spent over a century fixing. The infinitesimal itself was replaced within the calculus by delta-epsilon limit theory and much later resurrected within non-standard analysis.[5]

Let's first examine what it would take to divide a numeric form into N equal parts, each very close to zero but none zero itself. The form of a unit fraction is (<[N]>). We want an infinity of parts, each one-infinityith of the whole, each part with the hybrid form (<[∞]>) ☞ 1/∞.

$$\infty^{-1} = 1/\infty$$ ☞ (<[<[ ]>]>)

(< <[ ]> >)   infinite

void   ☞   0   unwrap/clarify

An **infinitesimal** is a unit fraction of ∞ that we refrain from reducing by Infinite Interpretation or by theorems that rely on Infinite Interpretation.

$$\infty^{-1} = 1/\infty$$ ☞   (<[<[ ]>]>)

Other than Infinite Interpretation, this form is *stable* although it does have a Promotion variant.

(<[<[ ]>]>) = <(<[[ ]]>)>   **infinitesimal**

Conventionally, 1/N approaches 0 *from above* in the limit as N approaches ∞, while 1/−N approaches 0 *from below*. This phraseology emphasizes the directional aspect of the sign of infinity. Thus there are both positive and negative infinitesimals. Positive infinitesimals are smaller than any positive number while negative infinitesimals are larger than any negative number. 0 itself is unreachable.

The difference between zero and an infinitesimal is that infinitesimals can be tallied. By construction we can collect infinitesimals.

1/∞ +..∞..+ 1/∞ ☞

(<[<[ ]>]>)..∞..(<[<[ ]>]>)

([(<[<[ ]>]>)][o..∞..o])   tally

(<[<[ ]>]> [o..∞..o])   clarify

(<[<[ ]>]> [<[ ]>])   substitute

(< <[ ]> >   <[ ]>)   infinite

([ ]   <[ ]>) ☞ *indeterminate* unwrap

The *product* of an infinity of infinitesimals is also indeterminate. It has the same form as the sum but without the tally.

expression ☞	form	reduced form
2^∞	(([[2]][<[ ]>]))	<[ ]>
1^∞	(([[o]][<[ ]>]))	*indeterminate*
$(1/2)^\infty$	(([[(<[2]>)]][<[ ]>]))	*void*
0^∞	(([[ ]][<[ ]>]))	*void*
$(-1/2)^\infty$	(([[<(<[2]>)>]][<[ ]>]))	([J]<[ ]>)<[ ]>
$(-1)^\infty$	(([[< o >]][<[ ]>]))	(([J]<[ ]>))
$(-2)^\infty$	(([[< 2 >]][<[ ]>]))	(([J]<[ ]>)<[ ]>)

Figure 43-4: *The diversity of an infinite exponent*

$1/\infty \times \infty$ ☞

	([[(<[<[ ]>]>)][<[ ]>])
clarify	(<[<[ ]>]> [<[ ]>])
infinite	(< <[ ]> > <[ ]>)
unwrap	([ ] <[ ]>) ☞ *indeterminate*

Just like $1/\infty$ is negligible compared to any substantive quantity, it is general practice to consider $(1/\infty)^2$ to be negligible compared to an infinitesimal quantity. This computational feature of infinitesimals keeps what are called **first-order terms** but ignores higher-order terms that are multiplications of infinitesimals by infinitesimals.

$$(1/\infty) > 0 \quad while \quad (1/\infty)^2 = 0$$

Checking this, we can observe that the characteristic form within the reduction of infinitesimals, (<[[ ]]>[[ ]]), does not occur when an infinitesimal is self-multiplied.

$(1/\infty) \times (1/\infty)$ ☞

	([[(<[<[ ]>]>)][(<[<[ ]>]>)])
clarify	(<[<[ ]>]> <[<[ ]>]>)
infinite	(< <[ ]> > < <[ ]> >)
unwrap	([ ] [ ])
unify/clarify	*void* ☞ 0

43.3 Infinite Concept

The apparently declarative use of symbols for infinity is backed up by a limit process that approaches what the infinite object is. Nonetheless, when we use boundary notation, we have a direct representation of the thing itself.

Infinite Exponents

Figure 43-4 shows a diversity of infinite self-multiplications. The James reductions conform with standard results except that [J] is not reduced in order to maintain our policy of preserving the polarity information embedded in J. When [J] is absorbed, only the form of $(-1/2)^\infty$ differs from expectation.[6] We'll focus on the algebraic rules of exponents, retracing the exploration in Chapter 36.4, but allowing base and power to be non-numeric.

$$(A \times B)^N = A^N \times B^N$$

When $N = \infty$, can we rely on distribution of exponents over multiplication?

$$(A \times 1/A)^N =?= A^N \times (1/A)^N$$

This question would normally be approached by a limit process. I'll assume that A is greater than 1. First the left-side:

$(A \times 1/A)^N$ ☞	`(([    A x 1/A    ]][N]))`	hybrid
	`(([[([A][(<[A]>)])]][N]))`	substitute
	`(([  [A]   <[A]>    ][N]))`	clarify
	`(([              ][N]))`	cancel

Reflection applies to the numeric A, however N cannot be absorbed since it is non-numeric. Now the right-side:

A^N ☞	`(([  [A]  ][N]))`
$(1/A)^N$ ☞	`(([[(<[A]>)][N]))`

$A^N \times (1/A)^N$ ☞

`([(((([A]][N]))][(((([<[A]>)][N]))])`		
`(  ([[A]][N])   (  <[A]>  [N])  )`		clarify
`(  ([[A]<[A]>][N])              )`		collect
`(  ([         ][N])             )`		cancel

We have reached an identity regardless of the numeric or non-numeric nature of N.

$$(([\ ][N])) = (([\ ][N]))$$

If N is numeric it will be absorbed. However if N is infinite (either positive or negative) the form $(([\ ][N]))$ is indeterminate. Let's take N to be positive infinity.

$$(([][\ N\ ]))$$

substitute

$$(([][<[\ ]>]))$$

infinite

$$(([\ ]\ <[\ ]>\ )) \qquad ☞\ \textit{indeterminate}$$

From $((([A]<[A]>][N]))$ above, prior to canceling we can see that if A = *void*, then again we would have an indeterminate form. The exponent rule also does not work in base-0. And if A rather than N is infinite, then again the result is indeterminate. Let's take A to be positive infinity.

$$((([\ A\ ]<[\ A\ ]>][N]))$$

substitute

$$((([<[\ ]>]<[<[\ ]>]>][N]))$$

infinite

$$((([\ <[\ ]>\ <\ <[\ ]>\ >][N]))$$

unwrap

$$(([\ <[\ ]>\qquad [\ ]\qquad][N]))\qquad ☞\ \textit{indeterminate}$$

Thus in all cases the distributive rule for exponents is indeterminate for infinite powers.

The Source of Indeterminacy

There is a more fundamental reason why infinite multiplication breaks the rules of exponents. It is hidden in the expression A x 1/A, which equals 1 whenever A is numeric. *Infinite unity* provides the indeterminism within infinite multiplication. The source of the problem is 1^∞. For example:

$$
\begin{array}{ccccc}
A^\infty & ☞ & <[\ ]> & ☞ & \infty \\
(A/1)^\infty & & <[\ ]> & & \infty \\
A^\infty/1^\infty & & ([A^\infty]<[1^\infty]>) & & \textit{indeterminate}
\end{array}
$$

Whenever we have an infinite exponent, the core of the issue is 1 x A. On similar grounds,

$$(1/A)^\infty \neq 1^\infty/A^\infty$$

0 and ∞ are incompatible indicators. Contrary to common conception, *infinity is not an accumulation of an infinite*

number of 1*s*. Rather it is a visitor from the incommensurable non-numeric world. This essentially degrades all
numeric forms of infinite multiplication. For *any* A other
than A = 1,

$$(1 \times A)^\infty \neq 1^\infty \times A^\infty$$

The issue is that 1^∞ is indeterminate while A^∞ is not when
A ≠ 1. First, the left-hand-side.

```
(1 x A)∞   ☞  ((([([o][A])]][<[ ]>]))
              ((C      [A]  ] <[ ]> ))        clarify/infinite
              ((                <[ ]> ))      absorb
                                <[ ]>    ☞ ∞  infinite
```

And the right-side,

```
1∞ x A∞  ☞
  ([[(([o]][<[ ]>])))][(((([A]][<[ ]>]))])
  ( ([   ][<[ ]>])   ([[A]][<[ ]>])  )       clarify
  ( ([   ] <[ ]> )   ([[A]][<[ ]>])  )       infinite
                           ☞ indeterminate
```

We have encountered the indeterminate form, so there is
no need to go further. Infinitely multiplying by 1 is not
benign. The unit 1 is a surprising exotic, clearly a number
yet with unexpected interaction with the other exotics.[7]

43.4 Exotic Bases

Other than the case of raising to the power of infinity, the
powers of 0 and 1 generate no exceptions. Except that 0^0
is also exotic. We will need to explore some other exotic
bases, particularly negative bases raised to infinite powers.

Negative Exponential Bases

What happens when a negative number, say −1, is self-multiplied without limit?

```
(-1)∞  ☞   ((([(J)]][<[ ]>]))
           ((C  J  ] <[ ]> ))  ☞ unresolved   clarify/infinite
```

The conventional value of $(-1)^\infty$ is *indeterminate*. But
even after the application of Infinite Interpretation,

this result does not reduce given the restriction of not absorbing [J] because of its embedded angle-bracket. We have yet to encounter square unit forms that fail to reduce even when indeterminacy is included. Perhaps the better descriptor is *unresolved*. This then brings up $(-1)^0$,

$$(-1)^0 \quad ☞ \quad ((\text{[J][ ]})) \qquad ☞ \textit{ unresolved}$$

The structure of $(-1)^0$ is the same as that of $(-1)^\infty$, but the first incorporates <[ ]> and the second [ ].

In general the polarity of a negative base can be separated from the magnitude itself and this is precisely what complex numbers do. Untangling orientation from magnitude is essential to complex numbers. As demonstrated in Chapter 35.5,

$$(-A)^N = (-1)^N \times (A)^N ☞$$

clarify/disperse

$$((\text{[[(J [A])]][N]})) = ((\text{[J][N]}) (\text{[[A]][N]}))$$

$$\textit{where } (\text{[J][N]}) ☞ J \times N$$

The ([J][N]) form carries parity information which can be reduced to the absence or presence of J by J-void tally.

In the case of $(-A)^\infty$, the same reduction steps apply to separate polarity from magnitude. With $N = \infty$,

$$(-A)^\infty ☞ ((\text{[J][N]})(\text{[[A]][N]}))$$

substitute

$$((\text{[J][<[ ]>]})(\text{[[A]][<[ ]>]}))$$

infinite/absorb

$$((\text{[J] <[ ]>)} \qquad <[ ]>)$$

$$☞ \textit{ unresolved}$$

The *magnitude* A can be absorbed by <[ ]> but the *polarity* cannot. Here is the dividing line. It is the decision to have different polarities of infinity that makes these forms unresolvable. This leads to the *complex infinities* introduced in Chapter 41.7. As was observed in Chapter 39.7, numeric polarity is the base case of complex orientation. And a reason for not absorbing polarity into infinity has come to light. Infinite sequences that oscillate in polarity are neither infinite nor indeterminate. In the James form they fail to reduce, creating a new class of structures, the *unresolved*. There are two types of unresolved forms, those that have an unknown numeric variable and those that are non-numeric. Unresolved variables are the standard unknowns from algebra. Now we'll take a look at unresolved infinities that are a direct consequence of allowing both positive and negative infinite forms.

Powers of Negative Infinity

The exponential expression ∞^{∞} is not indeterminate. Its reduction is direct.

∞^{∞} ☞

```
        (([[<[ ]>]] [<[ ]>]))
        ((  <[ ]>    <[ ]> ))        infinite
        ((  <[ ]>         ))          unify
            <[ ]>            ☞   ∞    infinite
```

A more challenging problem is the powers of *negative* infinity. The reason to look here is to try to separate self-multiplied polarity which is known to oscillate from self-multiplied infinity which should not oscillate. The powers of zero implicate [[ ]]. The powers of infinity lead us directly to [[[ ]]]. An auxiliary theorem to reduce triple square-brackets will be handy.[8]

```
[           [[ ]]         ]   ☞   loglog(-∞)
[<[ (<    [[ ]]   >) ]>]           log(-log(1/-∞))      wrap/enfold
[<[ (<[<o>]<[ ]>>) ]>]            log(-log #^(-∞+J))    double-square
[<[ (<[<o>]>[ ]  ) ]>]           log(-log(0/-1))       react
[<[<(<      >[ ] )>]>]           log(-log(-(#^-∞)))    promote/clarify
[<[<          >]>]                log(-log(-0))         void cancel/clarify
  <[          ]>                    -log 0 = ∞          void cancel/infinite
```

Now to accompany the Double-square theorem, we have

$$[[[ ]]] = <[ ]>$$ **triple-square**

We'll begin to explore the behavior of base-[ ] (i.e. the powers of negative infinity) by observing some simple cases of raising negative infinity to a power. What if the power of negative infinity is 1?

$(-\infty)^1$ ☞

```
        ((([[ ]]][o]))
            [ ]              ☞   -∞      clarify
```

So far, so good. Let's try the zero and infinite powers.

$(-\infty)^0$ ☞ `((([[ ]]][ ]))`

triple-square `(( <[ ]> [ ]))` ☞ *indeterminate*

$(-\infty)^\infty$ ☞ `((([[ ]]][<[ ]>]))`

triple/infinite `(( <[ ]> <[ ]> ))`

unify/infinite `<[ ]>` ☞ ∞

The standard result for $(-\infty)^\infty$ is a complex infinity. The triple-square theorem loses infinite oscillation, although it is difficult to determine which aspect, the theorem or the infinite oscillation, is problematic. Here's something potentially easier, a negative numeric exponent, $-A$. We would expect $1/\pm\infty$ to reduce to 0 regardless of the polarity of infinity.

$(-\infty)^{-A}$ ☞ `( ([[[ ]]][<A>]) )`

promote `(<([[[ ]]][ A ])>)`

triple-square `(<( <[ ]> [ A ])>)`

absorb `(<( <[ ]>        )>)`

infinite `(< <[ ]>        >)`

unwrap/clarify *void* ☞ 0

But now here's a serious polarity oscillation problem.

$(-\infty)^A$ ☞ `((([[ ]]][A]))`

triple-square `(( <[ ]> [A]))`

absorb ERROR `(( <[ ]>      ))`

infinite `<[ ]>` ☞ ∞ NOT

The absorption of A is *problematic* since the polarity of the result would depend upon whether the natural number A is *odd* or *even*.[9] In the case of infinity, as manifested by `[[[ ]]]`, to maintain polarity we may need to revert *conceptually* to

$$(-\infty)^A = (-1 \times \infty)^A \ne (-1)^A \times \infty^A$$

A quick look at the forms in Figure 43-5 shows that all powers of $-\infty$ include the triple-square-bracket. The experiment here though is to observe the interaction between infinite magnitude and polarity. We'll separate polarity from magnitude using the generic form of negative bases,

expression	form	exponent	value
$(-\infty)^A$	`(([[[ ]]][ A ]))`	positive	*unresolved*
$(-\infty)^{2k}$	`(([[[ ]]][2k ]))`	even positive integer	$+\infty$
$(-\infty)^{2k+1}$	`(([[[ ]]][2k o]))`	odd positive integer	$-\infty$
$(-\infty)^{-A}$	`(([[[ ]]][ <A> ]))`	negative integer	$\emptyset$
$(-\infty)^{-\infty}$	`(([[[ ]]][[ ]]))`	negative infinity	$\emptyset$
$(-\infty)^{\infty}$	`(([[[ ]]][[ ]]))`	positive infinity	∞
$(-\infty)^0$	`(([[[ ]]][ ]))`	zero	*indeterminate*

Figure 43-5: *Powers of negative infinity*

and look at even and odd positive powers. The form of 2k, with k a natural number, will be even and should reduce to ∞, while the form of 2k+1 should generate a result of $-\infty$.

$$(-\infty)^{2k}$$
$$(-1)^{2k} \times \infty^{2k}$$
$$((-1)^2)^k \times \infty$$
$$1^k \times \infty$$
$$\infty$$

$$(-\infty)^{2k+1}$$
$$(-1)^{2k+1} \times \infty^{2k+1}$$
$$(-1)^{2k} \times (-1)^1 \times \infty$$
$$(-1)^1 \times \infty$$
$$-\infty$$

Yes, polarity indicators cancel in pairs. Now the James form.

$(-\infty)^{2k}$ ☞ `(([[[ ]]][([2][k])]))`
              `(( <[ ]> [([2][k])]))`   triple-square
                  `<[ ]>`   absorb/infinite

Here the non-numeric form will absorb *any* value of k so we'll need to separate magnitude from polarity,

$(-1)^{2k} \times (\infty)^{2k}$ ☞

`([[( [J][([2] [k])])]) [((([<[ ]>]][([2][k])])))])`
`( ( [J]   [2] [k]  )    ([[<[ ]>]]  [2][k]  )  )`   clarify
`( ( [J]   [2] [k]  )       <[ ]>            )`   infinite/absorb
`( ([      ][k]  )       <[ ]>            )`   enfold/J-void tally
                         `<[ ]>`   ☞ ∞ absorb/infinite

The infinite subform on the right reduces to `<[ ]>` as expected. The polarity subform reduces to *void*. Using J-void tally is dubious since it converts [k] to an indeterminate. Comparing:

$$(-1)^{2k+1} \times (\infty)^{2k+1} \quad ☞$$

	([[([J][([2][k])o]))]	[[(([<[ ]>]][([2][k])o]))])	
clarify	(([J][([2][k])o])	([[<[ ]>]][([2][k])o]))
infinite/absorb	(([J][([2][k])o])	<[ ]>)
disperse/clarify	(([J][2][k]) ([J][o])	<[ ]>)
clarify/J-void tally	(([ ][k]) J	<[ ]>)
absorb/enfold	(J	[(<[ ]>)])
J-convert		<(<[ ]>)>
infinite/unwrap		[ ] ☞ −∞

If we separate the dynamics of the polarity information from the dynamics of infinity then the oscillation of polarity is maintained.[10] Non-numeric forms make this separation mandatory, however *a priori* identification the need for separate dynamics is generally intractable. Perhaps [[[ ]]] is a step too far since we have already left conventional results at double-square (Chapter 41.7):

$$[[ ]] = <[ ]> J \neq <[ ]>$$

43.5 Exotic Logarithms

The form of the logarithm with an explicit base provides the opportunity to explore conventionally unacceptable logarithmic bases. We have postponed until now three values for the logarithmic base: 0, 1, and ∞. What can we

logarithmic

R = ([[A]]<[[B]]>)

make of these exotic logarithms and their corresponding exponential forms? First of all there is an asymmetry in the two inverse functions, power and logarithm. Exotic exponential powers of 0, 1 and ∞ are not problematic. In contrast, these three exotic bases for *logarithms* each

exponential

A = ((([B]][R]))

create challenges for understanding and for usage. One tool to bring some order to exotic logarithmic bases is to convert logarithms into a common base, our generic #.

$$\log_B A = \log_\# A / \log_\# B$$

This relationship is built deeply into the James form: the form of a logarithm is also the form of division.

$$\log_B A \quad ☞ \quad ([[A]]<[[B]]>)_\#$$

hybrid

$$[A] \div [B] \quad ☞ \quad \log_\# A / \log_\# B$$

expression ☞	form	reduced form ☞	value
$\log_\# A$	([[A]]<[[(( ))]]>)	[A]	$\log_\# A$
$\log_{-N} A$	([[A]]<[[<N>]]>)	([[A]]<[J [N]]>)	*Chapter 35*
$\log_1 A$	([[A]]<[[( )]]>)	<[ ]>	∞
$\log_0 A$	([[A]]<[[ ]]>)	*void*	0
$\log_\infty A$	([[A]]<[[<[ ]>]]>)	*void*	0

Figure 43-6: *Values of exotic logarithms*

In Figure 43-6 the form of the logarithm directly shows the effect of each base. In the figure A and N are both assumed to be positive numeric. A **type error** is identified whenever an exponential form and its inverse logarithmic form generate incommensurable results. The dominant observation is that each of these exotic bases generates a type error.

Base-0 Logarithm

What does a logarithm in base-0 mean? We would immediately expect that base-0 would be 0 to some power, that is, 0. The base conversion formula yields the form of R.

$R = \log_0 A$ ☞   ([[A]] <[[]]>)$_\#$

                        <([[A]] <[<[ ]>]>)>   wrap/promote

                        <([[A]]   []   )>   infinite/unwrap

                        void   ☞   0   absorb/void cancel

Since A gets absorbed it is an *indeterminate variable*. Now to examine the exponential to determine its form for A.

$A = 0^R$ ☞   (([[]][R]))

                  (<([<[ ]>][R])>)   wrap/promote

                  (<(<[ ]> [R])>)   infinite

                  (< <[ ]>   >)   absorb/infinite

                  void   ☞   0   unwrap/clarify

R is also an *indeterminate variable*. It can be any numeric form but identifying *any specific form generates inconsistency*. For example,

Let R = 5   *therefore*   A = 0^5 = 0   *and* $\log_0 0$ = 5
but $\log_0 0$ ☞ ([[ ]] < [[ ]] >)

double-square   (J <[ ]> <J <[ ]>>)

react   (J <[ ]> <J> [ ]) ☞ *indeterminate*

The essential problem is that each *co-defined* function generates a specific value (i.e. 0) for a variable that the other
defines as indeterminate. In general if either of A or R is
specific then the other is indeterminate, which then makes
the specific variable indeterminate. This is quite apparent
since the composition of the two inverse functions of zero
(i.e. $f(f^{-1}(0))$) is indeterminate. Each function generates
a type error. This in another costume is the asymmetry
between the exponential and logarithmic inverses. $\log_0$ is
inherently non-computational. For completion here is the
base-0 logarithm of 1 and of ∞.

$\log_0 1$ ☞   ([[o]]<[[ ]]>)

clarify   <([   ]<[[ ]]>)>

wrap/promote   <([   ]<[<[ ]>]>)>

infinite/unwrap   <([   ]   [ ]   )>

unify/clarify   *void*   ☞   0

This result as an exponential, 0^0 = 1, is consistent with
Knuth's recommendation in Chapter 42.2 but does not
agree with the direct reduction of 0^0 as indeterminate.
Again $\log_0$ embodies a type error rather than an inconsistency. In comparison $\log_0 \infty$ is specifically indeterminate.

$\log_0 \infty$ ☞ ([[<[ ]>]]<[[ ]]>)

wrap/promote   <([[<[ ]>]]<[<[ ]>]>)>

infinite/unwrap   <(<[ ]>   [ ]   )> ☞ *indeterminate*

Base-1 Logarithm

The tally system is sometimes associated with base-1. But
the divisor in the logarithmic base conversion equation is
the *logarithm* of 1, not 1 itself, which results in a division
by zero and makes base-1 logarithms infinite.[11]

$\log_1 A$ ☞   ([[A]]<[[o]]>)   *with* A > 0

clarify   ([[A]]<[   ]>)

absorb   <[   ]>   ☞   ∞

If we let $R = \log_1 A$, then $A = 1^R$.

$$1^R \quad \text{☞} \quad ((([o]][R]))$$
$$((\,[\quad\,][R])) \qquad \text{clarify}$$
$$(\qquad\qquad) \quad \text{☞} \quad 1 \qquad \text{absorb}$$

The logarithmic form is infinite while the exponential form is 1. Given $R = <[ ]>$ though, it cannot be absorbed. We need to reexamine the exponential form.

$$1^\infty \quad \text{☞} \quad ((([o]][<[ ]>]))$$
$$((\,[\quad\,][<[ ]>])) \qquad \text{clarify}$$
$$((\,[\quad\,]\,<[\quad\,]>\,)) \quad \text{☞} \ \textit{indeterminate} \quad \text{infinite}$$

We have the same type error as with base-0, however this time the logarithm is infinite rather than 0. $\log_1 \infty$ does not encounter indeterminism. The infinite result is unambiguous.

$$\log_1 \infty \quad \text{☞} \quad ([[<[ ]>]]<[[o]]>)$$
$$(\ \ <[ ]>\ \ <[\quad\,]>) \qquad \text{infinite/clarify}$$
$$<[ ]> \qquad\qquad \text{☞} \quad \infty \qquad \text{unify/infinite}$$

Here we see again the fracture of the inverse relationship between powers and logarithms. The infinite power of 1 is indeterminate, while a logarithm in base-1 is simply infinite. This fracture has perhaps contributed to the interpretation of logarithms as complex numbers.

Base-∞ Logarithm

Finally, what does base-∞ look like?

$$\log_\infty A \quad \text{☞} \quad ([[A]]<[[<[ ]>]]>)$$
$$([[A]]\qquad[ ]\qquad) \qquad \text{infinite/unwrap}$$
$$\textit{void} \qquad\qquad \text{☞} \quad 0 \qquad \text{absorb}$$

The corresponding exponential form is $\infty^0 = A$.

$$\infty^0 \quad \text{☞} \quad ((([<[ ]>]][ ]))$$
$$((\ \ <[ ]>\ \ [\ ])) \quad \text{☞} \ \textit{indeterminate} \quad \text{infinite}$$

Again the same fracture, with one inverse pair being specifically 0 and the other being indeterminate. Finally

$$\log_\infty \infty \quad \text{☞} \quad ([[<[ ]>]]<[[<[ ]>]]>) \qquad \text{infinite}$$
$$(\ \ <[ ]>\qquad[ ]\qquad) \quad \text{☞} \ \textit{indeterminate} \quad \text{unwrap}$$

infinite powers

equal 0:

$$0^\infty$$

equal ∞:

$$0^{-\infty} \qquad \infty^\infty$$

negative bases

equal 0:

$$(-\infty)^{-A} \qquad (-\infty)^{-\infty}$$

equal infinity:

$$(-\infty)^\infty$$

indeterminate:

$$(-\infty)^0$$

unresolved:

$$(-1)^0 \qquad (-1)^\infty \qquad (-A)^\infty \qquad (-\infty)^A$$

logarithms with fundamental bases (*all are type errors*)

equal ∞:

$$\log_1 0 \quad \log_1 A \quad \log_1 \infty$$

equal 0:

$$\log_0 1 \quad \log_0 A \quad \log_\infty 1 \quad \log_\infty A$$

indeterminate:

$$\log_0 0 \quad \log_0 \infty \quad \log_1 1 \quad \log_\infty 0 \quad \log_\infty \infty$$

Figure 43-7: *Exotic results*

Conventionally these equations in base-0 and base-∞ are equal to 0. Base-1 logs are defined as complex infinities. Their James versions tend to expose type errors. Type errors are neither complex nor indeterminate.[12]

43.6 Remarks

Figure 43-7 captures the results of this chapter's exploration. The *unresolved* category is usually bundled with *indeterminate*. When logarithms are considered with their co-defined functions the results are *type errors* that render both functions mutually non-computable. It is the structure of operators rather than objects that creates anomalies.

This chapter has been overtly experimental. Rectifying these James results with conventional results is work yet to be done. The *logarithmic collapse at infinity* briefly mentioned in Section 43.4 is a significant difference between conventional and James imaginaries. It makes polarity preservation moot. In the next chapter we apply the visual forms introduced in Volume I to the content in this volume.

Endnotes

1. **opening quote:** D. Bressoud (2007) *A Radical Approach to Real Analysis* p.22.

2. **not a potentially infinite number of zeros:** Mistaking the representation for the concept it represents is the classical error of general semantics: a finger pointing to the moon is not the moon.

3. **indeterminate, a conceptual rather than algebraic error:** Mathematics avoids the concept of a *type error* by asserting a strong condition of **closure** for operations. Closure guarantees that transformation of objects within a set generates members of the same set. Usually these object sets are infinite, however the sets do not themselves include an *infinite object* such as [ ]. Infinite and indeterminate "objects" inherently violate closure constraints.

4. **without encountering some form of quanta:** Continuous functions are the foundation of numeric calculus and analysis.

5. **much later resurrected as non-standard analysis:** Robinson's non-standard analysis accepts infinitesimals as does Conway's surreal number system.

A. Robinson (1996) *Non-Standard Analysis*.
J. Conway (1976) *On Numbers and Games*.

6. **only the form of $(-1/2)^\infty$ differs from expectation:** The conventional value for this expression is 0. Infinite multiplication of a number less than 1 will certainly reduce to 0. The infinite oscillation of polarity must somehow reduce to ± 0 and thus become irrelevant. It is difficult to understand how this can be accomplished if polarity is considered to be independent of infinity, so it is tempting to identify this conventional result as an inconsistency compared to, for example, $(-3/2)^\infty$.

7. **unexpected interaction with the other exotics:** The ancient Greeks would clearly disagree that 1 is numeric. Plato and Euclid both make a distinction between the concept of unity and the concept of number. Euclid's *The Elements* (c. 300 BCE), Book VII Definition 1: "A unit is that by virtue of which each of the things that exist is called one." And Definition 2: "A number is a multitude composed of units." Euclid then constructs two separate proofs, VII 9 and 15, in recognition of this distinction. The concept of number herein is very close to Euclid's. A number is a unit ensemble. Euclid's numbers are geometrically determined relations and not abstract entities. James numbers in contrast are

contextual markers (`[o][N]`) collected in recognition of a cognitive choice to perceive shared properties. Thus there may be different types of unit for each measurement activity. *The Elements* is online in its entirety at `http://aleph0.clarku.edu/~djoyce/java/elements/elements.html`

8. auxiliary theorem to reduce triple square-brackets will be handy: This demonstration is undoubtedly the ugliest one in these volumes, and therefore the least desirable. A conventional demonstration might look like this:

$$\text{loglog} -\infty \quad \Rightarrow \quad \log \infty \quad \Rightarrow \quad \infty$$

The reason for the gyrations is to avoid the conventional collapse at infinity mentioned in Chapter 41.7, that $\log +\infty = \log -\infty$. Using a hybrid J, we have $\text{loglog} -\infty \Rightarrow \log(J + \log \infty)$, which then leaves us in uncharted territory. Did you notice how bizarre the interpretations of James transformations look?

9. whether the natural number A is *odd* or *even*: The villain here is probably the triple square unit `[[[ ]]]`. The Double-square theorem may have reached a limit here since the `[[[ ]]]` form itself may not respect manipulation of its polarity, if indeed it has a polarity.

10. the oscillation of polarity is maintained: Our cultural approach to mathematics has so reified *polarity* that we have endowed it with an importance more powerful than infinity itself. Certainly a design decision, but one that assures that our mathematics will be dichotomous rather than unified. Complex numbers are the finesse that keeps duality working, manifested as J within the James form. Nevertheless the difficulty with absorption of polarity information can no longer be handled by isolating angle-brackets directly.

11. makes base-1 logarithms infinite: The tally system is sometimes thought to be base-1, it has only one "digit". Logarithms to base-1 should identify the exponent of a tally mark. However, the unit 1 can be raised to an arbitrary numeric power without changing its unitary form. This implies that $\log_1 A$ is *not associated* with the base-1 tally system. If that were the case, then the form of the logarithm would be the same as the number of tallies. For example, a tally of four might look like | | | |. If tallies in base-1 were read like positional numbers, the rightmost stroke would be 1^0, while the leftmost stroke would represent a third power, 1^3. What is the logarithm base-1 of | | | | ? The results in this section indicate that all base-1 logarithms are infinite.

12. errors are neither complex nor indeterminate: The separation of real from imaginary in complex infinity does not resolve *indeterminate* forms.

Chapter 44

Concrete

*Closer to this book and equally illuminating are the
many problems triggered by a sound or a picture. Only
afterwards is a formula devised, and then proclaimed or
implied to be a full representation of reality.[1]
— Benoit Mandelbrot (1999)*

Academic knowledge has evolved over the last several
hundred years as the exclusive province of textual
symbols. Although these symbols find physical expression in typography and hand writing, their design and
intent is to isolate reasoning and computation as *cognitive*
skills divorced from physical experience. If a skill escapes
the realm of symbolic abstraction it is banished to the
nether worlds of extra-curricula activities. Humans love
sports and theater and film and exercise and gardening and traveling and music and dance and the internet,
but skills that involve our bodies are considered to be
inessential to thinking and to figuring. The Reading,
wRiting and aRithmetic of primary school reinforces
the cultural dominance of symbolic mind over dynamic
matter. Although both education and mathematics hold
onto the antiquated mind/body dichotomy, this century
recognizes the primacy of *embodied cognition*.

Volume I of *Iconic Arithmetic* invites our physical bodies to participate within simple arithmetic. Chapter 4

(( )( ))
parens

bounded

bucket

network

map

wall

path

room

block

introduces several non-linear and participatory dialects that unlike symbolic expressions allow us to observe and participate within numeric comprehension and computation. Chapter 13 introduces eight new postsymbolic dialects of James arithmetic. We'll revisit these interactive forms in this chapter. Can postsymbolic form help us to understand these potentially new ways to think about elementary mathematics? It's time again to free parens notation from the accidental structure inherited from its typography.

44.1 Revisiting Iconic Dialects

Figure 44-1 repeats Figure 13-1 of Volume I. It shows the transformations that convert parens notation into higher dimensional experiential forms. These simple topological and relational mappings confirm that parens notation is itself fully iconic, however its dimensional reduction obscures features that invite our eyes and hands to contribute their own unique forms of knowledge to our understanding of arithmetic.

Our initial intent is to revisit these iconic dialects but not to review their construction and dynamics. Rather we will look at the iconic forms of the new creatures unique to this volume: J, i, π, e, divide-by-zero and other forms of infinity. What does iconic imagery contribute to an understanding of algebraic computation, of calculus derivatives, of trigonometry, of Euler's identity? Can the iconic dialects inform the interface between symbolic and postsymbolic concepts such as void-equivalence, representational redundancy, sign-blindness, tally failure, incommensurability of J, ubiquity of e, non-primacy of i, reflective trigonometry and non-numeric forms?

An important caveat before beginning: the insight available from iconic dialects cannot be directly explained by an appeal to symbolic concepts. The new information is visceral, participatory and literal. All I will be able to

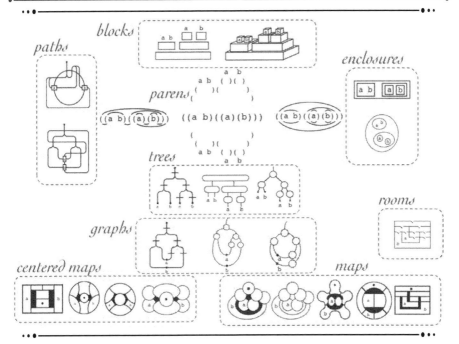

Figure 44-1: *Roadmap for generating iconic dialects (Figure 13-1)*

offer is: *Look at this!* More broadly we *think* in concert
with our senses, particularly touch and sight. In prior
chapters the approach has been to consider the boundary
forms of known symbolic expressions. In this chapter we
will reverse that approach to take postsymbolic form as
fundamental and then to observe that the structure and
symmetries of these forms lead us to consider symbolic
concepts in a new light.

For familiarity we'll look first at the forms of J and ÷0 in
several iconic dialects, and then focus on the bounded,
network, path and room representations of i, π and e.
The network dialect best exemplifies the postsymbolic
innovations of structure sharing, pattern substitution,
path analysis and computational parallelism. We'll use the
network form to demonstrate Euler's identity, to derive
the form of a boundary derivative, and to emphasize
transformational features associated with tallying J and
with dabbling in infinity.

[<( )>]

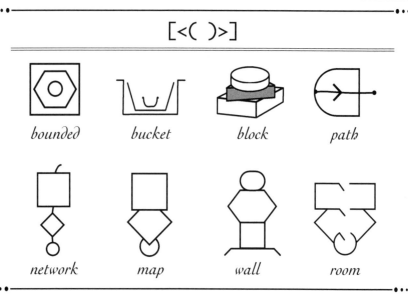

bounded   *bucket*   *block*   *path*

network   *map*   *wall*   *room*

Figure 44-2: *Iconic forms of* J

Varieties of J

The new creature on the block is J, an abbreviation for [<( )>]. Figure 44-2 shows the form of J in eight different iconic dialects as well as in parens notation. J is a *simply nested stable form* and thus can be considered to be a type of compound unit. Chapter 34.6 develops J as the *unit object* that replaces any occurrence of the angle-bracket operator. Figure 44-3, for contrast, shows divide-by-zero, a non-numeric form closely related to J that is interpreted as positive infinity. The iconic forms in Figures 44-2 and 44-3 have these constructive properties:

— **bounded**: The original surrounding enclosure form. **Parens** notation deletes the top and bottom edges.

— **bucket**: A bound notation with only the top edge deleted. This deletion effectively rotates the bounded form out of the plane of the page to create a cross-section containment form.

— **block**: A *manipulable* form constructed by rotating and extruding the bounded form upward

(<[ ]>)

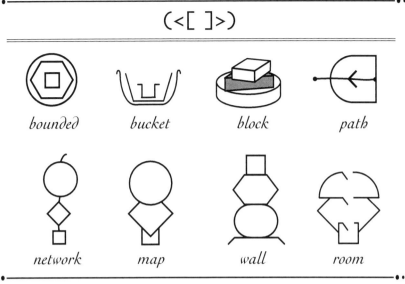

bounded　　　bucket　　　block　　　path

network　　　map　　　wall　　　room

Figure 44-3: *Iconic forms of* `divide-by-zero`

and outward. The innermost boundary is on top. Containment becomes gravitational stacking.[2]

— **path:** A traversable form with only one round/ square border. Multiple boundaries are represented by crossing the single border multiple times. The sequence of crossing replaces containment.

— **network:** An extruded form of parens in which nesting is replaced by top to bottom connectivity. This most useful form is also called a **dnet**.

— **map:** A network form in which links are converted into overlapping borders while nodes become territories.

— **wall:** A parens form extruded upward with containment implemented by gravity. Extruding the wall form out of the page generates the block form.

— **room:** A map form with borders replaced by sequentially traversed inward opening doors. The room form can be scaled to permit *physical participation* within the form.

These dialects demonstrate the relational morphism across containers, enclosures, stacks, paths, connections and borders. From a mathematical perspective each of these descriptions is an interpretation of the same essential structure. Each dialect though supports different types of experiential interaction, of computational implementation and of cognitive comprehension.

Perspective

Iconic forms embody a **viewpoint**, or perspective. The anchored perspective of English *text* is from outside the page, from above the script, and linearly from left-to-right for reading. The single fundamental difference of iconic forms is that they include an *inside*, thus providing a choice of viewing perspective. Parens, bounded and map dialects are read from above, sometimes called a God's-eye view. Bucket and wall dialects are viewed from the side, as if we were at the same level. The block dialect is a three-dimensional representation viewed and manipulated from an arbitrary location in space. Path, room and network dialects are path oriented. Although their representation on the page is from above, they invite a reading from inside. We participate by traveling along a path as time progresses. Dnets support multiple concurrent processes with localized perspectives that can act asynchronously and independently to achieve global transformation without global coordination.[3]

The variety of iconic dialects is achieved, as illustrated in Figure 44-1, by various rotations and extrusions either of the representation on the page or of the location of our imaginary viewpoint. These geometric and participatory transformations do not change the structure of containment relations but they do change the **cognitive look-and-feel**, which includes comprehension, understanding, mental modeling, learnability, retention, generalization and cognitive utility. When expressed in computing languages, the iconic dialects interact with implementation architectures, programming metaphors and models, functional partitioning, algorithmic efficiency, compiler techniques, parallelism, hardware/software co-design, and information storage and retrieval.[4]

About the Dialects

Foremost, James forms are abstract. They do not look like trees or houses although all can be embellished to look like familiar objects at the risk of introducing accidental features. They do look like some familiar objects such as boxes and floor plans, however the containment relations do not resemble natural containment processes such as putting lettuce into a bag and then putting the bag into a shopping cart or putting pots into the cupboard of the kitchen in a house. Containment relations are **abstract process descriptions**, as would be expected for a formal representation intended to facilitate dynamic pattern transformation.

The *bounded dialect* is a geometric form that may encourage holistic visualization. Bounded forms are essentially identical to parens forms, but without the habitual linearity of typography. The *parens dialect* itself is a unique typographical form since linear reading requires maintenance of the scope of an opening parenthesis until the accompanying closing parenthesis is encountered. Parens right/left fragments are non-local and thus context dependent, more like sentence and paragraph structure than letter and word structure. In programming languages opening (push) and closing (pop) delimiters differentiate between processes that require memory and those that do not.

Dnets, rooms and paths, like sentences, are temporal. Although their display structure shows an entire configuration concurrently, their process structure evolves over time. Unlike text, each dialect is a mixture of linear and parallel components. The *room dialect* is a minor modification of the dnet dialect that provides, given appropriate scaling, the opportunity to participate physically inside a computational process the same way that data is transferred between operations before finally being converted into a result. Divergent paths are choices of which door to go through. Computation implemented with the room model involves closing axiomatically specified doors.

The *path dialect* shows a traversal across fences rather than through doors. This dialect represents potential parallelism as diverging paths, however the traversal metaphor suggests that we must choose one path and backtrack to explore the other path. Uninformed choice of one path over another is the hallmark of a complex algorithmic process.[5] Paths end at units along the round border and at constants along the square border. Labeled variables lying on the round or square border identify subpaths with their own internal structure. Paths provide a unique parity count of crossings. They structurally distinguish odd and even depths of nestings. When a path terminates at a variable or constant on both sides of a border, the form is *binate*, another inherent marker of computational complexity.[6]

Finally the *∂net dialect* will be used extensively in the following sections since it provides unique information about **asynchronous processing** (i.e. the number of separate processes that can be constructively active at the same time) and **structure sharing** (i.e. the occurrence of identical subpatterns within a form).

44.2 i, π and e

Other than the units 1 and −1, the three ubiquitous constants in modern arithmetic are i (from imaginary numbers), π (from circular geometry) and e (from differential calculus). We will examine each as a compound James form using five different iconic dialects:

— **parens:** our convenient quasi-textual form
— **bounded:** a geometric form of containment
— **network:** a form with localized processing
— **room:** an exemplar experiential form
— **path:** an exemplar traversable form.

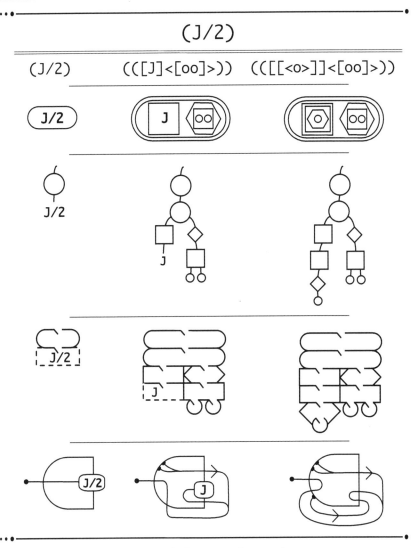

Figure 44-4: *Iconic forms of √-1*

Iconic i

Chapter 39.3 casts the four-cycle imaginary i as a compound expression composed of two out-of-phase cycles of the simpler two-cycle form J. In particular, i is one-half of J when expressed in a round space.[7]

$$i = (J/2) \qquad J = [i][i] = ([[i]][2])$$

Figure 44-4 presents √–1 in five dialects laid out in five rows. These forms each incorporate the constant J; all are J imaginary rather than i imaginary. The three columns in the figure show each dialect in three versions. The leftmost version incorporates the hybrid abbreviation J/2. The center version shows only the abbreviation J. And the right-most version includes no abbreviations, expressing J in its boundary form as [<o>].

Imagine that we have never seen the imaginary i, or for that matter, any conventional mathematical expression. What do the iconic forms tell us about the creature i? I'll adopt a structural perspective, considering containment relations but not conventional interpretations. In the leftmost column the structure J/2 does not show the boundary form because it is hybrid. It does tell us that i is a simple fraction of J, but the hypothesis is that we do not know what a fraction is. The center column includes the constant J and it also includes an abbreviation for a J-frame, the angle-bracket. The rightmost column keeps the angle-brackets as a visual abbreviation. By definition the boundary form of J cannot be expressed without an internal angle-bracket.[8]

Without angle-brackets

Omitting angle-brackets by embedding them within the constant J, we arrive at a James form that consists of two types of boundaries, each inverse to the other by the Inversion axiom, plus the unique James constant J and one common arithmetic unit, the constant o.

$$(J/2) = (([J]<[oo]>)) = (([J] (J [[oo]])))$$

For comparison, interpreting the iconic form of i yields a quite unconventional expression.

$$i = (([J] (J [[oo]])))_{\#} \quad ☞ \quad \#\#^{\log J + \#^{J} + \log\log 2}$$

Frame structure

We will focus on the center column of Figure 44-4. Nested within a round-bracket is a [J]-frame, (([J] [*content*])). The content is itself a J-frame also nested within a round-bracket: ((J [*content*])). Finally the content of the inner frame is [oo]. Visually,

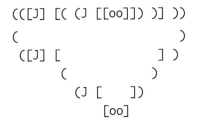

`((([J] [( (J [[oo]]]) )] ))`	
`(                          )`	round space
`([J] [            ] )`	[J]-frame
`(          )`	frame content
`(J [    ])`	J-frame
`[oo]`	frame content

[J]-frames support *fractional cardinality*, itself a generalized accumulation concept generated by Replication. J-frames support *polarity*, a numeric concept that from a James perspective expresses occlusion. Occlusion is equivalent to Reflection and to the assertion of identity. Both fractional Replication and Occlusion are imaginary J structures, neither inherently addresses what we have been interpreting as *numeric* concepts.

$$A = A$$
$$A <A> = void$$
$$A (J [A]) = void$$

The round-bracket containment of each frame shifts the entire form into round space. Counting each nested round-bracket as +1 and each nested square-bracket as –1 provides a metric of the **depth** of a form. A positive metric identifies a form as essentially round while a negative metric identifies a form as square. Both J and generic frames are balanced with nesting 0. The form of i has a nesting metric of 2 with two reflections indicated by the two occurrences of J.

Iconic π

The iconic structure of π comes directly from Euler's association of the circumference of a unit circle with exponential expressions. Figure 44-5 shows this structure in five dialects horizontally and with three types of abbreviation vertically.

(<J/2> [J])

(<J/2>[J])   ([J]<([J]<[oo]>)>) ([[<o>]]<([[<o>]]<[oo]>)>)

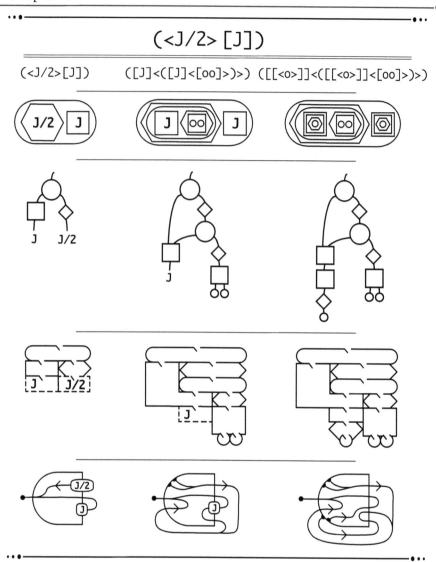

Figure 44-5: *Iconic forms of* π

The hybrid form of i can be reconstituted as (J/2 [o]), a J/2-frame with unitary content. Just like i, π is a J/2-frame with the frame contents of the unit J rather than the unit o. This provides a bridge between i, J and o.

$$i \quad \text{☞} \quad (\text{ J/2 } [o])_e$$
$$π \quad \text{☞} \quad (<J/2> [J])_e$$

The J/2-frame for π is inverted as <J/2>. Although J/2 is sign-blind, in conventional terms, the two approaches to π maintain a clockwise/counterclockwise rotational model.

$$(\ J/2 \ [J]) \quad ☞ \quad -π$$
$$(<J/2>[J]) \quad ☞ \quad π$$

Within the reflective J model, the direction of rotation around a unit circle does not exist, both are the same reflection of J. As a rotation ±π is sign-blind. Another caveat is that Euler's definition of π relies upon base-e. Although Euler also defines i in terms of base-e as $i = J/π$, the definition of i as $(-1)^{1/2}$ appears to be in base--1. As demonstrated in Chapter 43.5 unitary bases are structurally unsound.[9]

J-convert

Expanding the J/2 abbreviation we get the center column of Figure 44-5.

$$([J] < \quad J/2 \quad >)$$
$$([J] <([J]<[oo]>)>) \qquad \text{substitute}$$

All angle-brackets can be expressed in terms of J.

$$([J] \ (J \ [J]<[oo]>)) \qquad \text{J-convert}$$
$$([J] \ (J \ [J] \ (J \ [[oo]]))) \qquad \text{J-convert}$$

Both the network and the room dialects support structure sharing, shown as multiple upper connections in the dnet dialect and multiple doors opening into the same room in the room dialect. The path dialect supports structure sharing only in **unate** forms for which replicas occur only at depths with equal parity (replicas are solely either inside or outside the distinction border). In the case of π, J is binate, occurring both inside and outside. The path dialect then requires two path accesses to J, one on each side of the round/square border. This circumstance is clearest in the J-converted path version of π in the sidebar.

J-convert π path

The excessive parens structure is alleviated by the structure sharing network form illustrated in the sidebar. The depth metric of π is 2, the same as i, again displayed clearly in the dnet dialect by counting the round- and square-nodes in the longest dnet path.

J-convert π dnet

$$((([[Ln\ o]]\ <[Ln]>))$$

| bounded | network | room | path |

Figure 44-6: *Iconic forms of* e

enfold/clarify

π occurs often in many diverse mathematical structures, but it acquires a very specific meaning when associated with i due to Euler's co-definition of i, π and e. When the form of i is located within the form of π its complex boundary structure simplifies as illustrated below.

$$π = ([J] <\ ([J] <[oo]>)\ >)$$

enfold $\qquad ([J] <[(([J] <[oo]>))]>)$

substitute $\qquad ([J] <[\qquad i \qquad]>) \quad ☞\ J/i$

| π | enfold | match | substitute |

Iconic e

Figure 44-6 shows the limit-variable definition of the constant e in five dialects. The internal variable Ln is a limit variable that approaches 0, however if it is rendered void-equivalent then the definition becomes indeterminate. We will revisit the form of e in the next two sections.

$$e^{i\pi} + 1 = 0$$

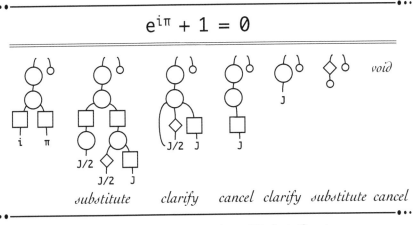

substitute   clarify   cancel   clarify   substitute cancel

Figure 44-7: *Demonstration of Euler's identity*

44.3 Euler Transformations

Here is the James analogy to Euler's identity as developed in Chapters 34.7 and 39.5.

`([o]([[e]][i][π])) o = ` *void*	☞	$1 \times e^{i\pi} + 1 = 0$
`([J]([[#]][ J ])) J = ` *void*	☞	$J \times \#^J + J = 0$

Euler identity

J-self-occlusion

Figure 44-7 demonstrates the validity of Euler's identity by substituting the forms of i and π within the James form of $e^{i\pi}$. The superfluous J/2 which encodes the concept of a rotational i "rotates" in the opposite direction for π and thus the imaginary components of the two cancel.

```
    (([i] [   π   ]))ₑ o
    ((J/2 <J/2> [J]))   o        substitute/clarify
    ((          [J]))   o        cancel
    (           J  )   o        clarify
              void               substitute/cancel
```

Similarly the James version of the Euler identity, *J-self-occlusion*, is reduced to *void* in Figure 44-8 without implicating a J/2-frame or a specific base.

```
    J ( J  [J])#
    J ([<o>][J])               substitute
    J <(    [J]}>              promote/clarify
    J <     J  >              clarify
         void                  cancel
```

J (J [J])

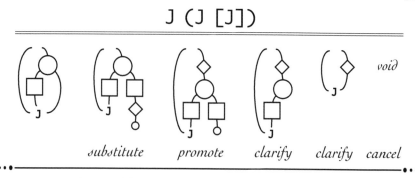

| substitute | promote | clarify | clarify | cancel |

Figure 44-8: *Demonstration of J-self-occlusion*

create/cancel

The substantive difference between these two void-equiv-alent identities is the constant e as a base, a consequence of Euler's definition of exponential rotation and not a necessity. Next we'll examine the role of e in differentiation of exponential forms.

demote/promote

44.4 Dnet Differentiation

The derivative of a function compares two small changes, one in the value of the function, f(x + Lh) – f(x), and one in the value of its argument, (x + Lh) – x. This essentially geometric concept can be abbreviated as df(x)/dx, where the d indicates the small change that approaches zero. The *approach to zero* is abbreviated as Lh. Below, this comparison is expressed iconically, without reference to geometric, functional or limit concepts.

(f(x+Lh) – f(x)) / Lh ☞ ([{x Lh}<{x}>]<[{Lh}]>)

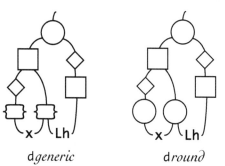

dgeneric   dround

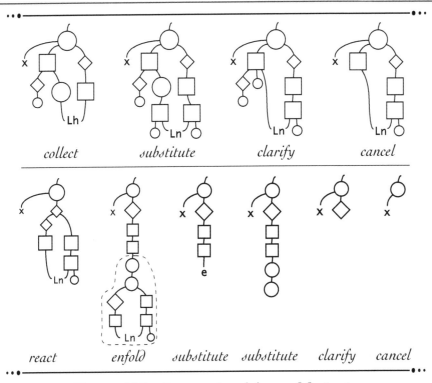

$$collect \qquad substitute \qquad clarify \qquad cancel$$

$$react \qquad enfold \qquad substitute \quad substitute \quad clarify \quad cancel$$

Figure 44-9: *Construction of the round derivative*

The curly-braces in the left dnet stand in place of any James boundary. On the right the round-node "function" has been substituted. The structural dilemma is that if the small change Lh were indeed zero, then its void-equivalence would leave an empty square-node that would render the entire form non-numeric.[10]

collect/disperse

The Round Derivative

Figure 44-9 shows the construction of the round derivative from the dnet definition. The objective is to consider function differentiation as a dnet transformation. The figure picks up from the dnet definition on the previous page. An initial structural goal is to eliminate the dual reference to x, that is, to untangle the variable replicas in the form. The implementation of Arrangement is particularly simple in the dnet dialect, we can relocate a

react/react

shared reference upward through an involution pair as illustrated by the first dnet in the figure. As described in Chapter 37.3 the next step is inspired: substitute [Ln o] for Lh. This results in two simplification steps, clarify and cancel, shown in the first row of the figure. The react step in the second row lays the groundwork for matching the limit pattern to the definition of e. A substitution replaces the dnet form of e by a label. At this point, the entire dnet is base-free. The second substitution of e = (( )) anchors the form to base-e and simplifies the derivative to (x).

Compared to the bracket derivatives in Chapter 37, the dnet dialect facilitates structure sharing. Seeing a form as having only *one* occurrence of a given variable leads to a more integrated, relational display of the overall structure. The initial substitution of [Ln o] for Lh creates an internal shared structure which then supports structural abstraction, as illustrated in the sidebar. Rather than reading the token Lh as *approach-to-zero*, it can be read as an abbreviation for the compound subform [Ln o] throughout the form.[11]

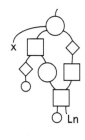

x

Ln

The Chain Rule

(a b)

parens

∂net

a b

a b

error

Chapter 37.4 provides a rather elaborate explanation of the necessity of the chain rule to manage the context of a limit variable. The chain rule itself can be seen as accidental structure imposed by a typography that does not accommodate substitution *on the inside*. The left-hand column of Figure 44-10 shows the three dnet substitution patterns that define the derivatives of angle-, round- and square-nodes. The fourth pattern at the top of the left column shows the rule for addition, at least within the interpretation. The concept of addition in the James form has been replaced by the concept of *independence*. This is easily seen in the dnet dialect as separate content links. A single link to more than one content node is an error. As well, the angle-node is *transparent* to differentiation.

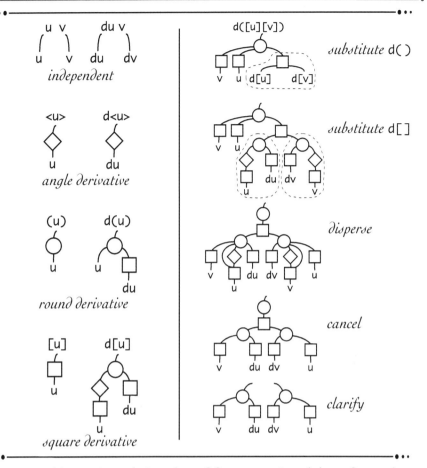

Figure 44-10: *Dnet chain rules and demonstration of the product rule*

We are left with two simple substitution patterns that structurally incorporate the chain rule. Implementing the chain rule is the same as implementing successive pattern substitutions. From a network perspective, the importance of the chain rule is that it provides *labels* for subnetworks.

The right-hand column of Figure 44-10 shows the construction of the product rule. Of course there is no concept of a *product*, there are just three nested nodes. The first substitution shown as the top dnet is the form of the round derivative. Since the round-node has two content forms they are attached independently. The result calls

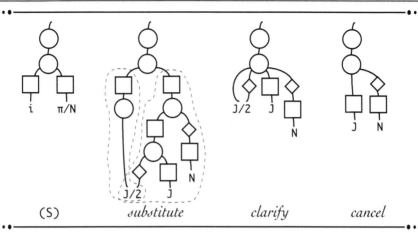

Figure 44-11: *The reflective* rcosine

for two instances of substitution of the square derivative. The second dnet completes the differentiation. The chain rule remains as unspecified variables du and dv. The next three lower dnets show a structural simplification. The forms [u] and [v] are both dispersed downward, which then triggers two instances of cancellation. Again we see that the most complex axiom for linear representations, Arrangement, is simply moving subnets up and down the network structure. The Reflection axiom is triggered by the structure sharing pattern [u][v] that initially motivates their dispersal. In an implementation these rules coalesce into a single rule defined by specific *path patterns*. As is typical, the Inversion axiom cleans up the remaining inverse container pairs.

44.5 Dnet Rcosine

In Chapter 40.6 the reflective rcosine is defined as (S) where S connects both James reflection and Euler rotation.

$$e^{i\pi/N} \quad \text{☞} \quad (([i][\pi/N])) = (J/N) = (S)$$

The dnets in Figure 44-11 show the conversion between the Euler expression and the James form. The figure illustrates that the exponential form of rotation simplifies significantly

Collecting J causes a tally error

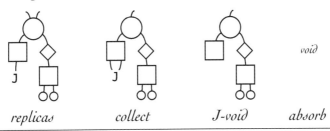

| *replicas* | *collect* | *J-void* | *absorb* |

Collecting (<[oo]>) maintains J parity

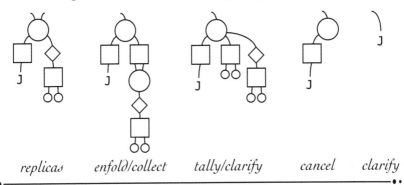

| *replicas* | *enfold/collect* | *tally/clarify* | *cancel* | *clarify* |

Figure 44-12: *Tally failure*

when converted into the James notation. The quantized angle π/N becomes the distance J/N along the i-axis, obviating the need for the concept of rotation. This transformation effectively maps the unit circle circumference onto the number line, with the value of the rcosine carried along as the real component of the imaginary number $e^{J/N}$.

44.6 Tally Failure in Dnets

Tally failure is a loss of confluence, an inconsistency in pattern-matching, that occurs when replicas of J are tallied. As discussed in Chapter 35.3 it is an initially disconcerting but essential behavior of an additive imaginary. As described by Euler,

$$2 \times J = 0 \quad but \quad J \neq 0$$

This feature plays havoc with the Distributive Rule.

$\backslash_J{}^J$ = *void*

J-void

= *void*

emit/absorb

= *replicate/tally*

replicate/tally

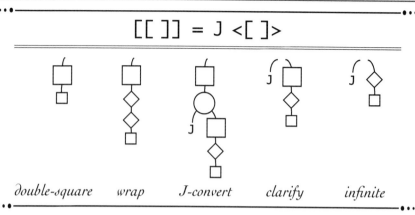

double-square   wrap   J-convert   clarify   infinite

Figure 44-13: *Double-square theorem*

Figure 44-12 shows how a structural choice of which forms to collect becomes a choice of structure sharing in dnets. We begin with two replicas of the form of J/2, represented by the two top links to context. The upper display shifts structure sharing down to J, triggering absorption of the entire dnet. The lower display shifts structure sharing down to the numeric component (<[2]>), allowing a tally of the fractional cardinality of J without voiding J itself. To avoid the tally error, pattern-matching is forbidden to tally J.

wrap/unwrap

infinite

44.7 Dnet Non-numeric Form

Finally we'll visit the dnet reduction of two non-numeric forms. Figure 44-13 demonstrates the **double-square theorem** that converts [[ ]] into a simpler structure that incorporates the basic non-numeric form <[ ]>. Both an application of Infinite Interpretation and the existence of J are necessary. If the angle-nodes of <[ ]> are J-converted, the reduced structure is lost.[12]

```
              [  []   ]
wrap          [< <[]> >]
infinite      [<(<[]>)>]
J-transparent [<(    )>] <[]>
substitute        J     <[]>
```

[[[ ]]] = <[ ]>

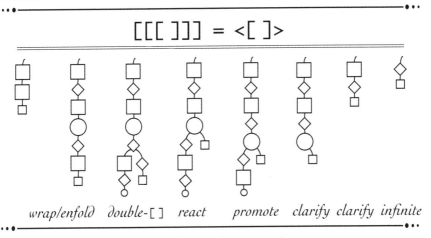

wrap/enfold ∂ouble-[ ] react promote clarify clarify infinite

Figure 44-14: *Triple-square theorem*

Directly absorbing J is not an option. Compare these two sequences:

```
(  J   <[ ]>)        (J <[ ]>)
([<( )>]<[ ]>)       (  <[ ]>)   ERROR   substitute--absorb
<([ ( ) ]<[ ]>)>          <[ ]>          promote--infinite
<(        <[ ]>)>         <[ ]>          clarify
<         <[ ]> >         infinite
          [ ]             unwrap
```

Triple Square

Figure 44-14 demonstrates the Triple-square theorem which as it turns out requires some subtlety, thus qualifying it for the second most challenging theorem in the three volumes.[13] The strategy is to apply the double-square theorem after isolating a double-square. Reduction requires both wrapping a double-square with intervening angle-brackets, [<<[[ ]]>>], and separating the angle-brackets with an inversion pair, [<[(<[[ ]]>)]>]. Note that absorb is never applied since absorbing single angle-nodes is an error.

wrap

[<<[[ ]]>>]
parens ∂ialect

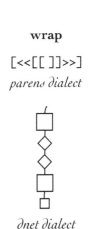

∂net ∂ialect

As observed in Chapters 41.4 and 43.1, one remarkably strange design decision of modern mathematics is to give polarity dominance over infinity, thereby creating both $+\infty$ and $-\infty$. Thus ∞ can *absorb* negative magnitude but not negative polarity![14] Design decisions reflect a priority of conceptual values. The duality of $+1$ and -1 supports two commensurable worlds of natural numbers, joined together as the *integers*. ∞ establishes an unreachable limit to natural numbers. Both -1 and ∞ are imaginary and thus *design choices*. As a culture we have elected to value bidirectionality, *conceptual duality*, over bounded possibility. This choice leaves us with dual infinities, $+\infty$ and $-\infty$. We could consider a sign-blind infinite, $\pm\infty$, as an alternative design choice by asserting [ ] = <[ ]>. This would lead to a unified Dominion,

$$(A \ [\ ]) = (A \ <[\ ]>) = void$$

and a different way of understanding reality.

44.8 Remarks

The intention of this chapter is to encourage a visual pattern-matching approach to both computation and comprehension. The chapter's narration is heavily *structural*. At this point a symbolic narration that might provide guidance about iconic thinking is both premature and presumptive. If my personal experiences are a guide, then the development of a cognitive understanding of iconic form is idiosyncratic, transitory during learning and continually self-referencing. There is an intuition that comes with familiarity, but the path of deconstructing symbolic habits instilled by culture and education since early childhood is very challenging.

Although the metalanguage relies upon arithmetic concepts (additive, fraction, base, function, and yes, even *number*), they are all interpretations of containment patterns. Modest modifications of the James axioms can turn the same patterns into sets, into logic and into imaginative new domains of structure.

Endnotes

1. **opening quote:** B. Mandelbrot (1999) *Multifractals and 1/f Noise* p. 9.

2. **Containment becomes gravitational stacking:** The shading of the angle-block is a display artifact intended to distinguish the block's type when it is occluded by another block.

3. **achieve global transformation without global coordination:** W. Bricken (1995) Distinction networks. In I. Wachsmuth, C. Rollinger & W. Brauer (eds.) *KI-95: Advances in Artificial Intelligence* p.35-48. Online 8/18 at http://wbricken.com/pdfs/01bm/05arch/01dnets/04distinction-networks.pdf

4. **parallelism, and information storage and retrieval:** Classical mathematical technique places mathematics above and beyond physical and cognitive constraints. The indulgence of Platonic reality assures the construction of artifacts that are as physically detached as those generated by playing video games. This opinion is antithetical to the assertion of mathematical primacy, however I would suggest that the illusion of primacy characterizes a mathematics only in its infancy.

5. **the hallmark of a complex algorithmic process:** Polynomial processes (P) do not require backtracking, while exponential processes (NP) do.

6. **form is *binate*, another inherent marker of computational complexity:** Binate is a technical term from Boolean optimization that identifies expressions in which a variable appears both negated and non-negated, for example, A AND NOT A. Here it is expanded to refer to a form in which a variable occurs at both an odd and an even depth of nesting within square-brackets.

7. **one-half of J when expressed in a round space:** *Round space* is a new term, an attempt to avoid the interpretative term *exponential space*. We have encountered very little direct analysis of James forms in these volumes, and now is not the time to begin in earnest. Description in terms of frames and nestings and balance of round- and square-brackets remains a frontier.

8. **cannot be expressed without an internal angle-bracket:** The complexity of J compared to that of i can be seen by comparing the James forms in Figure 44-2 (J) to those in Figure 44-4 (i). Of course the dialects of James arithmetic are designed to express logarithms with ease, however a notation

designed to express square roots with ease, such as √N, cannot extend easily to express the range for functions that the James forms do. A square-root centered language cannot manage the integration of multiplication and logarithms.

9. **unitary bases are structurally unsound:** Conveniently 1^n remains 1 so long as n remains numeric. $(-1)^n$ is not uncommon; it oscillates but in a controlled binary manner. However the concept of a base is rarely applied to a *unit* since the exponential base is associated with repeated multiplication.

10. **that would render the entire form non-numeric:** The situation is slightly more complex because the angle-bracket containing the potentially empty square-bracket does not allow that bracket to be clarified out of existence.

11. **for the compound subform [Ln o] throughout the form:** In software development finding common dynamic patterns throughout a program is called *function partitioning*, and is essential for optimizing control flow through functional and object-oriented code.

12. **are J-converted, the reduced structure is lost:** This demonstration differs from the demonstration of the Double-square theorem in Chapter 41.7.

13. **the second most challenging theorem in the three volumes:** I consider the demonstration of the Promotion theorem in Chapter 10.1 to be the most challenging, although still quite trivial for an automated pattern-matching search algorithm.

14. **can *absorb* negative magnitude but not negative polarity:** As discussed in Chapter 41.7, the decision to maintain a directionality for infinity supports not only $+\infty$ and $-\infty$, it also is critical for the display of all imaginary numbers on the complex plane. A complex number displays its real component as a magnitude along the x-axis and its imaginary component as a *polar coordinate rotation* along the y-axis. The distinction breaks down at real $\pm\infty$, under the logarithmic transform, $\log +\infty = \log -\infty$. This polarity collapse is not reflected in the James translation, $[<[ ]>] \neq [[ ]]$. The use of J to carry polarity within exponential space requires $\log +\infty \neq \log -\infty$. The experimentation over the last few chapters attempting to maintain J in the presence of square-brackets might be due to the incompatibility with the imaginary i and the imaginary J.

Chapter 45

Return

Math was always my bad subject.
I couldn't convince my teachers
that many of my answers were meant ironically.[1]
— Calvin Trillin (1988)

Volume I presents two iconic approaches to the representation of the formal structure of arithmetic. It also serves as an introduction to a different way of thinking about formality. Volume II contrasts postsymbolic arithmetic to the established symbolic foundations of arithmetic developed well over a century ago. This volume explores the iconic constant J and applies void-based thinking to several areas of elementary mathematics.

45.1 Evolution

At the turn of the twentieth century the mathematical community adopted a radical plan to put mathematics on a firm foundation. The idea was **symbolic formalization**, the representation of concepts using encoded symbols that bear no resemblance to what they mean. Also at the turn of the twentieth century the American logician C.S. Peirce contrasted *symbolic, indexical* and *iconic* notations within his development of the field of **semiotics**. Peirce was the first to formalize iconic logic with his **Existential**

iconic forms look like what they mean

Graphs, a form of logic based on containment within two dimensional spatial boundaries.[2] Peirce believed that his graphs *illustrated* the process of logical thinking. In 1967 G. Spencer Brown reintroduced Peirce's iconic system in a more general algebraic style as *Laws of Form*.

Return to Postsymbolism

Today mathematics remains symbolic while other communication media have evolved into visual and interactive experiences. We write on lines of paper but what of the communication of artists and sculptors and film-makers? We speak in a linear flow of words, but what of the non-linear flow of music and poetry and dance? We read books that display strings of tokens but what of the display of illustrations and photographs and videos and websites? Our digital computation tools can render both lines of text and dynamic images but that which is encoded within huge strings of binary digits has no knowledge of context or environment. Symbolic computation cannot make a distinction, cannot have an idea; it can neither know nor deceive itself.[3]

Although symbolic mathematics may be eternal, the context, meaning, relevance, interpretation and worthiness of any aspect of mathematical symbolism is involuted by physical time and by cultural change. **Belief in mathematics** is *not* eternal. Indeed a theme of postsymbolism is that formal decisions and commitments made in one era can in a later era become dubious. Hilbert sought to design a mathematics that supported entirely its own validity, without reference to the context that contains it. Prior to our modern understanding of cybernetics, ecology and embodiment, Hilbert's dream of metamathematics was a great improvement that literally laid the groundwork for the computational age. But by design metamathematics cannot be *relevant*. Symbols are necessarily obscured, obliterated, by their meaning. Formal symbol systems are designed to deceive. There is no there there.[4]

Digital technology has spurred an evolution in the representation and acquisition of mathematical knowledge. Mathematics is shifting to visual rather than textual forms of expression. Venn diagrams, Feynman diagrams, diagrammatic reasoning, cellular automata, fractals, knot theory, string theory, category theory, silicon circuit design; each of these fields relies upon the iconic representation of formal systems. Like geometry these fields can be seen as addressing inherently multidimensional concepts. Formalism is escaping its symbolic constraints.

But we face a severe limitation: *formalism itself is currently defined by symbolic strings*. Created in an era without film and television and video gaming and telephones-that-are-cameras and social media, symbolic formalism is permeated with accidental structure imposed by a medium of expression that obscures the content being expressed. Via the syntax/semantics barrier, symbolic form is intentionally blind. It cannot access its own meaning. It lacks a direct facility for feedback and self-modification. Attempting to isolate any aspect of reality or fantasy from the context/environment that provides its sustenance and vitality is delusional behavior. *Thought is a system*, integrated with its mental carrier which is itself integrated with its physical carrier which is itself integrated with its experiential context which is itself inseparable from the warp and weft of reality. Today it is both dangerous and destructive to believe in a Platonic reality separate from the actual reality since existential questions stretch well beyond the isolated security of formal and philosophical thought and well outside of the contextual disassociation of silicon computation.

45.2 Crossing the Boundary

After working with *Laws of Form* for over a decade, I learned to recognize the depths to which Spencer Brown had deconstructed our notions of Truth and rationality. In my mind, axiomatic Crossing and Calling boiled over from logic into the neurophysiology of thought and into the fundamental philosophies of Western culture. Taking *void* seriously forces one to look at the unity of life rather than escaping into the ease of dualism. It is no longer appropriate to pretend that our thoughts can be separate from our actions. In *boundary logic* this is particularly clear since logical boundaries are **semipermeable**, the outside has complete access to the inside. I explored a void-based perspective for two more decades, applying semipermeability to the most challenging logical tasks available: programming languages that support provably correct code and the optimization of million gate silicon circuitry. Iconic *arithmetic* grew from the rigorously computational foundation of iconic *logic*. Learning how to interpret Spencer Brown's work involves connecting abstraction to experience.

logic

Logic Begets Numerics

An impassible chasm became obvious. Aside from a few professionals, folks don't really understand or have much interest in *logic*. People are extensively irrational.[5] We all however must face numeric arithmetic from an early age onward. It seemed like a good idea to construct *iconic arithmetic* as a basis for communicating the importance of iconic thought to cybernetic philosophy.

numeric

Which shared beliefs are most universal and most entrenched across the cultures of the world? What would it be like to deconstruct and then to reconstruct the skills taught to every school child? Mathematics and language are the universal basis for modern primary education. In schools logic never shows up. Language skills are of course fragmented across the many human languages, but the arithmetic of whole numbers is relentlessly present in every child's schooling. What fascinates me is the exotic challenge of exploring an *alternative* to one of the few things that nearly every culture considers to be a vital necessity.[6] This effort is particularly appropriate in today's age of the **tyranny of numbers**.[7] Our institutions and businesses are becoming increasingly reliant on AI pattern-recognition systems combined with unimaginable amounts of digital data to make decisions about both the strategies of organizations and the fate of individuals.

The task then was set: To demonstrate that *what we take as universal is simply a design decision* that we have chosen from a diversity of alternatives. The motivation is grounded in a belief that humankind is not at its apex of sophistication. What we believe today, I believe, will look as antiquated in the coming century as the pre-computational construction of formal mathematics a century ago looks today. For proof of principle what is needed is a clear, equally capable alternative that provides an entirely different way to think about arithmetic, an alternative that is *not isomorphic* but rather that is constructed on a completely different ground. Spencer Brown has provided that ground at the absolute minimum: *void* rather than zero. The accumulating round-boundary is an easy analog for tally arithmetic. Kauffman arithmetic provides an iconic resolution to the grouping problem encountered by every civilization that has accumulated too many individual tally marks. Addition and multiplication of numbers is thus addressed by tally arithmetic augmented by substitution.

Spencer Brown's tectonic shift in the structure of formal thinking suggests how to extend tally arithmetic into rational and real numbers. The innovation is to construct a second kind of boundary unit that is non-accumulating (Unify) and that cancels the round unit (void Inversion). The Law of Calling is a model for a non-accumulating distinction. The Law of Crossing provides a model of how to compose distinctions with their inverses. Refocusing on *containment as the only relation* eliminates the numeric processes of **counting** and **functions**. The singular relation removes addition and multiplication from James patterns, placing these numeric functions

accumulate
( ) ( ) ≠ ( )

group base-2
o o = (o)
merge
(A)(B) = (A B)

unify
[ ] [ ] = [ ]
void inversion
([ ]) = [( )] = *void*

call
⟨ ⟩ ⟨ ⟩ = ⟨ ⟩
cross
⟨ ⟨ ⟩ ⟩ = *void*

instead into the interpretation. The James calculus then stands solely on *containment patterns* rather than on our familiar arithmetic constants and operations. The operations of iconic arithmetic consist of putting parts into mutually inverse containers, ([.]). When we add we put the part inside the dual container, ([a b c]). When we multiply we put each part into a container and then put those together into the inverse container, ([a][b][c]). Divide and subtract require that we toss the constant J into an appropriate location within the containment pattern. Computation proceeds by *pattern-recognition and rule-based substitution* that implements replacement subforms by axiomatically equivalent alternatives.

45.3 Violation of Symbolic Canons

Iconic Arithmetic is an attempt to meet mathematics on its own ground, not at the psychological underpinnings of philosophy but at the formal rigor of axiomatic structure. The enterprise is constructed on several Principles that guide and determine the structural constraints on numeric iconic form.

void =

Principle of Void: *Void* has no properties.

( ) ≠ *void*

Principle of Existence: Something is not nothing.

( ) = ( )

Principle of Identity: A distinction distinguishes itself.

(a b)

Principle of Containment: There is the only relation, containment.

(a b) = (a) (b)

Principle of Independence: All forms are mutually independent.

a = *void* ⇒ *void*

Principle of Void-equivalence: Void-equivalent forms are syntactically inert and semantically meaningless.

One other Principle constrains the alien numeric creature J.

(a J) ⇏ (b)

Principle of Incommensurability: J does not interact with other numeric forms.

In a final affront to arithmetic, the empty square-bracket is even stranger than J, [ ] is not numeric. The non-accumulating square unit is guided by two Principles that isolate numeric form from the erosive tendencies of its antithesis.

Principle of Non-numeric Form: After reduction, non-numeric forms include a square unit.

$$(a\ [\ ])\ \nRightarrow\ (b)$$

Principle of Indeterminacy: Any numeric form in the same container as a square unit is indeterminate.

$$(a\ [\ ])\ \Rightarrow\ ?a?$$

Needless to say, there is very little in the above Principles that reminds one of the foundations of symbolic arithmetic.

Symbolic Dogma

It's not surprising that the structure and transformation of postsymbolic form immediately violates several canons of the symbolic dogma.

- *Meaning is stored and manipulated in strings of symbols.*

Pattern-matching exposes the *accidental structure* manifest in the representation of concepts by token strings. The symbolic doctrine casts strings as the static data structure within which control algorithms enact transformations. It is posited that knowledge can be gleaned by rearranging the linear ordering of tokens. Iconic containment, nesting itself, erodes the symbolic canon of separation of object and process, of data from algorithm. James forms are purely *patterns of containment*. Containment embodies parallelism, distributed processes, transformation *across* nested forms, and independence of every form within every container. Meaning is perceptual, interactive, experiential.

$$(a\ b\ c)\ \Rightarrow\ (b\ c\ a)$$

$$\begin{array}{c} foo \\ baz\ \ bar \end{array} \Rightarrow \begin{array}{c} foo\ \ \ baz \\ bar \end{array}$$

- *Image and experience do not support formalism.*

The 19th century trauma of non-Euclidean geometry grew into a ban on embedding formal meaning into diagrams and pictures. Careful structural definition can of course overcome this overt bias. A common difficulty with pictorial formalism is the distinction between figure

ground
as context

ground
as content

figure

and ground. A container *cleaves* the ground and *is* the figure. Containment not only eliminates the figure/ground duality, it also allows both figure and ground to have mutually defined meaning as content and context.[8] Containers both separate and connect.

- *All concepts must have a representation.*

String languages treat the "blank space" as just another type of token, one that is given a specific meaning as a separator of strings that represent concepts. Concept, to exist, must be expressed by an arranged sequence of encoded tokens. Containers in contrast provide an internal emptiness that is not enlisted to distinguish concept from structure. The container boundary itself provides conceptual distinction. Emptiness, a contextual *void*, is then free to be employed as a structural tool. Concept can be implicit. Structure can be void-equivalent.

- *Replication is free.*

Symbolic replication is the source of symbolic complexity. Rearrangement is the primary mechanism for decoding concepts that are tangled and obscured within an arrangement of symbolic replicas. When the sequence

yada yada yada yada yada...

of rearrangement steps is ambiguous, the art of finding meaning explodes combinatorially. Iconic display in contrast is spacious enough to support unique forms without replication. Illusory forms are *pervasive* throughout an iconic structure. These forms can be freely deleted and

freely constructed anywhere while inducing minimal structural complexity. During computation void-equivalent forms can act as catalysts for reduction of significant form.[9] Only irrelevant replication is free. Irrelevant replicas are *motivated* only as ephemerals and once identified can be discarded without loss.

- *Process is rearrangement, not deletion, of structure.*

Strings collect and store structure that might be information. The pernicious NOT of logic allows storage of contradictory information. Structure is converted into information via accumulation, via the construction and retention of more structure. Strings cannot self-prune via occlusion, instead they encourage redundancy. Information is positively associated with quantity. Massive redundancy has been discovered within string representations, due not only to accidental structure supported by the linear medium but also due to irrelevant structure embedded within the string representation of concepts and operations.

this

this
or that

this
or that
and not this

this
or that
and not this
therefore that
!

Spencer Brown's startling innovation of defining specific forms to be void-equivalent permits iconic structure to be identified as irrelevant. Iconic transformation increases information by deleting structure. Deletion increases the density and quality of information. This new perspective has evolved into **constraint-based reasoning**. *Eliminate* what is NOT to arrive at what is possible. Rather than considering a solution, consider all solutions by omitting the non-solutions. Computation moves forward by deletion of contextually irrelevant and redundant form. The structural independence of all forms makes rearrangement in space unnecessary.[10]

• *Meaning requires dualism.*

The void-based structure of Peirce's and Spencer Brown's iconic logics challenge a foundational assumption of Western thought, that rationality requires dualism. Duality is subtly embedded within the arithmetic and algebra of numbers as inverse operations, as the self-similar structure of repeated addition and multiplication, as polarity of value, and as the object/process distinction. Duality is embedded in string notation as group theoretic structure (commutativity, associativity, arity), as absence of parallelism in both expressions and processes, as the semantics/syntax barrier, as forced representation of both relevant and irrelevant expressions, and as the exclusion of the active Agent (the mathematician) from the notation.

duality

unity

Dualism dominates logic as the concepts TRUE and FALSE and as the dual perspectives of AND and OR. In contrast, the *logic* boundary ⟨ ⟩ can be interpreted as TRUE, in which case FALSE is the *void* within TRUE. Since FALSE is void-equivalent in iconic logic its non-existence makes *Laws of Form* a logic of *unity rather than duality*. Truth is confounded with existence.[11] A distinction, as represented by a single boundary, accommodates both independence and unity. Context, concept and content are a singular system.

45.4 Non-conformity

There have been several occasions during this exploration when the James calculus has lead to results that do not conform with conventional mathematics. The easy observation is that non-conforming results may require further work to understand, or they may be errors, or inappropriate, or excessively deviant, or simply wrong, or not even wrong.[12] There are certainly circumstances in which I have attempted to push James calculus to the limits of my understanding. It should not be surprising that some anomalies occur, particularly in places where conventional mathematics behaves anomalously within itself. There are a very few areas in which the James calculus appears to be self-contradictory, most of these have been addressed by imposition of rather arbitrary constraints to eliminate destructive forms. The occasions in which James forms substantively deviate from a consistent interpretation are indeed rare, given the very substantive differences between iconic and symbolic technique. There are a few occasions in which poor computational technique embedded within conventional mathematics is a source of problematic behavior. And there are a few occasions in which the mapping to exponential and logarithmic expressions appears to be presumptive. In these cases the James formal structure stands out as underneath and independent of conventional arithmetic. There are of course large tracts of conventional mathematics that I've elected not to address. The guiding theme has been to limit exploration to elementary, high school and first year college mathematics for non-STEM students, with the obvious exception of innovations such as J and some applications to calculus derivatives, complex numbers and infinity. Here is a brief overview of the innovative and the non-conforming results in this volume.

General Computational Technique

Mathematical systems use a wide variety of computational methods (deductive inference, induction, recursion, iteration, substitution of various types, infinite series, mapping, etc.). Almost all eventually reduce to rule-based transformation of formal textual structure, what might be called *algebraic technique*. Iconic form supports a much wider diversity of transformational strategies including parallelism, structure sharing and elimination of accidental structure. Iconic pattern-matching is very challenging to implement within digital software while maintaining the purity of iconic principles. Software is of course string-based, however the networks of transistors that comprise digital hardware are inherently parallel, spatial and void-based. Software embraces the textual duality of 0 *and* 1; hardware operates by the *presence or absence* of an electrical signal along a wire.

Behavior of J *(Chapters 34-36)*

Figure 34-1 lists the features of this resurrected imaginary value while Figure 34-6 lists some of the worrisome properties of J.

Tally failure (Chapters 34.4, 35.3 and 44.6): The equation $x + x \neq 2x$ violates the Distributive property that connects addition to multiplication. However tally failure is a natural consequence of the J-void theorem. An intervention is to recognize that J does not accumulate even though it is numeric. Suppression of accumulation is quite

J-void

$J\ J = void$

natural when one considers the extra-logical attachment of a counting mechanism required for iterative, inductive, oscillating and circular functions. *Counting repetitions requires explicit mechanism.* This weakness is attributable to hidden assumptions in conventional technique.

$a + J \Rrightarrow b$

Incommensurable *(Chapter 35.3):* That J does not add to natural numbers is a property already pioneered by i.

Sign-blind *(Chapter 35.3):* The bipolar property is shared by i, square root and many other conventional functions. In order to maintain a working concept of equality, J-self-inverse cannot be used for local replacement of equals by equals. All J forms (explicit and implicit) must be replaced globally and concurrently within an equation. Euler's intervention is better: recognize the prevalence of bipolar and multivalued functions within the laws of algebra.

J-self-inverse

$J = <J>$

Arrangement inconsistency *(Chapter 35.3 and 36.6):* **Loss of confluence** is a serious issue associated with tally failure and is the reason for suppressing accumulation of J tokens. The constraint not to collect or disperse replicas of J is necessary to avoid contradictory conclusions. J-fractions also rely on a non-accumulating J.

$([J][2]<[2]>)$
$\Rrightarrow ([J \ J]<[2]>)$

J *as a polarity exponent* *(Chapter 38.6):* The computational use of J is unique, particularly the creation of sign-free numbers by moving polarity information into the exponential space as the presence or absence of J.

$a^{k+J} \Rightarrow -a^k$

J *as a more elementary imaginary* *(Chapter 39):* The imaginary constant J is additive and structurally simpler than the multiplicative i.

$i = (J/2)$

Base-free Differentiation *(Chapter 37)*

Differentiation of base-free forms suppresses the logarithmic conversion constant that occurs when changing from one base to another. There is no equivalent conventional concept.

Rational Reflection *(Chapters 39-40)*

***Fractional reflection** (Chapters 39.7 and 40):* Reflection along a single axis suppresses the complex plane by quantizing irrational rotation into rational fractions.

***Fractional polarity** (Chapter 40.6):* Positive and negative polarity, as well as the complex plane, are special cases of arbitrary rational fractions of polarity.

***Reflective trigonometry** (Chapter 40.6):* Rational reflection without polarity changes a few trigonometric identities. Euler's equation and the double-angle and half-angle formulas are reduced by a factor of 2. The Pythagorean theorem and the tangent function collapse.

Infinity *(Chapters 41-43)*

Numeric and non-numeric forms are intimately integrated within the James notation as *iconic polymorphism* of object and operator, removing the type confusion of infinite expressions.

numeric unit ( )
non-numeric unit [ ]

***The form of infinity** (Chapter 41.3 and 41.4):* The representation of negative infinity as [ ] and positive infinity as <[ ]> is a reversal of the interpretation of the angle-bracket that points to an unusual relationship between infinity and polarity.

***Absorption of polarity and magnitude** (Chapter 35.3):* The choice and sequencing of valid transformation must be managed with structural restrictions so that the square unit does not absorb magnitude and polarity information. Since positive infinity and negative infinity are deemed in all cases to be different, absorption of polarity information must be managed closely.

***Infinite Interpretation axiom** (Chapter 41):* Mixing an external interpretation of a formal system with the internal axioms of that system has substantive negative effects on interpretability and application. The mitigation is to restrict Infinite Interpretation to forms with rare applicability that have no other avenue for reduction.

Complex infinity *(Chapter 41.7 and 41.8):* The double-square unit [[ ]] carries complex infinity into James forms with dubious results. A central issue is whether or not an infinite unit can or should *absorb* polarity, or in the James case *absorb* J. The triple-square unit might be inaccessible to consistent computation.

Reflective infinities *(Chapter 41.8):* The dimensionality of a complex infinity with both magnitude and direction are exacerbated by James reflective infinities that support a different imaginary axis for each of the N unit fractions of J/N.

Indeterminate forms *(Chapter 42):* The easily identified single indeterminate form [ ]<[ ]> provides an innovative tool for organizing indeterminate forms, although it does come with further restrictions to avoid sign-blindness and inappropriate absorption.

Non-conforming exotics *(Chapter 43):* James exotic forms sometimes reduce to non-standard results. Infinite summation of zero yields an indeterminate conventional expression but a James *void*. It is more difficult to ignore the indeterminism of 1^∞ and 0^0 in James form. Several conventional results yield a complex infinity while James forms result in specific forms of infinity or indeterminism. The polarity of $-\infty$ needs to be specifically factored into $(-1 \times \infty)$ for James reduction to yield consistent results. J exacerbates the conventional logarithmic collapse of polarity at infinity.

45.5 Grand Strategy

Daniel Kahneman
1934-
Nobel prize 2002

Introducing the innovative world of iconic formal thinking is bound to be extremely challenging. Daniel Kahneman observes, "People tend to assess the relative importance of issues by the ease with which they are retrieved from memory."[13] Not only is there virtually no memory of nor experience with iconic formalism, almost all memory associated with arithmetic is saturated by experience with symbolic expressions. Further, our interpretation of James patterns lands in unfamiliar territories within symbolic arithmetic.

There seems to be little motivation for conceptual justification of an *exploration*. Instead these volumes launch us into an experiential postsymbolic territory where interactive structure condenses symbolic complexity, where form and meaning are united, where objects merge with processes, where absence is a primary conceptual tool, and where the viewing perspective of the reader is directly implicated within the form.

There is a fairly wide awareness of the integrative beliefs driving postsymbolism: Haeckel's ecological holism, Peirce's iconic rationality, Spencer Brown's void-based axioms, von Bertalanffy's general systems, Bateson's cybernetic pattern-that-connects, Lovelock's Gaia, Prigogine's self-organizing systems, Tufte's visual information, Varela's embodied cognition, Wolfram's new kind of science, Buddhist and Vedic metaphysics.[14] Although arithmetic is often enlisted to provide examples that support holism, none reach in to *define arithmetic as a form of experience*. In contrast to Hilbert's metamathematical formalism built solely on isolated abstraction, postsymbolism as a philosophical perspective lies beneath the surface of iconic form as concrete experience. The postsymbolic alternative holds within it an implicit critique of both Western dualism and objective rationality. Dualism is the mechanism, the *excuse* so to speak, that allows us to indulge in the fantasy of an objective reality external to our experiential context. Radical reconstruction of cherished formal beliefs incorporates a broader commentary on the conceptual underpinnings of rational thought in particular and of epistemology in general. *Symbolic representation does not lead to embodied knowledge.*

45.6 Remarks

> *Necessity*
>   *— the author (1980)*

> *Like an empty mirror reflecting an empty room*
> *With nothing around and nothing within*
> *The blank pages of an unwritten book,*
> *The fountain pen still full of ink,*
> *The author without thoughts*
> *Fills the empty page*
> *Expressing without necessity*
> *Nothing at all.*

Endnotes

1. **Opening quote:** C. Trillin (1988/2012) *Quite Enough of Calvin Trillin* p.4.

2. **logic based on containment within two dimensional spatial boundaries:** C. S. Peirce (1909) MS 514 Existential graphs. Online at http://www.jfsowa.com/peirce/ms514.htm

3. **it can neither know nor deceive itself:** The conceptual limits of computation are illustrated by many self-referential questions that cannot be addressed by a computation. The famous **halting problem** asks a computational process: *When will this process be done?* If a computation is able to know when it finishes, it must have sufficient information to actually complete the computation, and therefore can use the information of when it finishes to reach the finish *faster* than is indicated by its answer. There are **modal logics** that provide operators with enticing names such as *undecided* and *know*. Similarly I can write words like *I know that I do not know.* Neither qualify, of course, as self-knowledge.

4. **designed to deceive. There is no there there**: More accurately what remains is metaphysics, an appeal to a semantic magic that connects symbolic structure to experience. We provide that magic by disembodying cognition.

5. **are extensively irrational:** D. Kahneman (2011) *Thinking, Fast and Slow.*

6. **nearly every culture considers to be a vital necessity:** This perspective was somewhat inspired by Stephen Wolfram's book *A New Kind of Science* (2002). Wolfram addresses the universal belief that the physical sciences are fundamentally united with symbolic mathematics by providing an alternative description of Science based on the iconic form of cellular automata.

7. **appropriate in the age of the tyranny of numbers:** "So number will now manifest itself, without limit, as tyranny." A. Badiou (1990) *Number and Numbers* § 6.14. Here Alain Badiou is referring to the abstract structure of our number system. More political and sociological examples include:

N. Eberstadt (1995) *The Tyranny of Numbers: Mismeasurement and misrule.*

D. Boyle (2001) *The Tyranny of Numbers: Why counting can't make us happy.*

J. Williams (2016) *Quantifying Measurement: The tyranny of numbers.*

S. Ball (2017) *Governing by Numbers: Education, governance, and the tyranny of numbers.*

J. Muller (2018) *The Tyranny of Metrics.*

8. **to have mutually defined meaning as content and context:** The page provides a ground for typography, but it is also a dynamic container that *contextualizes* as well as holds structure.

9. **act as catalysts for reduction of significant form:** Although deletion can be conceptualized as *void substitution* and thus integrated into a standard computational model, **catalytic reduction** which permits void-equivalent forms to be introduced arbitrarily, used to trigger transformation of significant structure, and then freely deleted is an entirely new computational paradigm.

10. **makes rearrangement in space unnecessary:** The side bar illustrates a chain of deduction in text and the same reasoning in the path dialect of iconic logic. The untangling of the path logic is clearly visible.

11. **Truth is confounded with existence:** "The concept of truth can be expressed in an extremely simple and formal manner thus: 'What exists is and what does not does not.'" H. Matsuo (1987) K. Inada (trans.). *The Logic of Unity* p.12.

12. **deviant, or simply wrong, or not even wrong:** A common academic finesse is to leave some problems as *an exercise for the student*. I suspect that the entirety of these three volumes leaves iconic arithmetic as an exercise for any reader.

13. **the ease with which they are retrieved from memory:** Kahneman, p.8.

14. **Varela's embodied cognition, Buddhist and Vedic metaphysics:** See

E. Haeckel (1866) *Generelle Morphologie der Organismen*

C.S. Peirce (1931-1935) *Collected Papers of Charles Sanders Peirce*

L. von Bertalanffy (1968) *General Systems Theory*

G. Bateson (1979) *Mind and Nature*

J. Lovelock (1979) *Gaia: A new look a life on Earth*

I. Prigogine (1980) *From Being to Becoming*

E. Tufte (1983) *The Visual Display of Quantitative Information*

F. Varela, E. Thompson & E. Rosch (1991) *The Embodied Mind*

S. Wolfram (2002) *A New Kind of Science.*

Māyā, the void concept in Vedic texts, has many meanings including *illusion*, the appearance of things that are not present. Buddhist texts as well describe māyā as illusory, a sign without substance.

Bibliography

All entries in the bibliography are from the chapter endnotes.

Aristotle (350 BCE) *Physics*. R. Hardie & R. Gaye (trans.). Online at `http://classics.mit.edu/Aristotle/physics.3.iii.html#485`.

A. Artaud (1947) Van Gogh, the man suicided by society. In S. Sontag (ed.) (1988) *Antonin Artaud: Selected writings*.

A. Badiou (1990) *Number and Numbers*.

D. Bal (2006) Leibniz, Bernoulli and the logarithms of negative numbers. Online at `https://msuweb.montclair.edu/~bald/files/LeibBernLogs.pdf`.

S. Ball (2017) *Governing by Numbers: Education, governance, and the tyranny of numbers*.

G. Baron (1804) *The Mathematical Correspondent* Vol.1.

J. Barrow (1992) *Pi in the Sky*.

G. Bateson (1979) *Mind and Nature*.

E. Berlekamp, J. Conway & R. Guy (1982) *Winning Ways*.

C. Bernard (1865/1957) *An Introduction to the Study of Experimental Medicine*.

L. von Bertalanffy (1968) *General Systems Theory*.

J. Bolyai (1823) Letter to father 11/3/1823. Péter Körtesi (trans.). Online at `http://mathshistory.st-andrews.ac.uk/DSB/Bolyai.pdf`.

J.L. Borges (1962) Avatars of the tortoise. *Labyrinths: Selected stories & other writings*.

D. Boyle (2001) *The Tyranny of Numbers: Why counting can't make us happy*.

D. Bressoud (2007) *A Radical Approach to Real Analysis*.

W. Bricken (1995) Distinction networks. In I. Wachsmuth, C. Rollinger & W. Brauer (eds.) *KI-95: Advances in Artificial Intelligence* p.35-48. Online at `http://wbricken.com/pdfs/01bm/05arch/01dnets/04distinction-networks.pdf`.

W. Bryant (1907) *A History of Astronomy*.

F. Cajori (1928) *History of Mathematical Notations*.

G. Cardano (1545) *The Great Art*.

G. Chaitin (2004) *Meta Math!*

W. Churchill (1930) *My Early Life*.

K. Cole (2001) *The Hole in the Universe.*

A. Connes (2010) *A View of Mathematics.* Online at http://www.alainconnes.org/en/downloads.php.

J. Conway (1976) *On Numbers and Games.*

J. Conway & R. Guy (1996) *The Book of Numbers.*

R. Courant & H. Robbins (1941) *What is Mathematics?*

T. Danzig (1930) *Number.*

A. DeMorgan (1831) *On the Study and Difficulties of Mathematics.*

_____ (1915) *A Budget of Paradoxes Vol1.* Online at http://www-history.mcs.st-andrews.ac.uk/Quotations/De_Morgan.html and at books.google.com.

W. Dunham (1994) *The Mathematical Universe.*

N. Eberstadt (1995) *The Tyranny of Numbers: Mismeasurement and misrule.*

Euclid (c. 300 BCE) *The Elements.* Online at http://aleph0.clarku.edu/~djoyce/java/elements/elements.html.

L. Euler (1747) On the controversy between Messrs. Leibniz and Bernoulli concerning logarithms of negative and imaginary numbers. *Berlin Academy of Sciences* [5] 1751 p139-179.

_____ (1747) On the logarithms of negative and imaginary numbers. *Actor. Acad. Berolinensis tomo V.A.* Number 807.

_____ (1770) *Elements of Algebra.*

_____ (1771) *Complete Guide to Algebra.*

J. Fauvel & J. Gray (1987) *The History of Mathematics: A reader.*

T. Gowers (2002) *Mathematics: A very short introduction.*

R. Graham, D. Knuth & O. Patashnik (1989) *Concrete Mathematics: A foundation for computer science.*

I. Gratton-Guiness (1997) *The Rainbow of Mathematics.*

J. Hadamard (1945) *An Essay on the Psychology of Invention in the Mathematical Field.*

E. Haeckel (1866) *Generelle Morphologie der Organismen.*

G. Hardy (1940) *A Mathematician's Apology.*

D. Hilbert (1925) On the infinite. In P. Benacerraf & H. Putnam (eds.) (1983) *Philosophy of Mathematics 2nd Edition.*

D. Kahneman (2011) *Thinking, Fast and Slow.*

E. Kasner & J. Newman (1940) *Mathematics and the Imagination.*

V. Katz (2009) *A History of Mathematics.*

L. Kauffman (2002) Time, imaginary value, paradox, sign and space. Online at `http://homepages.math.uic.edu/~kauffman/TimeParadox.pdf`.

F. Klein (1932) *Elementary Mathematics from an Advanced Standpoint.*

M. Kline (1980) *Mathematics: The loss of certainty.*

J. Lovelock (1979) *Gaia: A new look a life on Earth.*

P. Maddy (2014) A second philosophy of arithmetic. *The Review of Symbolic Logic* 7(2).

B. Mandelbrot (1999) *Multifractals and 1/f Noise.*

A. Martínez (2006) *Negative Math.*

_____ (2007) Euler's "mistake"? The radical product rule in historical perspective. *Mathematical Association of America* 114 April 2007.

_____ (2012) *The Cult of Pythagoras.*

F. Maseres (1758) *A Dissertation on the Use of the Negative Sign in Algebra: Containing a demonstration of the rules usually given concerning it; and shewing how quadratic and cubic equations may be explained, without the consideration of negative roots. To which is added, as an appendix, Mr. Machin's quadrature of the circle.*

_____ (1759) In *Complete Dictionary of Scientific Biography* 2008. Online at `http://www.encyclopedia.com` and at `http://www-history.mcs.st-and.ac.uk/Biographies/Maseres.html`.

H. Matsuo (1987) K. Inada (trans.) *The Logic of Unity.*

B. Mazur (2003) *Imagining Number.*

J. Muller (2018) *The Tyranny of Metrics.*

P. Nahin (1998) *An Imaginary Tale.*

_____ (2011) *Dr. Euler's Fabulous Formula.*

T. Needham (1997) *Visual Complex Analysis.*

J. vonNeumann (1951) Various techniques used in connection with random digits. In A. Householder, G. Forsythe & H. Germond (eds.) *Monte Carlo Method.*

P. Painlevé (1900) *Analyse des travaux scientifiques.*

B. Pascal (1670/1966) *Pensées.* XV. From knowledge of man to knowledge of God. A. Krailsheimer (trans.) (2011).

R. Penrose (2004) *The Road to Reality.*

C. S. Peirce (1909) MS 514 Existential graphs.

_____ (1931-1935) *Collected Papers of Charles Sanders Peirce.* C. Hartshorne & P. Weiss (eds.).

J. Playfair (1778) On the arithmetic of impossible quantities. In Hutton, Shaw & Pearson (1809) *The Philosophical Transactions of the Royal Society of London* XIV p.356.

G. Pólya (1963/1977) *Mathematical Methods in Science.*

I. Prigogine (1980) *From Being to Becoming.*

A. Robinson (1996) *Non-Standard Analysis.*

G. Schubring (2005) *Conflicts between Generalization, Rigor, and Intuition: Number concepts underlying the development of analysis in 17-19th century France and Germany.*

G. Spencer Brown (1969) *Laws of Form.*

G. Spencer Brown (1969/1996) Introduction to Appendix 4: An algebra for the natural numbers. *Laws of Form, revised fifth English edition* (2009).

J. Stillwell (2010) *Mathematics and its History 3rd Edition.*

_____ (2016) *Elements of Mathematics.*

_____ (2018) *Reverse Mathematics: Proofs from the inside out.*

P. Suppes (1960) *Axiomatic Set Theory.*

G. Thomas (1951) *Calculus and Analytic Geometry.*

C. Trillin (1988/2012) *Quite Enough of Calvin Trillin.*

E. Tufte (1983) *The Visual Display of Quantitative Information.*

F. Varela, E. Thompson & E. Rosch (1991) *The Embodied Mind.*

C. Wessel (1797) On the analytic representation of direction: An attempt. *Philosophical Transactions,* Royal Danish Academy of Sciences (1799).

E. Wigner (1960) The unreasonable effectiveness of mathematics in the natural sciences. *Communications in Pure and Applied Mathematics* **13**(1).

J. Williams (2016) *Quantifying Measurement: The tyranny of numbers.*

L. Wittgenstein (1930/1980) *Philosophical Remarks.*

S. Wolfram (2002) *A New Kind of Science.*

G. Zukav (1979) *The Dancing Wu Li Masters: An overview of the new physics.*

Index to the Index

The six **Primary Reference Figures** summarize the structural forms of James algebra and have been isolated from the alphabetical Index as globally applicable. Plurals have been collapsed into their root word. Page ranges separated by double dashes, --, indicate ubiquitous occurrence of a term throughout the range, but not necessarily on every page.

The index is organized by several *semantic reference categories*. The main distinction is between **Symbolic** and **Iconic** concepts. Generally the Iconic Section isolates dominantly iconic concepts. Within the Symbolic Section the separation of algebra from geometry from logic is somewhat arbitrary; these distinctions are made from a perspective of high school mathematics. Another challenge is the categorization of Euler's innovations as algebra or trigonometry or complex numbers, since Euler's equation mixes the three together.

PEOPLE

PRIMARY REFERENCE FIGURES

TYPOGRAPHIC DELIMITERS

SYMBOLIC CONCEPTS
 general
 arithmetic and algebra
 geometry and trigonometry
 imaginary and complex
 infinite and indeterminate
 logic and proof
 computer science
 education
 history and philosophy
 typography

ICONIC CONCEPTS
 general
 applications

JAMES STRUCTURE
 brackets
 axioms and theorems
 applied patterns

SYMBOLS AND ICONS

VOLUMES

COVER
 cover words

BUMPER STICKERS

WEBSITES

Index

PEOPLE

quotations in bold

page

Anaximander 272

Jean-Robert Argand 217

Aristotle 182, 272, **273**, 274, **281**, 283, 285, 302, 304

Antonin Artaud **143**, 173

Alain Badiou **390**

Deepak Bal **57**

S. Ball 390

G. Baron 56

John Barrow **11**, 26

Gregory Bateson 388, 391

Benacerraf & Putnam 302, 304

Berlekamp, Conway & Guy 86

Claude Bernard **307**

Johann Bernoulli 25, 30-31, 36-45, 47-**49**-50, 54-55, 57-58, 83, 110

Ludwig von Bertalanffy 388, 391

Bhaskar 285

János Bolyai **27**, 55

Bernard Bolzano 285, 323

Rafael Bombelli 207

Jorge Luis Borges **272**, 302

D. Boyle 390

David Bressoud **325**, 347

W. Bricken 373

W. Bryant 56

Florian Cajori 237

Georg Cantor 272, 274-275, 303

Gerolamo Cardano **32**, 55, 207

Gregory Chaitin 304

Winston Churchill **87**, 110

K. Cole 306

Alain Connes **274**, 303

John Horton Conway 85-**86**, 347

Conway & Guy 303

Courant & Robbins 237

Jean D'Alembert 31, 37

Tobias Dantzig **36**, 57, **276**, 304

Richard Dedekind 8

Abraham DeMoivre 256, 262, 265

Augustus DeMorgan **33**-34, 56, **224**, 238

René Descartes 36, 178, 268

Keith Devlin **222**, 237

William Dunham **306**

N. Eberstadt 390

Euclid 55, 306, **327**, **348**

Leonhard Euler 18-**19**, 25-27, 29-**30**-31, 34, **37**-39, 41, 43, 45, 47-**48**-49-**50**, 51-**53**-54-58, 62, 66, 70, 73-74, 80, 83, 85-86, 99, 111-112, **114**-**116**-**117**, 119, 126, 135, 137, 141, 159, 175, 178, 186-**187**, 205, 219-221, 224, 231, 233, 244, 259, 261, 301, 313, 323, 361, 369, 386

Fauvel & Grey 57

Harvey Friedman 9

Carl Gauss 127, 217, **274**, 302

Kurt Gödel 319

Timothy Gowers **274**, 303, **308**-309, 323

Graham, Knuth & Patashnik 323

Ivor Gratten-Guiness   **34**, 56-57

John Graves   61

Jacques Hadamard   **207, 236**

Ernst Haeckel   388, 391

William Hamilton   61

Hardie & Gaye   302

Godfrey Hardy   **59**, 85

Hartshorne & Weiss   391

Felix Hausdorff   327

David Hilbert   9, 273-**274**, 276, 302-304, 376, 388

Householder, Forsythe & Germond   304

Hutton, Shaw & Pearson   56

K. Inada   26, 391

Daniel Kahneman   **388**, 390-391

Kasner & Newman   237

V. Katz   57

Louis Kauffman   97, **110**, 379

F. Klein   56

Morris Kline   56, 302, 323

Donald Knuth   **316**, 323, 344

P. Körtesi   55

A. Krailsheimer   302

Leopold Kronecker   112, **303**

Pierre-Simon Laplace   **36**, 56

Gottfried Leibniz   25, 30-31, **36**-40, 50, 55, 58, 146, 160, 273, 288, 319, 332

James Lovelock   388, 391

Penelope Maddy   **275**-276, **303**

Benoit Mandelbrot   325, **347**, 371

Alberto Martínez   **34**, 56, **68**, 85, **122**-126, 135, 142, **285**, 306

Francis Maseres   **33**, 37, 55-56

Hōsaku Matsuo   **26, 391**

Barry Mazur   **118**-119, **127**, 141-142

J. Muller   390

Paul Nahin   **56**, 237

Tristan Needham   **204**

John vonNeumann   **113**, 141

Isaac Newton   30, 39, 273, 288-289, 319, 332

Paul Painlevé   **236**

Blaise Pascal   **269**, 302

Guiseppe Peano   11-12, 66, 198, 236, 292

Benjamin Peirce   **221**, 237

Charles Peirce   375-376, 382, 388, 390-391

Roger Penrose   237

Plato   347

John Playfair   **35**, 56

Henri Poincaré   **274**, 302

George Pólya   **239**, 267

Ilya Prigogine   388, 391

Pythagoras   122, 142, 265, 306

Bernhard Riemann   289, 297

A. Robinson   347

G. Schubring   57

A. Shtern   236

F. Smith   141

S. Sontag   173

George Spencer Brown   **xxi**, xxiv, 28, 376-377, 379, 382, 388

John Stillwell   **1**, 10, 70-**71**, **85**, 216-**217**, 237

Patrick Suppes   **272**, 302

G. Thomas   237

Calvin Trillin   **375**, 390

Edward Tufte   **175**, 204, 388, 391

Varela, Thompson & Rosch   388, 391

Wachsmuth, Rollinger & Brauer   373

Caspar Wessel   217, 237

Eugene Wigner   35, 56

J. Williams   390

Ludwig Wittgenstein   304, **324**

Stephen Wolfram   388, 391

Gary Zukav   **141**

PRIMARY REFERENCE FIGURES

		page
FIGURE 31–1	Summary of definitions, axioms and theorems	6
FIGURE 34–2	J theorems	63
FIGURE 34–5	Angle-bracket theorems to J-frame theorems	81
FIGURE 37–3	Derivatives of boundary forms	155
FIGURE 38–7	The entire composite number line	195
FIGURE 41–2	Theorems of [ ] and <[ ]>	291
FIGURE 44–1	Roadmap for generating iconic dialects	351

TYPOGRAPHIC DELIMITERS

bracket	name	use	chapters
		JAMES ALGEBRA	
o, ( )	round	numeric, exponential	all
[ ]	square	non-numeric, logarithmic	all
< >	angle	reflection, inverse	all
{ }	curly	generic boundary	32, 34, 37, 44
		TEXTUAL MATHEMATICS	
(.)	parenthesis	textual scoping	all
{,}	brace	set delimiter	33-35, 39-43
{.,.}	brace	coordinate pair	38-41
I.I	double bar	absolute value	32-33, 35, 39
".″	quotation mark	emphasis	32, all
		INCIDENTAL	**page**
⌐	cross, mark	LoF distinction	xxiv
(.)	shell	void-equivalent outermost	147, 380
*[.]	star square	bode operator	**124**
⟦...⟧	double shell	substitution operator	**120**-121
⟦ ⟧	double square	two-boundary system	304
⟨ ⟩	large angle	logic, not numeric	379, 383
{.I.}	surreal	surreal number	85-**86**
*	surreal {0I0}	surreal analog of J	**85**-86

SYMBOLIC CONCEPTS

main topics in bold

GENERAL

archetype   32, 64, 281, 300, 314
cognitive   5, 7, 354, 372-373
confusion   329-330, 332
counting   112, 348
meaningless   85, 285, 309-311
  imaginary i 19, 27, 32, 34, 36-37
  imaginary J 29, 40, 65
neurological   3, 377
logic as skill   349
pre-computational   2, 379
processes   1, 236
deconstruct   286, 378
Euler   240
symbolic   201, 372
truth   377
finite   281, 292, 301, 303, 328
formal   28, 201, 285, 306, 355, 381
logical inference   324
rigor   274, 380
rule-based   385
structure   4, 325, 375, 380, 385
thinking   1, 3-5, 377, 379, 389
incommensurable   84, 207
algebraic numbers   8
commensurable   208, 217, 372
imaginary i   8, 111, 139, 207
imaginary J   87, 93-94, 99, 106, 108, 350, 386
infinity   287-288, 338
indicator   160, 199
  1   207, 209, 217, 336
  i   220, 235, 241
  J   98-99, 101-102
type error   140, 331, 343-344, 347
mathematics
constructive   9, 112, 277, 285
inventing   12--25
model   227   *Figure 39-4 227*
reverse   10

measurement   181, 218, 220, 228, 238
octonions   61
pragmatic   9-10, 276-277, 322
quaternions   61
space
complex   240, 262
empty   332
exponential   24, 171, 259, 373
imaginary   149
infinite   269
linear   171, 208, 219, 250, 254
logarithmic   127, 191, 208, 261-262
quadratic   184
symbolic   12, 90, 372, 381
abstraction   2, 349
algebra   37, 117, 151, 199, 201
and iconic   35, 144, 173, 198-189, 201, 350, 376
assumption   44, 99, 199
blind to meaning   377
canon   380-381
complexity   202, 382, 389
concepts   5, 199, 350-351
existence   36, 57, 100
illusory diversity   202
logic   303
mathematics   4, 44, 330, 376
rearrangement   1, 201, 205, 381-383
redundancy   202, 244, 260, 264, 304
replication   64, 72, 102, 330
  not 0 or ∞   70, 85
  not free   43-44, 99, 142, 311, 382
  of tokens   85, 101, 284
representation   35, 44, 74, 118, 184, 389
system   1, 5, 198-199, 204, 321, 331, 376-377

ARITHMETIC AND ALGEBRA

absolute value   25, 28, 96, 110
anticommutative   123
arithmetic   2-4, 9, 25, 27, 35, 202, 275, 316, 375, 389
basis   66-67, 78, 259, 263

contradiction 28, 45-46, 109, 128
distribute exponent 335-336
distribute square root 123, 132-135
natural 139
asymptotic 289
base 22-23, 60, 64-67, 134, 136, 219, 286-287, 363-364
base-0 336
base-2 21, 379
base-10 191, 194, 323
base-e 77, 157, 192, 228, 231-232, 237, 244, 366
base--1 337, 348, 361
conversion 92, 146, 343-344
negative 92, 104, 106, 112, 326, 337-339, 357-338
binary 2, 30, 376
bivalent laws 104
oscillation 111, 216, 373
calculus 30--33, 85, 143-145, 160, 172-173, 288, 319, 332
closure 8, 277, 287, 323, 347
continuity 160, 173, 204, 302, 332
decimal 10, 196, 275, 277
differentiation
chain rule 160
limit 52, 143, 314
approach 230-231, 312-313, 340
above/below 234, 333
to-zero 289, 366
delta-epsilon 145, 332
variable 145, 160, 313
discrete 4, 112, 273, 302-303
exponential *Figure 38-4 189*
asymmetry 166, 289, 342, 344
base 188-189, 205
function 85, 129, 133, 157, 188-190, 205, 220, 239, 266
multiplication 133, 166, 237
inverse operation *Figure 34-4 77*
62, 95, 188, 211, 383
logarithm 36-37, 57, 241
imaginary 29, 31, 43, 49--53, 74, 197
negative 38, 42, 195, 212, 293
base 93, 104, 146, 189, 311,

328, 342-346
log0 326, 328, 343-344, 346
log1 326, 344-346, 348
log2 13, 21, 24
log10 146, 197
loge (ln) 23-24, 29-31, 37--53, 74, 146, 150-155, 169-171, 223, 233, 262, 361
log∞ 345-346
mapping *Figure 38-10 199*
198, 206
isomorphism 199, 379
one-to-one 319-320, 324
one-to-two 186
many-to-one 198, 202, 231, 309
morphism 198-199, 202-203, 206
structure preserving 199
two-to-one 186
multivalued *Figure 32-2 24*
71, 85, 110, 124, 126, 142, 217, 234
function 54, 139, 386
number *Figure 38-6 194*
domain *Figure 38-8 196*
12, 196, 287
irrational 8-9, 12, 189, 277
e 145, 220
logarithmic 190
lawless real 8, 278, 304
natural 7, 99-104, 184, 210, 226, 274--278, 320, 324
rational 7, 16, 197
surreal 12, 86, 347
system 86, 122, 139, 173, 237, 323, 347
types of 12, 14, 210, 235-236, 287
number line 176, 182, 185, 191, 306, 369
composite *Figure 38-7 195*
193-197, 203, 205, 300
exponential 188, 197
infinite 300
linear 242-243
logarithmic 229
ordering 124, 206, 284, 306, 381

polarity *Figure 35-3 104*

  assumed 217

  confounded 133

  negative 91, 278, 296

  partition 103, 133, 173, 293

  symmetry 127, 182

polynomial 8, 19, 32, 48, 144, 167, 173, 207, 373

  binomial 166, 316

  quadratic 17, 55, 91, 205, 211

reciprocal 91, 184, 286

  function 192-193

  geometric 314

  inversion 176

  unit fraction 15-16, 133, 184, 205

relation

  arity 198, 206, 383

  associativity 61, 121, 201, 308, 323

  commutativity 61, 120-121, 201, 284, 383

  distribution 48, 115-120, 129

    non-distributive 84

  transitivity 47

reentrant 18, 21, 157, 211-213

self-multiplication *Figure 38-2 185*

  42, 60, 186--193, 235-236

  i 186, 208

  infinite 334--339

  lossy 133

  squaring 127-128, 133-138, 184-185

  negative units 45-46, 90, 104, 113, 119-120

  units 66, 69, 90

  zero 331-332

series 58, 85, 275

sign calculus *Figure 36-1 119*

  25, 89, 114, 117--126, 141

  minus times minus *Figure 36-3 125*

  123, 128

square root 20, 45-47, 59, 67, 127, 129, 180, 187, 218, 234

  information gain 133

  inverse 184, 187

  multivalued 18, 34, 97, 124, 130--135

  of 1 126-132

  two-valued 46

unity

  bifurcation of 16, 128, 234

  logical 384

  negative 13, 65, 77

    roots of 228-229

  roots of 126-127, 262

GEOMETRY AND TRIGONOMETRY

angle

  double 116, 247-248, 265, 387

  half 244, 265, 387

  multiple 247, 256

angular distance 181

circle

  circumference 110, 238, 369

    infinite 177

    π 224, 226, 243, 206, 277, 359, 369

    radians 181-182, 219-220, 238, 242-243, 274

  counterclockwise 182, 230, 232, 245

  curvature 179, 238

  quadrant 49, 196-197, 215, 217

  radius 110, 176--181, 219, 231, 238, 243

  revolution 29, 50, 52, 89, 180

  semicircle 243, 261, 277

conic section

  ellipse 192

  hyperbola, unit 192-193

  parabola 184, 186, 192, 243

coordinates 191-193, 204, 295

  Cartesian 178-179, 184, 243, 258

  orthogonal 179, 241, 243, 262

    decomposition 179, 219, 268

    non-orthogonal 263

  orthogonal-to-polar 180

  polar 178-179, 238

  polar-to-orthogonal 180

dimension

  dimensionless 238, 240

  one-dimensional 184, 240, 260

  three-dimensional 217, 179, 204, 354

  two-dimensional 38, 176, 184, 216-217, 240, 245, 260, 267, 376

geometry   151, 178, 183, 294, 356
   anticonformal   177, 314
   conformal   314
   hyperbolic   177-178
   inversive   176-177, 192, 226, 314
   non-Euclidean   55, 177, 204, 381
   projective   306, 314
inversion   *Figure 38-1 176*
    181, 184, 186, 203, 306
   through line   176-178, 182, 205, 208
   through circle   176, 204
   through function   178
perspective
   extrinsic   179-181, 204, 219
   intrinsic   179-180, 220, 226
Pythagorean theorem   111, 180, 247, 253-254, 266, 387
sphere   204, 274, 289
triangle   180, 239-240, 259, 264
trigonometry   180, 192, 235, 239-241
   arctan   180, 204, 233, 243
   cosine   49-50, 180, 204, 220, 229, 243-254, 257--267
   sine   180, 204, 220, 229, 239-240, 249--267
   symmetry   244, 251, 260, 263
   tangent   144, 159, 204, 239, 254-255, 266, 387

IMAGINARY AND COMPLEX

complex
   analysis   87, 207, 235, 239, 256, 321
   conjugate   48, 231, 244-245
   logarithm   233
   of complex number 53
    infinity of   29, 43, 52-55, 74, 85, 99, 102, 175, 232-233
   number   7-8, 32--38, 49, 94, 99, 111-112, 207, 215-220, 232--238, 244-245, 260-261, 291--298, 348, 379
   plane   38, 175, 187, 203, 210, 216--219, 289, 294, 387

rotation   38-39, 217--235, 240, 261
   principle value   231, 261, 263
cyclotomic equation   127, 262-263, 268
DeMoivre's theorem   256, 262, 265
Euler
   angle α 50, 219, 241, 247, 256-257
   coordinates   203, 219-220
   equation   49, 203, 207--210, 219--223, 231-232, 241, 243, 256-258, 263, 267, 387
   formula   175, 231, 237, 260
   identity   38, 62, 79, 221-224, 232, 237, 350-351, 363
   polar to logarithmic   244, 261-262
i-land   186, 191, 207
imaginary number   *Figure 38-3 187*
    27--39, 59--64, 123, 139-140, 184, 186, 213-218, 235
   meaning   223
   unit i   20, 59, 67, 131, 214, 220-221, 356

INFINITE AND INDETERMINATE

compactification   297
continuous   204, 274, 302-303
countable   272, 274-275, 292, 324
indeterminate   307, 336-337
   contradiction   309, 313, 318-319, 322
   direction   292
   expression   311-313
   object   274
   series   319-320
   variable   308-309, 312
infinite   *Figure 41-3 299*
    231--307, 312--322, 328-348, 370-372
   accumulation   66, 111, 300, 309, 336
   contradiction   296
   exponent   336-337
   extent   280, 316
   limitless   272
   line   292
   magnitude   273-274, 293, 296, 298, 302, 340
   multiplication   332, 336-337, 347

number of 176, 231-232, 275, 300, 330, 336, 347
number line *Figure 41-4 300*
object 276-277, 335, 347
oscillation 320, 347
power *Figure 43-4 334*
 286, 326, 336, 339-342, 345-346
ray 292-293
rotation 294-298, 305-306
sequence 7, 338
series 58, 267, 276, 319-320, 384
set 179, 232, 319-320, 324
sum 330, 388
universe 5, 281, 306, 327

infinity
actual 273-275, 324
approaches to 275-277, 279, 300-301
base, exponent 333-334, 339-342
base, logarithm 345-346
bounded 275, 281, 287, 303, 305
completed 112, 276-277, 304, 324
complex 271, 285, 291--299, 388
countable 292, 324, 330
 uncountable 274-275, 284, 305
directional 271, 288-289, 292, 297-298, 306, 313, 333
illusion 274, 284
inward/outward 184, 303, 328
meaningful 269, 301, 310, 326
negative *Figure 43-5 341*
 195, 271, 278--317, 327, 332-333, 339, 341, 387
point at 177, 314
positive 194, 271, 280-289, 295, 301, 307, 327, 333, 336, 341, 352, 387
potential 272--277, 324
reciprocal 279
types of 292, 306
unbounded 273, 280-281, 303, 305
infinitesimal 31, 143-144, 273, 287-289, 301, 319, 332-334, 347
L'Hôpital's formula 314
zero 289, 332, 329, 365

LOGIC AND PROOF
ambiguity 87, 109, 181, 205, 233, 237, 317-318
ambiguous 106, 234, 285, 319, 382
anomaly 279, 295, 298, 346, 384
arithmetization 9-10
co-defined 221, 293, 344, 346, 362
completeness 231, 319
consistent 121, 308, 316, 319, 323 384
 expert 324
 inconsistent 98, 126, 139, 289, 347, 369
 paraconsistency 324
deductive 138, 274, 385, 391
equivalence 139, 186
 pattern 4-5
 structural 13
 systems 198
idempotent 28, 69, 270, 302
incomplete 319, 324
logic
 contradiction 324, 384
 dialectic 26
 operators 64, 205, 384
 metalanguage 151, 200, 239, 301, 372
 metamathematics 376, 389
 paradox 35, 56, 110, 221, 238
proof 379
 algebraic 113, 247
 computational 164
 conventional 160
 deductive 138
 formal 285
 inductive 256
semantics 126, 276
 and syntax 4, 304, 311, 377, 383
 existence of 200
 general 347
 intention 284
 interpretation 180, 304
 structural 84-85
substitution 17-18, 160, 309-310, 319
 as multiplication 120 *Figure 36-2 120*
 choices 138
 constraint 45, 97
 failed 120

Flagg resolution	97, 110-111	non-computable	344, 346
global	97, 111	object-oriented	71, 111, 374
of equals	138, 317	optimize	1, 373-374, 378
of limit	150-152	**pattern matching**	144, 200-202, 282, 304,
of patterns	97, 156, 159, 366-368		309, 317, 319, 369--
partial	97, 111		374, 380-381, 385
replacement	97, 110-111, 124	polymorphism	206, 387
structural	84, 239	recursion	66, 292, 305
valid	45, 120, 178, 317	rewrite	129, 138, 331
truth	1, 377, 384, 392	signature, function	201, 206
validity	35, 363, 376	silicon	2-3, 5, 173, 206, 268,
axiomatic	142, 318		377-378
structural	63	situated	243, 318
		software	5, 173, 355, 374, 385

COMPUTER SCIENCE

		system	138, 285, 324, 378
algorithm	2-3, 173, 267, 381	structural perspective	227, 282, 358
backtracking	205, 356, 373	unate	361
binate	356, 361, 373	Wikipedia	237, 303
Boolean	270, 373		
co-design	355		

EDUCATION

complexity		arithmetic	321, 324, 349, 378
algorithmic	148, 355-356, 373-374	curriculum	2, 306
computational	205, 322, 356, 373	education	2-3, 60, 141, 204, 206,
in design	124, 126		324, 349, 372, 378
visual	170	humanistic	236
computational age	376	learnability	354
computer science	206, 323	psychology	236, 380
confluence, loss of	83, 109, 131, 137-139,	quadrivium	306
	369, 386	student	60, 144, 184, 311, 324, 385
constraint	101, 231	teachers	183, 303, 375
computational	323	textbook	33, 64, 110, 117, 144, 151,
formal	4		170, 223, 237, 267, 316
reasoning	383	Thomas' Calculus	237
digital	10, 376--379, 385	universal schooling	2
halting problem	391		
intractable	205, 342		

HISTORY AND PHILOSOPHY

lossy	96, 124, 126, 135, 308	Babylonian	15, 182, 239
Mathematica	5, 306	BCE	108, 275, 302, 306, 347
memory	135, 232-233, 262, 355	Buddhist	389
accumulation	100-103, 112, 386, 389	creation-from-nothing	13
revolution	112, 181	**dualism**	348, 372, 382-384
serial counter	102	dichotomy	306, 348-349
storage	238, 355, 373, 382	Western	268, 378, 389
with	72, 101	ecological	328, 376, 389
without	72, 94, 100, 183		

Egyptian — 15, 108, 239
epistemology — 389
Greece
  ancient — 8, 39, 181, 192, 239, 347
  aperion — 272
  concepts — 48, 184, 272, 328
  Pythagoreans — 122, 273
holistic — 26, 355, 389
India
  Ananta — 275
  Asmkhyata — 275
  Jaina — 275
  Lilavati — 285
  māyā — 392
  Vedic — 285, 389, 391
magic — 391
metaphysics — 30, 389, 390-391
One — 124, 269, 272-273, 328
philosophy — 30-31, 268, 275-276, 303, 324, 378, 380
Platonic reality — 373, 377
rationality — 378, 383, 389
thesis-antithesis — 13
Through the Looking Glass — 186
tyranny of number — 379, 391

TYPOGRAPHY

blank space — 382
curly brace — 154, 179, 204
double-struck — 7, 10
finger — xxiv, 199, 201-203
Greek letters — 110, 219, 241
hybrid language — 88
juxtaposition — 141
parenthesis — 355
quasi-token *void* — xxiv
string — 3, 62, 144, 166, 174, 198, 240, 320, 376--385
text — 354-355, 376, 391
textual — 124, 349, 377, 385
typographic — 10, 349-350, 355, 366, 392

ICONIC CONCEPTS

GENERAL

accidental structure — 284, 331, 350, 355, 366, 377, 381, 383, 385
accumulation — 6, 111
  frame — 359
  round — 269, 272-273
axioms — 81, 122, 256, 269, 372
  arithmetic — 174
  derivatives — 144, 148
  non-numeric — 290-291
  pattern — 7, 9, 54, 64, 239, 379
  void-based — 270-271, 329
base
  arbitrary — 150, 156, 167, 201, 208
  base-free — 146--156, 169, 223, 227, 238, 366, 386
    exponent — 5, 144, 158
    logarithm — 21, 29, 64
  explicit — 158, 190, 196, 286, 342
  generic — 146, 151, 159, 173, 196
  independence — 157, 223, 286
boundary
  environment — 281, 376
  innermost — 65-66, 269, 271, 353
  math — 1, 281
  outermost — 65, 197, 280-281, 295, 303, 305, 328
  topological — 94, 350
container/containment
  as border — 353-354
  as connection — 353-354
  as enclosure — 352-354
  as path — 353-354
  as stack — 352-354
  capacity — 328
  cardinality — 200
  context-dependent — 216, 318-319, 355
  empty — 69, 90, 292, 329
  finite — 328
  internal structure — 61, 286, 328, 356, 358, 366, 382
  non-commutative — 123--126, 134-135
  relation — 7, 198, 354-355, 358

cybernetics	376, 389
design choice	54, 268, 316, 372
distinction	303
cognitive	4
context/content	281, 382
identity	380
inside/outside	75
number/non	271, 276
object/process	277, 383
one/many	269, 347, 384
positive/negative	96, 280
emergent	54, 90, 138, 170, 322
ensemble	1, 4, 10, 82, 86, 120, 197, 205, 347
Existential graphs	376, 391
frame	xxiv
cardinality	89
content	76, 89, 147, 208-209, 359
form	147-148
inversion	68, 89, 270
magnitude	208
numeric	109
type	89, 208
group	10
iconic	*Figure 35-1* **88**
arithmetic	4, 83-84, 378, 380
dialects	350--356
form	4-5, 184, 199, 202, 380
formal system	1, 198, 201, 204, 376, 389
logic	302, 378--380, 385
methods	1, 144, 173, 206
pattern	9, 149, 159, 201-202, 217, 381--385
semiotics	375
thought	4-5, 7, 142, 199, 203, 378, 388-389
mark of priority	124-125
nested	4, 64, 94, 191, 300, 316
inverse	60, 75
exponents	78
power tower	162, 214, 236
non-accumulating	
call	379
full rotation	242
infinity	112, 284

J	68-70, 385
logic	302
square-bracket	270, 272, 277, 284, 305
surreal	86
void	85, 329-330
non-conforming	384, 388
non-numeric	307, 313-314, 326
incommensurable	287--296
indeterminate	321-322
square-bracket	7, 26, 65, 145, 172, 179, 270-271, 276--280, 335--342, 370, 381
void	69, 289, 325, 329
notation	9, 113, 161, 350, 375, 387
parens	xxiii, 350, 352-356, 361
permeability	74, 325, 377
semipermeable	85, 378
transparent	74-75, 157, 328
perspective	
geometric	64, 226-227, 250
iconic	13, 100, 144, 260, 311, 354-355
James algebra	65, 82, 71, 213, 223, 291, 322
symbolic	62, 200
void-based	71, 153, 305
phase	103 *Figure 39-2* **214**
cyclic	29, 50--54, 87, 101-102, 214-216, 232--235
four-cycle	216, 357
multiplicative	215
quantized	214
shift	216, 220, 226, 249-250, 258, 264-266, 357
two-cycle	214-216, 357
polarity	132, 209, 297
collapse at infinity	295-296, 346, 348, 388
fractional	263, 387
partial	208-210, 293
preservation	134, 332, 336, 346
postsymbolic	4-5, 350-351, 376-377, 381, 389
reduction	95, 124, 338, 342
angle-bracket	60, 280
asynchronous	354, 356

catalytic 382, 392
concurrent 102, 200, 205, 354
deletion 382-383, 392
irreducible 67, 109, 301, 316--321
non-confluent 129-131
path 97, 132-136, 139
parallelism 1, 3, 83, 102, 201, 205, 351, 355-356, 381--385
unresolved 337-339, 346
reflection *Figure 39-5 235*
87, 89, 101, 230
as negation 182
binary, discrete 182
constant J 183, 209, 222
generalized 282
imaginary 39, 64, 186, 195
independence 281
infinite 280, 282, 297
sign change 182
square-bracket 280, 297-298
turn around 64, 235, 305
sign-blind 33-34, 71, 93, 96
absolute value 25, 28, 110
bipolar 21, 25, 34, 40, 70, 97, 110, 124--136, 139, 186-189, 217, 296, 301, 306
cosine 25, 260
double value 34, 48, 187
function 20, 37, 45, 137, 234, 244
imaginary 21, 184, 186, 211, 217, 231, 261
infinity 301, 342, 372
logarithm 37
multiply by zero 43
numbers 40, 68, 127, 187-188
sign-free 128, 196, 209, 386
signless 68, 110, 203, 217
sine 250
spatial 185, 240, 385
stable form 271, 280, 291, 333, 352
unit fraction 90-91
void *Figure 32-1 13*
Figure 43-3 328
absence 65, 327, 389
bounded 281, 328

no zero 183
omnipresent 269
pervasive 200, 382
substitution 144, 156, 392
sum of nothing 329
void-based 71, 153, 375, 378
construction 156, 212
demonstration 69, 76, 117, 192-193, 283
differentiation 155, 386
equality 78-79
identity 79, 156
reasoning 22, 124
systems 44, 200
technique 13-14, 144, 203
void-equivalent 1, 91, 117-118, 151, 171, 201 -202, 284, 380--384
absorbed 100, 270, 278, 296, 300, 309-310
illusory 44, 151, 171, 200-202, 284
permeable 74, 157-158
theorem 45, 71, 103, 140, 305, 329

APPLICATIONS

absorption 270, 311-313, 330, 370
polarity 295-297, 301, 307, 321-322, 340, 348, 387
infinity 293-295, 301, 306, 338, 346, 371-372
derivative 143 *Figure 37-2 147*
Figure 37-3 155
chain rule 147, 161, 366-368
base conversion 146, 151, 156, 169, 173
derivative of
angle d<.> 153, 367
dconstant 154
dcosine 257-258
double round d((.)) 162
double square d[[.]] 163
round d(.) 149, 151-152, 155, 173, 364--367
dsine 257-259
square d[.] 152-153, 159, 167, 367-368
dvariable 154, 257
differentiation
frame 144, 147-148, 160-161

template 147, 161, 163, 167, 170, 173
  double round 162
  double square 163
  generic 148, 167-172, 169
  power 168-169
  product 165
  type-trails 161
inflection point 171-172
integration 172
limit *Figure 37-1 146*
  154--159, 364
limit variable 146, 150--154, 157, 173-174, 362
power rule 165-166, 268
product rule 163--166, 367
quotient rule 165, 174
transparency 171, 362
  angle-bracket 153-154, 161, 165-166
  limit process 145-146, 153, 159
  round unit 157-159
  unit fraction 169

dialects *Figure 44-1 351*
  7, 350--366
block 352-354, 373
bound 352-356, 362
bucket 352-354
map 352-354
network (dnet) 351--356, 361--370
path 351--356, 361-362, 368, 372
room 351-356, 361-362
wall 352-354

dialect examples
chain rule 366-368 *Figure 44-10 367*
double-square 370-371 *Figure 44-13 370*
divide-by-zero 352-354 *Figure 44-3 353*
e 362 *Figure 44-6 362*
Euler identity 363 *Figure 44-7 363*
i 357-359 *Figure 44-4 357*
J 352-354 *Figure 44-2 352*
J-self-occlusion 363 *Figure 44-8 364*
π 359-362 *Figure 44-5 360*
rcosine 368-369 *Figure 44-11 368*
round d(.) 364-366 *Figure 44-9 365*
tally failure 369-370 *Figure 44-12 369*
triple-square 371-372 *Figure 44-14 371*

dialect properties
border 353-354, 356, 361
depth parity 356, 359-361
dynamics 74, 228, 232, 355
embodied 1, 349, 389, 391
gravity 353, 373
look-and-feel 354
multisensory 1
participatory 89, 261, 275, 349-350, 354-355
path analysis 351
physical 1, 29, 64, 349
physical participation 353
physiological 236
round/square path border 353, 356, 361
same as parens 355-356
shared structure 92, 213, 366
traversable 353, 356

exotics 143 *Figure 43-1 326*
  Figure 43-7 346
bases 112, 173, 337, 342-343
exponential 342
form 113, 325-327, 388
logarithms *Figure 43-6 343*
  342-343
zero 329-332

fractional reflection *Figure 40-1 242*
  100, 208, 210, 226-229, 237, 387
discrete 208, 227, 229
generalized 282
half 187, 216, 221, 226-260, 298
half-negation 188, 216, 221, 254
partial 226-227, 229, 240, 261
quantized 216, 297, 387
rotation as 181-184, 203, 222, 226-230, 235, 240-241, 245-249, 256--266
trigonometry 239--266

indeterminate *Figure 42-1 315*
  Figure 42-2 318
  130, 138-139, 173, 270, 274, 285--288, 309--331, 336--348, 381, 388

conditional dominion   322
negotiable   315-319
J [<o>]   *Figure 34-1   62*
                               Figure 34-6   83
absence/presence 68, 96, 99--102, 111-112,
                  183, 338, 386
additive   39, 54, 61, 87, 100, 137,
                  215, 235, 268, 369, 386
breaks distribution   369, 385
can't replicate   18, 26, 64, 69-70, 101, 131
contradiction   73, 83-84, 137, 139,
                  383--386
discrete object   39, 54, 106
domain   62, 79-80, 87
imaginary unit   *Figure 38-5   190*
                  61, 64, 66-69, 74, 189
imaginary logarithm 74, 121, 132, 137
imaginary marker 94
independent   68, 73, 94, 109, 195, 229
interior   66, 73
invariant   80
issues   83
magnitude-blind   43
object form   66
parity   233, 338, 369
process form   66, 73
reflection   100, 102, 175-176, 184,
                  210, 226, 239
self-addition   66, 69, 235-236
self-definition   71
self-inverse   25, 64, 97, 107, 225, 230
self-multiplication 66
self-voiding   64, 69-70, 72, 89-90,
                  100-103, 112
sign-blind   20, 22, 25, 96-97, 136,
                  213, 230
stable   64, 74
tokens   44, 72, 95, 99, 102-103
transparency   73-75, 83, 225
J/2 ([<o>]<[2]>)
J/2-frame   210, 225--229, 241-242,
                  248--256, 360
  i (J/2)   *Figure 39-1   213*
  π (<J/2>[J])   *Figure 39-3   225*
                  218--254, 277, 359-362

J-fractions   99, 131-132, 386
cardinality   210, 370
cosine   *Figure 40-2   246*
                  244, 246-249
no denominator   285--288
numerator   98, 106, 108, 127, 309
power function   228
rational   87, 98, 106-109
quantized   262, 265-266, 297
sine   *Figure 40-3   252*
                  251-253
unit   106-109, 218
J-frame   *Figure 35-2   89*
                  108, 188, 208-209, 352,
                  358-359
  inverse operation   *Figure 34-3   76*
                  60, 75-77, 82, 96
  J-angle frame   89
  J-conversion frame 76, 78, 82, 89, 183
  J-involution frame 89
  J-self frame   89
  [J]-frame   359
J-land   190-191, 195, 208
J-self-occlusion
  Euler identity 79-80, 222, 363-364
reflective   177, 218, 222, 230, 242,
                  361, 388
  rcos-squared   265
  rcosine   244, 260-266, 368-369
  rsin-squared   265
  rsine   262-266
  rtan   266
  trigonometry   259--266
tally
  arrangement   98, 131
  consistent   99
  constraint   108, 385
  failure   53, 73, 85, 87, 98-99,
                  106, 301, 350, 369-
                  370, 385-386
  infinite   72, 330
  square-bracket 283-284, 305
  system   344, 348, 379

STRUCTURE

Figure 31-2	8	*numbers*
Figure 38-9	197	*number line*
Figure 43-2	327	*concepts*

Principle of

Composition   15
Containment   380
Existence   380
Identity   380
Incommensurability   94, 106, 108, 380
Independence   144, 148, 161, 366-367, 380, 383
Indeterminacy   309-310, 381
Non-numeric Form   278, 381
Void   303, 380
Void-equivalence   380

BRACKETS

angle <.>   *Figure 34-5*   *81*
   10, 17, 60, 66, 75, 188
divide-by-zero (<[ ]>)
   143, 285--290, 313, 352
double-round (( ))   162
double-square [[ ]]
   163, 271, 291, 293-294, 299, 371, 388
infinitesimal   332-334
round (.)   193, 268, 269, 277, 281
round unit ( )   65, 146, 269-270
square [.]   65, 193
square unit [ ]   *Figure 41-1*   *282*
   269-271, 277-281, 284, 307, 380-381
triple-square [[[ ]]]   339-342, 371

AXIOMS AND THEOREMS

| Figure 31-1 | 6 | *summary* |
| Figure 41-2 | 291 | *non-numeric* |

Arrangement Axiom

   48, 82, 95, 98-99, 102, 106, 115--119, 122, 131, 135, 142, 149, 170-171, 329, 365, 368, 386
collect   72, 98--102, 149, 152, 170-171, 250, 258-259, 330, 333, 348, 370, 386

disperse   48, 115, 118, 131, 134, 152, 161, 165, 167, 249, 368, 386
Bode   125, 142
Cross   64, 377, 379
Composition
cover   15, 159, 287
decompose   128
move   15, 119
Dominion Theorem
   14, 96, 98, 131-132, 138, 171, 201, 270, 279, 283, 296, 309-310, 313, 317-318, 321-322, 330, 342, 372
absorb   154, 280, 283, 285, 294--298, 301, 307--313, 317, 322, 330-331, 335--338, 341--345, 371-372, 388
emit   117
Dominion II Theorem   283, 285
Dominion III Theorem   294-295
Double-square Theorem
   294, 301, 339, 348, 370-371, 374
Indeterminacy Axiom   173, 321
Indication Theorem   100, 102, 330
mark   72, 330, 348
Infinite Interpretation Axiom
   269, 290, 295--301, 307, 312, 314, 321-322, 326, 333, 370, 387-388
Inversion Axiom
   14, 42, 82, 91, 107, 233, 281, 331, 358, 368
bracket inversion   178
clarify   65, 91, 161, 165, 202, 280, 287, 364, 366, 374
enfold   78, 151, 156
void enfold   44
void inversion   65, 136, 270, 279, 321, 328-329, 379
Involution Theorem
   17, 42, 76, 105, 116-119, 121, 321, 365
unwrap   105, 259
wrap   371
J Theorems   *Figure 34-2*   *63*
J-conversion Theorem
   66, 75--78, 82, 89, 92-93, 122, 149, 153, 170, 183, 209, 225, 230, 361, 370
J-invariant Theorem   80

J-occlusion Theorem
78--82, 86, 94-95, 114, 204
J-parity Theorem
99, 103--106, 125, 230, 233
J-self-inverse Theorem
40, 70-71, 80, 107, 213, 386
J-self-occlusion Theorem   79, 222
J-transparency Theorem
49, 52, 73--76, 86, 94, 97, 125, 183,
195, 301
J-void Theorem
17, 23, 70, 90, 95, 105--108, 129-
131, 134, 140, 183, 247, 268, 369, 385
J-void object   69, 71-72, 76, 98-99
J-void process   71
J-void tally   72-73, 98, 103, 130,
132, 137, 232, 338, 341
J/2 Toggle Theorem 212, 225, 230
Promotion Theorem
17, 42, 46, 65, 82, 115, 118-120, 130-
131, 137, 321, 332-333, 374
demote   48
promote   73, 98, 116, 295, 364
Reaction Theorem 96
react   151, 366
Reflection Axiom
14-15, 45, 60, 75, 78-79, 95--98, 114--
121, 124, 130, 154, 204, 280-281, 311,
317-318, 335, 368
cancel   15, 70, 89, 98, 105, 118,
129, 139, 152-154, 176, 178, 249, 254,
259-260, 266, 336, 341, 363, 366, 368,
379
unit reflection   114, 119, 122, 243, 260
void reflection   23, 40-41, 151, 172,
231, 301, 305, 329, 339
Replication Theorem
42, 72, 128-129, 131, 142, 213, 330, 359
replicate   18, 102, 128, 330
Separation Theorem
52, 82, 94-95, 139, 278, 342, 348
Triple-square Theorem   339, 371
Unify Axiom
272, 283-284, 329, 379

APPLIED PATTERNS

*Brackets on the right count
demonstrations of each transformation
within the volume*

Arrangement Axiom		[39]
collect	[24]	
disperse	[15]	
Bode		[4]
Composition		[10]
Cover		[58]
Dominion		[44]
absorb	[39]	
emit	[5]	
Double-Square		[8]
Indeterminacy Axiom		[17]
Indication		[7]
mark	[3]	
unmark	[4]	
Infinite Interpretation Axiom		[63]
Inversion Axiom		[258]
clarify	[216]	
enfold	[42]	
Involution		[50]
unwrap	[36]	
wrap	[14]	
J-convert		[35]
J-occlude		[7]
J-self-inverse		[2]
J-transparent		[9]
J-void object		[23]
J-void tally		[10]
Move		[32]
Promotion		[56]
demote	[12]	
promote	[44]	
Reaction		[13]
Reflection Axiom		[84]
cancel	[72]	
create	[12]	
Replication		[22]
replicate	[12]	
tally	[10]	
Separation		[13]
join	[9]	
split	[4]	

Substitute		[160]
Triple-square		[5]
Unify Axiom		[7]

Symbols and Icons

definitions in bold
*asterisk * indicates ubiquitous token*

☞	interpretation finger	**xxiv**, **201**, *
±	bipolar number	21, *
=	equal sign	11, *
≠	difference sign	12, *
⇒	process arrow	6, *
⇏	does not convert to	62, 101, 380
⇔	transformation equality	15
⟼	mapping arrow	176--190
=∂ef=	definition	*
=?=	equality to be determined	133
~	similar	151
··N··	N replications	6
··∞··	infinite cardinality	330, 333
ℕ	the natural numbers	7-8
ℤ	the integers	7-8
ℚ	the rational numbers	7-8
ℝ	the real numbers	7-8
ℂ	the complex numbers	7-8
⊂	subset	7
CIƆ	Roman numeral 1000	**303**
⏐⏐⏐⏐	tally number	**348**
τ	tau, 2π	**110**
∞	countable infinity	*
∃	existential quantification	75
{.}	not empty container	*
Re(.)	real component	**260**, 264
Im(.)	imaginary component	**260**
(( ))	James base	**30**, 114
#	arbitrary base	62, *
(( ))$_b$	imposed base-b	*
d{x}	generic derivative	**149**
d(u)$_#$	round derivative	**149**, 155
d[u]$_#$	square derivative	**152**, 155
d<u>$_#$	angle derivative	**153**, 155
d{.}	applied derivative	153--174
dcos	cosine derivative	**257**-258
dsin	sine derivative	**258**-259
Δx	small change in x	**160**
Lh, Ln	limit variable	**146**--159
[<o>]	J	*
void	non-symbol	*
{x,y}	Cartesian coordinate	**179**, *
{r,θ}	polar coordinate	**179**, *
✱	generic mapping	**196**--201
¤	generic mapping	**196**--201
(A [B])	James frame	xxiv, **208**, *
x, *, <blank>	multiply (contextual)	*

Volumes

VOLUME I		4--7, 78, 82, 120, 203, 205, 302, 346, 349-350, 375
Chapter 2		120, 205
Figure 2-7		120
Chapter 3		10
Chapter 4		349
Chapter 8		208
Chapter 9		112
Chapter 10		141, 374
Chapter 13		350
Figure 13-1		350
Figure 15-1		302
VOLUME II		5, 11, 140, 201, 301, 375
Figure 16-1		5
Chapter 18		15
Chapter 20		66, 75, 271, 291, 304
Figure 20-5		271
Figure 20-7		271
Chapter 22		11
Figure 26-1		201
Chapter 27		8, 301

COVER

page 360
the form of π,
room dialect

page 292
complex infinity

page 190
imaginary
exponential

page 367
dnet proof of
product rule
for
derivatives

page 269
unit
axioms

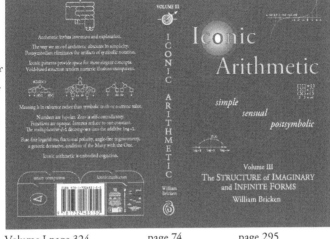

Volume I page 324
Arrangement axiom,
room dialect

page 74
opaque
boundary

page 295
absorption of
polarity at infinity

COVER WORDS

Arithmetic invites invention and exploration.

The way we record arithmetic obscures its simplicity.
Postsymbolism eliminates the artifacts of symbolic notation.

Iconic patterns provide space for more elegant concepts.
Void-based structure renders numeric illusions transparent.

Meaning is in existence rather than symbolic truth or numeric value.

Numbers are bipolar. Zero is self-contradictory.
Functions are opaque. Inverses reduce to one constant.
The multiplicative $\sqrt{-1}$ decomposes into an additive log -1.

Base-free logarithms, fractional polarity, angle-free trigonometry,
one generic derivative, coalition of the Many with the One.

Iconic arithmetic is embodied cognition.

BUMPER STICKERS

(some are paraphrased)

Iconic methods encourage embodied cognition. 1

Iconic arithmetic is an adventure, an exploration of a foreign territory. 3

James arithmetic has no concepts of addition or multiplication. 4

Real numbers are lawless, almost all are both indescribable and unknowable. 8

Arithmetic is sufficient for all constructive mathematics. 9

Negative one is the arch-villain. 13

Fractions are not designed to be added together. 15

A sign-blind expression is equal to its own negation. 20

Every mathematical object is imaginary. 27

An imaginary concept can be completely real in an imaginary world. 28

Every number has an infinity of logarithms. 29

Algebra is insensitive to what humans would call absurd. 36

Identity requires replication but it does not require repetition. 64

±1 is both +1 and –1 at the same time. 73

Reflection is the void-based form of identity. 78

J can be seen as an alternative to 1 as a basis for arithmetic. 82

Void cannot be collected since it cannot be indicated. 99

Cardinality counts indications. 102

Every rational number is a sum of unit fractions in multiple ways. 108

J replaces the concepts of negation, subtraction, division and logarithm. 114

Multivalued functions create tears or folds in the fabric of the plane. 127

Multivalued functions are the rule rather than the exception. 127

At the foundation of the arithmetic of signs is a type error. 140

Replication is not free. 142

The form of e is the form of round unit transparency. 157

Presence of J is not the inverse of its absence. 183

We translate, rotate, reflect and scale by changing viewing perspective. 184

i is a half-reflection operator. 187

Self-multiplication leads to bipolarism.   188

Magnitude is signless while exponents carry polarity.   196

Fractional reflection and partial polarity take the place of rotation.   210

J is a simpler, more elementary imaginary number than i.   213

Round units describe the Many, square units describe the One.   272

Infinity is inside.   275

Replication of infinity is an illusion.   284

Infinity is not a homogeneous singular concept.   288

We fantasize an unbounded universe so we can pretend to be outside of it.   305

Infinity cannot be tallied.   309

The utility of a definition is as important as its mathematical consistency.   316

Complexity is an emergent property of the accumulation of units.   322

Language embraces inconsistency and interdependent webs of meaning.   323

Exotics illuminate rules, exposing their biases and their weaknesses.   326

Zero is non-numeric.   329

Infinity is not an accumulation of an infinite number of 1s.   336

Look at this!   350

We think in concert with our senses.   350

Transformation of containment relations changes their look-and-feel.   354

As a culture we value duality over bounded possibility.   372

Belief in mathematics is not eternal.   376

By design metamathematics cannot be relevant.   376

Thought is a system.   377

Our thoughts are not separate from our actions.   378

What we believe today will look antiquated in the next century.   379

Containment eliminates the concepts of counting and function.   379

A container identifies the ground and is the figure.   381

Eliminate what is not to arrive at what is possible.   382

Truth is confounded with existence.   383

Arithmetic is a form of experience.   388

Postsymbolism is a critique of Western dualism and objective rationality.   388

WEBSITES

page

http://aleph0.clarku.edu/~djoyce/java/elements/elements.html   348

https://books.google.com   238

http://classics.mit.edu/Aristotle/physics.3.iii.html#485   302

https://en.wikipedia.org/wiki/Controversy_over_Cantor%27s_theory   303

http://homepages.math.uic.edu/~kauffman/TimeParadox.pdf   110

http://mathshistory.st-andrews.ac.uk/DSB/Bolyai.pdf   55

https://mathworld.wolfram.com/Doublestruck.html   10

https://msuweb.montclair.edu/~bald/files/LeibBernLogs.pdf   57

http://wbricken.com/pdfs/01bm/05arch/01dnets/04distinction-networks.pdf   373

http://www.alainconnes.org/en/downloads.php   303

http://www.encyclopedia.com.   55

http://www-history.mcs.st-and.ac.uk/Biographies/Maseres.html   55

http://www-history.mcs.st-andrews.ac.uk/Quotations/De_Morgan.html   238

http://www.jfsowa.com/peirce/ms514.htm   391

https://www.scientificamerican.com/article/let-s-use-tau-it-s-easier-than-pi/   110

Printed in Great Britain
by Amazon

77321404R00255